STEPHEN H. UNGER, Professor of Electrical Engineering at Columbia University, received his B.E.E. degree from Brooklyn Polytechnic Institute in 1952 and his S.M. and Sc.D. degrees from M.I.T. in 1953 and 1957 respectively. His very active career includes research and development work for Bell Telephone Laboratories from 1957 to 1961, consulting work for RCA Laboratories and G. C. Dewey Company, and summer employment at RCA Laboratories, Bell Telephone Laboratories, IBM, and General Electric.

He was a visiting faculty member at Berkeley in 1967, and lectured at the Advanced Institute on Network and Switching Theory in Trieste, Italy in the summer of 1966.

The author is a Guggenheim Fellow (1967) and a Senior Member of the Institute of Electrical and Electronics Engineers. He has written extensively about switching circuits, digital systems, and computer programming theory in leading journals.

D1496373

Asynchronous Sequential Switching Circuits

Asynchronous Sequential Switching Circuits

STEPHEN H. UNGER

Department of Electrical Engineering
Columbia University

WILEY-INTERSCIENCE   A Division of John Wiley & Sons
New York · London · Sydney · Toronto

10 9 8 7 6 5 4 3 2 1

Library of Congress Catalogue Card Number: 70-88320

SBN 471 89632 2

Printed in the United States of America

To My Mother

Preface

Switching theory is concerned with the techniques of analyzing and synthesizing distinct portions of systems in which the variables of primary
concern are restricted to a finite number of values. Such systems include
digital computers, telephone switching systems, and many types of control
systems. The switching theory aspect of the problem is distinct from the
electronic engineering aspect in that the basic building blocks are generally
assumed to be given at the outset and they are already fairly complex circuits.
The switching theorist (in another guise, the logic designer) does not deal with
voltages, currents, reactances, or energy but with idealized versions of the
building blocks in which the external signals are usually assumed to be ones
and zeros. On the other hand, switching theory is distinct from digital systems
design in that it consists of a fairly extensive and precise set of concepts
applicable to the solution of certain well-defined problems of a certain range
of complexity. The design of a large system is usually a more intuitive affair
concerned with the specification and assembly of many subsystems that are
themselves perhaps more susceptible to the tools of the logical designer.
Needless to say, in real life the boundaries are not so well drawn and the
identities of the electronics engineer, logical designer, and system designer
are often merged and blurred. One of the goals of switching theory is to shed
more light on the adjacent disciplines.

The basic aspect of the subject is classified as *combinational-circuit theory*,
the study of switching circuits without memory. When the facility to store
information is added, we have *sequential circuits*. A subclass may be classified
as *synchronous sequential-circuit theory*, the study of sequential circuits in
which *time* as well as the signal amplitudes, is assumed to be quantized.
The subject of this book is *asynchronous* sequential-circuit theory, in which
events are *not* constrained to occur at discrete intervals. It should be understood that these definitions are intended only to give an intuitive notion of
the concepts involved.

The reader is assumed to have a general knowledge of combinational-
switching theory and of the use of the Karnaugh map. A qualitative

understanding of electronic circuit design would enhance his appreciation of some of the points discussed but it is not essential. Readers who lack this knowledge can skip over the very few places that refer to this area. No special mathematical background is required (other than that acquired while learning about combinational circuits), although the usual qualification of "mathematical maturity" is pertinent, since the material is certainly mathematical in nature and a number of fairly involved chains of reasoning must be followed through.

An effort has been made to minimize formalism and to address the reader as a human being rather than an automaton for validating proofs. I feel that a high degree of formalism is not essential to rigor; hence many steps in the proofs presented here are stated in a somewhat informal, though hopefully clear and precise manner. In some cases the judgement has been made that a sketchy outline of a proof is all that is warranted by the importance of the idea involved relative to the space that a complete argument would require. A good deal of reliance has been placed on the use of examples to clarify concepts and procedures.

The goal of the book is to present a clear, unified, and essentially complete picture of the subject that will place the reader in a position to exploit the ideas in a practical manner or to do research aimed at adding further to our understanding of the field. With reference to the first point, it is not expected that a designer will be able to find in these pages pat solutions to all his problems but rather that he will acquire an insight into the subject that will enable him to set bounds on what is feasible and to adapt general methods to specific cases.

Asynchronous Sequential Switching Circuits can be used as a textbook or for self-study. A full set of problems follows each chapter, and solutions to about a third of them (those marked by * or ‡) are provided at the end of the text. The starred problems introduce significant ideas that are not dealt with in the text and should receive special attention.

It should be possible to cover the bulk of the material in a one-semester three-hour-per-week graduate course, although the instructor may wish to gloss over certain topics. I have been teaching a course of this kind in the Electrical Engineering Department at Columbia University, for which the prerequisite is any first course in switching theory.

The reader is advised to go through the book in sequence, skipping material that does not interest him and returning to it when he finds it necessary in order to comprehend later topics. Since the introductory chapter constitutes a survey of the later chapters, it is advisable to reread the appropriate part of the introduction before beginning each new chapter.

To avoid cluttering up the text with footnotes I have confined almost all references and discussions of the origin of the ideas in each chapter to concluding sections entitled "Sources." Citations in these sections, and in a few other places, refer to a single alphabetized list of references at the end of the book. This list is prefixed by a brief note that calls attention to sources not mentioned elsewhere in the text.

As recently as 1953, all of the published work in the field of switching theory could have been incorporated in one modest sized volume. The situation is very different now, even with respect to the one area of the field that is being treated here. Choices had to be made concerning the material to be included and inevitably differences of opinion will occur, particularly with respect to peripheral subjects. Nevertheless, I feel that the principal points have been thoroughly treated.

In Chapter 1 an effort has been made to orient the reader and to survey the major problems to be discussed. Chapter 2 provides a comprehensive treatment of the state reduction problem for both synchronous and asynchronous functions. The asynchronous-circuit, row-assignment problem is treated in Chapter 3 with respect to minimizing the number of state variables, transition times, and circuit complexity. Delays, hazards, and timing problems in general are the subject of Chapter 4 under several different assumptions regarding stray delays; Chapter 5 deals with feedback, its consequences in asynchronous circuits, and how minimal feedback circuits can be synthesized. In Chapter 6 several different modes of operation are considered, including a synthesis procedure for circuits that generate completion signals (sometimes called *speed-independent circuits*), timing and tolerance problems in pulsed or synchronous circuits, and the synthesis of double-rank sequential circuits. Finally, in Chapter 7 a number of different kinds of binary counter are considered in the light of the various concepts introduced in the preceding chapters.

I am grateful to the John Simon Guggenheim Foundation for granting me a fellowship that made possible the writing of this book and to the Department of Electrical Engineering and Computer Science of the University of California at Berkeley, where I spent the fellowship period, for providing an atmosphere conducive to such work. Special thanks are due Drs. Armstrong, Friedman, and Menon of the Bell Telephone Laboratories for making available to me prepublication versions of several very interesting papers they have produced, thus making possible the inclusion of material that would not normally appear in a book at such an early date. A number of errors and unclear points were pointed out by some of my students. Finally, mention must be made of the skillfull and conscientious work done by Miss Betty Geenty of Columbia University and by Mrs. Billy Vrtiak of Berkeley who typed the manuscript.

New York, New York   STEPHEN H. UNGER
September 1969

Contents

CHAPTER 1

Introduction

In order to establish clearly the kinds of problems to be treated in this work, and to introduce some basic terminology, it is useful to begin with a plausible, concrete, synthesis example. The themes introduced here are developed and varied in subsequent chapters.

1.1 Problem Specification—the Flow Table

Consider Route 1, a heavily traveled highway, intersected by Crumb Road, a rural road frequented only by an occasional car. If there were no traffic light at the intersection, it would be almost impossible for a car to safely Cross Route 1 on Crumb Road because of the density of high-speed traffic on the former. However, a traffic light halting the flow on the main highway every minute or two, regardless of the fact that during nine-tenths of these stoppages there would be no cars at all waiting to cross, is feasible only if the local farmers can muster the considerable political leverage that would be required to foist such an outrage on the much larger body of travelers on the main highway. Assuming that this is not the case and that the rather substantial cost of an overpass is clearly unjustified, a reasonable, and fairly common compromise in such situations is to install a signal light that halts highway traffic only when there are cars waiting to cross the intersection; that is, Route 1 traffic would normally see a green light and would be halted by a red light only after a car approached the highway on Crumb Road. This can be accomplished by a control circuit operating with inputs from a timer and from parallel-connected pressure-actuated switches embedded in Crumb Road at appropriate points.

The control circuit to be developed here is to function as follows:

The timing signal x_1 alternates between being off for 60 seconds ($x_1 = 0$) and on for 30 seconds ($x_1 = 1$). The only time Route 1 traffic can see a red light, a condition designated by $z = 1$, is during an interval in which $x_1 = 1$. Only at the start of an $x_1 = 1$ interval can z

1

go on, and once on, it must remain on for the full interval. If a car on Crumb Road actuates a switch, a condition designated by $x_2 = 1$ (when no car is over such a switch $x_2 = 0$), while $z = 0$, then z should go on the next time x_1 goes on.†

The requirement that the "red" interval be in phase with a fixed timing interval makes possible the synchronizing of traffic lights along Route 1 for speed-control purposes. If this were not required, the problem would be simplified.

Our problem now is to design a circuit with two binary (that is, binary *valued*) inputs x_1 and x_2 and one binary output z. A significant aspect of the situation is that the input signals are mutually independent. One cannot, for example, exclude the possibility of x_1 and x_2 changing simultaneously.

It is obvious at the outset that no combinational switching circuit can realize the specified behavior. This is because the output of a combinational circuit is a function only of the *present* values of the input variables; whereas in this case *past* input values are also relevant. For instance, when $x_1 = 1$ and $x_2 = 0$, z would be 1 if x_2 had been 1 35 seconds ago, and z would be 0 if x_2 had been 0 for the past 120 seconds. Thus, the desired circuit is a *sequential* one in that it must store information concerning past input states.

Such information is stored in terms of *internal states* of the circuit. At any given time, the circuit is in one of a finite number of states (as determined by the values of a set of internal *state variables*). The internal state serves to summarize the pertinent history of the circuit. The combination of the internal state and the input state is called the *total state*.

Both the output of a sequential circuit and the next internal state are functions of the current total state. When the next internal state is the same as the current internal state, then the total state is said to be *stable*, referring to the fact that nothing significant is scheduled to happen until an input change occurs.

The above definitions are couched in terms of circuits. It is useful to apply the same terminology to behavioral descriptions of circuits, or, to use a better term, to *sequential functions*. A *sequential function* relates output sequences to input sequences assuming some particular initial internal state. The specification of the behavior of the traffic-light controller given earlier is an example of an informal, verbal description of a sequential function. In order to make such a description more precise and more amenable to formal manipulation, we now describe the function by specifying the total states, output functions, and next-state functions of a circuit realizing the desired sequential function. The description does not necessarily correspond to that of the circuit ultimately developed (except, of course, that it realizes the same sequential function) but is in a form that is particularly convenient

---

† Note that although no mention has been made of the use of a yellow warning light, this could be included as the initial part of the 30-second "red" interval.

for initial specification. Subsequently it will be transformed into a more desirable form.

The general format that is used here for the above purposes is called a *flow table* and consists of a two-dimensional array. The columns correspond to input states, the rows to internal states, and the entries are ordered pairs representing the next internal state and the current output, respectively. Entries representing stable states are circled.

Initial specifications of sequential functions are made in the form of flow tables having exactly *one* stable state per row. They are called *primitive* flow tables. The formation of such a table for a given problem is now illustrated in terms of the traffic-light controller under discussion.

First we consider a static situation, which corresponds to a stable state. Suppose that the timer is in the off-state ($x_1 = 0$), no car is presently operating a switch ($x_2 = 0$), and no switches have been operated for several minutes. Then $z = 0$, and the internal state is such that unless x_2 goes on before x_1, z is to remain 0 during the next $x_1 = 1$ interval. Designating the internal state as 1, we can label the total state as 1-00 (the first digit indicating the internal state and the last two the input state $x_1 x_2$). Since this state is stable, it should be circled (see Table 1.1a).

Now, if while the system is in this total state, x_1 changes to 1 (that is, the total state becomes 1-10), z remains 0, and the next-state entry must change to something other than 1 (only *one* stable state is permitted in any row of a primitive flow table). Let this entry be 2. Thus, in position 1-10, the entry is (2, 0). Consider now the total state 2-10. The internal state corresponds to the situation in which no $x_2 = 1$ signal has occurred for a long time, and hence z should remain 0 at least for the duration of the current $x_1 = 1$ interval. Thus, 2-10 should be stable with entry (2, 0).

Suppose now that x_1 reverts to 0 while the system is in 2-10. Then the situation becomes the same as that described initially; hence the 2-00 entry should be (1, 0). The incomplete flow-table fragment shown as Table 1.1a indicates precisely what happens in the steady state when the timer x_1 goes through its paces in the absence of traffic on Crumb Road. The total state of the system cycles through 1-00, 1-10, 2-10, 2-00, 1-00, ... with z remaining fixed at 0.

Table 1.1a Partial Flow Table Describing Situation When No Traffic Is on Crumb Road

	$x_1 x_2$			
	00	01	11	10
1	①, 0			2, 0
2	1, 0			②, 0

The construction is continued by filling in the blanks in rows 1 and 2, adding new rows as new states are found to be necessary, until the process (hopefully) comes to a halt with a completed table.

The next step (see Table 1.1*b*) may be to enter a 3, 0 in position 1-01 and 3, 0 in 3-01. Note that, after each input change, the system moves from its initial stable to an unstable state in the same row and then to a stable state in the column corresponding to the new input. This pattern of behavior is characteristic of primitive flow tables that describe functions in which the output state changes at most once after a change in the input state.

Table 1.1*b*   Flow Table Complete Except for Some Conditions Involving Double Input Changes

	00	01	11	10
1	①, 0	3 , 0		2 , 0
2	1 , 0	3 , 0	7 , 0	②, 0
3	4 , 0	③, 0	6 , 1	
4	④, 0	3 , 0		5 , 1
5	1 , 0	3 , 0	6 , 1	⑤, 1
6		3 , 0	⑥, 1	5 , 1
7		3 , 0	⑦, 0	8 , 0
8	4 , 0	3 , 0	7 , 0	⑧, 0

When the system is in total state 3-01 and x_2 changes to 0, the next stable state is, of course, in the 00 column. If this state were the 1-00 stable state, then, in effect, the system would be "forgetting" that x_2 had been on. Thus, a new stable state is needed in column 00, and it is designated as 4-00. One property of this state is that z is to be switched on for the next interval during which $x_1 = 1$, which accounts for the entries in total states 4-10 and 5-10. At this point we observe that, *regardless of the present state*, the consequences of a 01-input (car at intersection while $x_1 = 0$) are always the same. Hence, *all* entries in the 01 column must be (3, 0).

Since, once z goes on, it must remain on as long as x_1 is on, there must also be a stable state in the 11 column in which $z = 1$, and it must be possible to cycle between this state and 5-10 as x_2 goes on and off (corresponding to a surge of traffic on Crumb Road—due perhaps to a county fair). These requirements account for entries in states 5-11, 6-11, and 6-10. State 6-11 is the obvious destination when x_1 goes on with the system in 3-01. This explains the entry in 3-11.

Returning now to row 2, we note that if x_2 goes on while x_1 is on, the z-signal should remain at 0, but should go on the *next* time x_1 goes on. This accounts for the entries in 2-11 and 7-11. If x_2 goes off while the system is in 7-11 the next state must record the occurrence of the $x_2 = 1$ signal. Hence a transition to a new state, 8-10, is needed. The other row-8 entries follow in a straightforward manner.

When the system is in 5-10, z is on and no cars are operating the x_2-switch. Hence, when x_1 goes off, the system may be returned to the quiescent state by means of the 5-00 entry. At this point the table has been developed to the point shown in Table 1.1b, where the remaining unspecified entries all result from simultaneous changes in x_1 and x_2.

When simultaneous input changes occur with the system in 3-01, 4-00, or 7-11, the corresponding entries in 3-10, 4-11, and 7-00, respectively, should obviously be as shown in Table 1.1c. When the system is in 6-11 and both inputs go off together, it is probably advisable to have the system go to 1-00 as specified by the 6-00 entry. If there is some doubt concerning the possibility that the last car may have moved off the switch but not have crossed Route 1, then the destination state would be 4-00.

Table 1.1c The Completed Primitive Flow Table

$x_1 x_2$

	00	01	11	10
1	①, 0	3 , 0	6 , 1/7, 0	2 , 0
2	1 , 0	3 , 0	7 , 0	②, 0
3	4 , 0	③, 0	6 , 1	5 , 1
4	④, 0	3 , 0	6 , 1	5 , 1
5	1 , 0	3 , 0	6 , 1	⑤, 1
6	1 , 0	3 , 0	⑥, 1	5 , 1
7	4 , 0	3 , 0	⑦, 0	8 , 0
8	4 , 0	3 , 0	7 , 0	⑧, 0

Consider now the case in which, with the system 1-00, a car on Crumb Road arrives at the Route 1 intersection switching on x_2 just as x_1 changes from 0 to 1. One possibility is to specify that z should immediately go on. This would give this car the green light immediately and would be indicated in the flow table by a (6, 1) entry in 1-11. The alternative is to make the car wait for the next cycle by sending the system to state 7. Clearly this point is not important, since both choices are reasonable and the situation will occur only occasionally. In such cases, the decision is best made so as to lead to the simplest circuit. Since, at the problem-specification stage, which will be the simplest is not usually evident, the option should be indicated in the flow table by specifying *both* of the acceptable entries (separating them with a slash), as shown in position 1-11 of Table 1.1c. Now that all the entries of the flow table have been filled in, Table 1.1c represents a complete, formal description of what we wish the control circuit of our traffic light to do. The word "complete" in the preceding sentence should perhaps be qualified by noting that a flow table says nothing about such significant matters as time scales and power levels; but it does fully describe the desired *logical* behavior.

Before proceeding to the next step in developing a solution for our example, it may be well to make some general comments on the process of flow-table formulation that is illustrated above. First note that, when converting a natural-language description, or mental image, into a precise form, no algorithmic procedure is possible. One can develop only heuristic approaches and constantly check to see if the resulting formal description is consistent with the original informal idea. Frequently the process of writing a formal specification generates questions about what is desired in situations not originally considered. Thus, the process of constructing a flow table may clarify the problem even if no further use is made of the table.

1.2 Flow-table Reduction

An alternative approach to the one illustrated here is to consider what stable states are needed for each input column. Starting with these states as the basis for the primitive flow table, the appropriate transitions among these states are then filled in. It may occur in the course of this process that not enough stable states were chosen; in this event they can be added as required. As becomes evident later, no serious harm is done if too many states are used. In fact, the next step in the synthesis procedure is to find a minimal-state flow table that satisfies the specifications implicit in the original primitive flow table.

The reasons for state reduction and the methods for accomplishing it are the subject of Chapter 2. Suffice it to point out for the present that, in our example, with the appropriate choice for the 1-11 entry, the entries in the corresponding columns for rows 1, 3, 5, and 7 are the same as those for rows 2, 4, 6, and 8, respectively. This makes it evident that Table 1.1c can be reduced to Table 1.2, and in fact no table with fewer rows satisfies our specifications.

1.3 Coding The Internal States

Having arrived at a flow table that satisfactorily describes the desired sequential function, we must, as the next step in the synthesis, select a finite set of binary state variables and assign to each row of the flow table one or more states of these variables. Once this has been accomplished, it is a straightforward matter to obtain truth tables specifying the circuit outputs and next values of the state variables as functions of the current values of the input and state variables.

Table 1.2   Reduced Flow Table

$x_1 x_2$

	00	01	11	10
1	①, 0	2, 0	4, 0	①, 0
2	②, 0	②, 0	3, 1	3, 1
3	1, 0	2, 0	③, 1	③, 1
4	2, 0	2, 0	④, 0	④, 0

In order to have enough states of the state variables to permit a unique coding for each row of the flow table, the number of state variables n must be such that $2^n \geq r$, where r is the number of rows. It is useful to write this as $n \geq \lceil \log_2 r \rceil$, where $\lceil x \rceil$ is the smallest integer at least equal to x. (The quantity $\lceil \log_2 r \rceil$ is commonly designated as s_0.) For the flow table labeled Table 1.2 in which $r = 4$, at least two state variables are needed. Suppose that this minimum number is chosen, that the variables are labeled y_1 and y_2 (our convention is to call the ith state variable y_i and to designate as Y_i the *next* value of y_i), and that the states of $y_1 y_2$ are assigned as in Table 1.3. A flow table such as this with a y-state assigned to each row is called a *flow matrix*.

A set of Karnaugh maps (Table 1.3b, c, and d) can now be derived specifying z, Y_1, and Y_2 as functions of x_1, x_2, y_1, and y_2. The columns of the Karnaugh maps are ordered in the same manner as those of the flow matrix. The rows however are permuted, and at the left of Table 1.3b are the row numbers of the flow matrix that correspond to the rows of the maps. The z-map is obtained by filling in 1's in the positions corresponding to the $z = 1$ entries of the flow matrix (the right halves of rows 2 and 3). In order to obtain the Y_1-map, we note from the flow matrix that $y_1 = 1$ for the codes assigned to rows 3 and 4. Hence, for each total state with a *next-state* entry of 3 or 4, there should be a 1 in the Y_1-map. *Every* next-state entry in the 11 column is a 3 or a 4; hence all the entries in the 11 column of the Y_1-map (Table 1.3c) are 1's. In the 10 column, only the row-1 entry of the flow matrix is neither 3 nor 4; hence only in row 1 is there a blank in the Y_1-map. Similarly, noting

Table 1.3 a Flow Matrix

$x_1 x_2$

	00	01	11	10	y_1	y_2
1	①, 0	2, 0	4, 0	①, 0	0	0
2	②, 0	②, 0	3, 1	3, 1	0	1
3	1, 0	2, 0	③, 1	③, 1	1	0
4	2, 0	2, 0	④, 0	④, 0	1	1

Table 1.3 _b, c, d,_

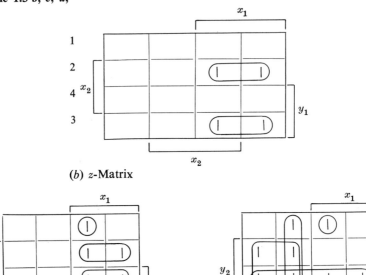

(_b_) _z_-Matrix

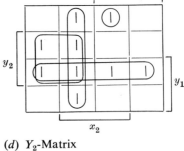

(_c_) Y_1-Matrix   (_d_) Y_2-Matrix

that Y_2 should be 1 whenever the next-state entry is 2 or 4, we obtain Table 1.3_d_.

Applying standard techniques of combinational-circuit design (this is not a trivial case), we obtain the expressions

(1.1) $$z = x_1 \bar{y}_1 y_2 + x_1 y_1 \bar{y}_2,$$

(1.2) $$Y_1 = x_1 x_2 \bar{y}_1 \bar{y}_2 + x_1 \bar{y}_1 y_2 + x_1 y_1,$$

(1.3) $$Y_2 = \bar{x}_1 x_2 + y_1 y_2 + \bar{x}_1 y_2 + x_1 x_2 \bar{y}_1 \bar{y}_2.$$

(Note the product terms shared by Y_1 and z and by Y_1 and Y_2.)
These expressions in turn lead to the circuit of Fig. 1.1 in which z, Y_1, and Y_2 are realized with an economical two-stage logic circuit.

It is assumed that the complement of each input is available (_double-rail inputs_) and that for each i, y_i is obtained from Y_i through a delay element. This is how we implement the notion that Y_i is the _next_ value of y_i.

There is a good deal to be said about these delay elements, the need for them, and their properties, but for the present it is assumed that one is

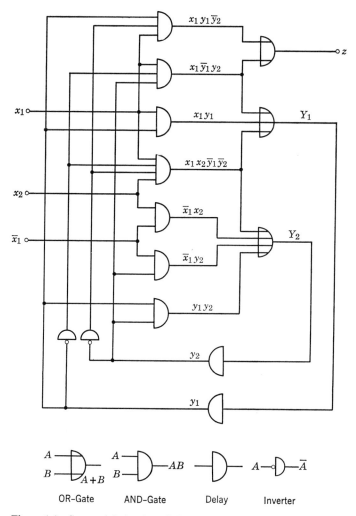

Figure 1.1   Sequential circuit realizing Equations 1.1 to 1.3.

associated with each state variable and that they do not respond to overly rapid input changes.† These are both conservative assumptions as is seen later.

In order to gain some insight into how such a sequential circuit operates,

† To be more precise, if such a delay (called an *inertial-delay element*) has a value D, then its output changes after the input change has persisted for time D. Thus, for example, if the input to such a delay is 1 for a long time, changes to 0 for a time *less* than D, and then reverts to 1, the output will remain at 0 and ignore the two changes.

it is useful to examine in some detail the action involved in a few transitions. First, we examine the transition resulting when x_2 changes from 0 to 1 with the system initially in 1-00.

In the initial state $x_1 = x_2 = y_1 = y_2 = 0$ an examination of the circuit (or the K-maps) indicates that $Y_1 = Y_2 = 0$ for this total state; hence, since the input of each delay element is the same as its output, the system is indeed in a stable state as indicated in the matrix. Now, if x_2 is turned on (making the total state 01-1), Y_1 remains 0, but the $\bar{x}_1 x_2$ gate produces a 1-output which switches on Y_2. After a delay, this signal penetrates the y_2-delay and y_2 changes to 1 so that the next total state is 2-01. With $x_1 = 0, x_2 = 1, y_1 = 0$, and $y_2 = 1$, it is clear from the circuit diagram that $Y_1 = 0$ and $Y_2 = 1$, and hence again the system is in a stable state. Thus far, the derived circuit behaves according to the flow table.

Consider now what happens if, with the system in 2-01, x_1 is switched on. One effect is that the $x_1 \bar{y}_1 y_2$ gate goes on, thus switching on Y_1. Another effect is that the two gates that were holding Y_2 on, $\bar{x}_1 x_2$ and $\bar{x}_1 y_2$, both go off and no other Y_2 gate goes on. Hence, Y_2 switches to 0. Now note that $Y_1 \neq y_1$ and $Y_2 \neq y_2$ so that both delay elements are unstable. We may envision a 1-signal moving through the y_1-delay element and a 0-signal moving through the y_2-delay element. Suppose that both arrive at their respective destinations simultaneously. Then the new total state would be 3-11; an inspection of the circuit reveals that this state is stable and that the behavior of the circuit would have conformed to that specified by the flow table. But what if the y_1-signal changes first? This would occur if the y_1-delay were smaller than the y_2-delay. Then after this change we would have $x_1 = x_2 = y_1 = y_2 = 1$, the $x_1 y_1$ gate would hold Y_1 on, and the $y_1 y_2$ gate would go on, switching Y_2 back to 1. But now, because of its inertial nature, the y_2-delay would revert to a stable condition ("forgetting" the brief period during which Y_2 had been 0) and the system would be stable in 4-11! This possibility of course conflicts with the flow-table specifications.

The situation appears even worse when we note (and the reader may verify) that if y_2 wins the race, the system will enter 1-11 and *then* proceed to 4-11. Thus only if the race ends in a tie, an event possible only if the delays are exactly equal, does the circuit work properly.

The detailed examination of the circuit action, and indeed even the execution of the synthesis procedure beyond the formation of the flow matrix, were unnecessary in detecting this condition. Simply by inspection of Table 1.3a, it is evident that in the course of the 2-11 $\rightarrow$ 3-11 transition, *two* state variables must change; that is $y_1 y_2$ must change from 01 to 10. If it is assumed that y_1 changes first, then the y-state becomes 11, which has been assigned to internal state 4, which is stable in the 11 column. Hence, the possibility of ending up in 4-11 exists. Furthermore, if y_2 changes first, then the system enters 1-11, where the next-state entry is 4, and so a second possibility for malfunction exists.

A situation whereby more than one state variable must change in the course of a transition is called a *race* condition. If correct behavior of the circuit depends upon the outcome of the race, then it is called a *critical race*. A race is *noncritical* if, regardless of the outcome, the behavior of the circuit still conforms to that specified by the flow table. For example, the transition 3-01 → 2-01 in Table 1.3*a*, also involves a race condition. However, regardless of which *y*-variable changes first, the next-state entry encountered is always a 2, and hence the outcome will be as specified. (The *z*-values will also be correct in all of the possible intermediate states.)

Another type of critical race is illustrated in Table 1.4*a*, which should be

Table 1.4

	y_1	y_2	y_3			y_1	y_2	y_3
4	7 , 0	0	0	1	4	5 , 0	0	0	1
5	7 , 0	0	1	1	5	7 , 0	0	1	1
6	⑥, 1	1	0	1	6	⑥, 1	1	0	1
7	⑦, 0	1	1	1	7	⑦, 0	1	1	1

(*a*) A critical race.   (*b*) Eliminating the race.

considered as a portion of a larger flow matrix. The transition from state 4 to state 7 involves a race between y_1 and y_2 which is critical since if y_1 wins, the system will stop in state 6. However, correct operation results if y_2 wins, as well as if the race ends in a tie. This is because the intermediate state to which *y*-state 011 has been assigned also has 7 as its next-state entry. Hence, it is possible to "fix" this race by specifying that the delay element associated with y_1 be significantly larger than that associated with y_2. Such a solution has two drawbacks:

1. There may be other analogous races in the flow matrix that call for y_1 to win a race with y_2.
2. More fundamentally, it is undesirable to have to specify more than one magnitude for *y*-delays, since a second magnitude imposes more stringent tolerance constraints that cost money or longer delays; in addition a proliferation of parts requirements is in itself inconvenient for manufacturing and maintenance purposes.

There is however a second method for circumventing the type of critical race under discussion. Since satisfactory operation results if the 4 → 7 transition is executed with 5 as an intermediate state (that is, if it becomes 4 → 5 → 7), we can alter the flow matrix so that the transition *always* occurs this way. This has been done in Table 1.4*b*, where the next-state entry in 4 has been changed to a 5. Now the $4 \rightarrow 7$ transition takes place in two steps, neither of which involves a critical race (in this case, no races at all are involved). The drawback here is that the transition takes longer, in that the two variables change in sequence.

Because of the existence of the second solution, we may refer to a critical race of the type arising in Table 1.4*a* as a *removable* critical race, as opposed to the type illustrated in Table 1.3*a* which is not removable.

As a result of the above discussion, it should be evident that the state-assignment problem is by no means a simple one. Not only must each row be assigned a unique code, but the codes must be so interrelated that no transition involves a nonremovable critical race. It is desirable to achieve this end while minimizing transition time (that is, the number of steps for each transition), the number of state variables, and the complexity of the resulting logic circuit. In different situations, varying importance may be attached to the above factors, and perhaps still other factors may be considered as significant. A number of general approaches to this very basic problem are treated in Chapter 3. For the present, we simply present a solution for the illustrative example under discussion.

Table 1.5 depicts a row assignment for Table 1.2 which assigns a single, unique y-state to each row and which is free of critical races (there are non-critical races in the 01 column).

It is interesting to note that if Table 1.2 is altered by changing the entry for total state 2-10 to $(1, 0)$, then there exists *no* two-variable state assignment for the resulting new table that is free of critical races. However, a number of valid three-variable assignments can be found using the techniques to be developed in Chapter 3.

1.4   Effects of Stray Delays—Hazards

Having found a satisfactory row assignment, we now proceed as illustrated earlier to develop maps for z, Y_1, and Y_2 (parts *b*, *c*, and *d* of Table 1.5) and

Table 1.5

	x_1x_2				y_1	y_2
	00	01	11	10		
1	①, 0	2, 0	4, 0	①, 0	0	0
2	②, 0	②, 0	3, 1	3, 1	1	1
3	1, 0	2, 0	③, 1	③, 1	0	1
4	2, 0	2, 0	④, 0	④, 0	1	0

(a) A valid row assignment.

Table 1.5 *b*, *c*, *d*

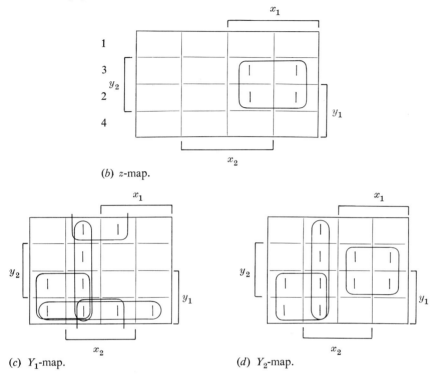

(*b*) *z*-map.

(*c*) Y_1-map.

(*d*) Y_2-map.

derive the algebraic expressions

$$z = x_1 y_2,$$
$$Y_1 = \bar{x}_1 y_1 + y_1 \bar{y}_2 + x_2 \bar{y}_2 + \bar{x}_1 x_2,$$
$$Y_2 = x_1 y_2 + \bar{x}_1 y_1 + \bar{x}_1 x_2.$$

A circuit realizing these expressions is shown in Fig. 1.2. (In order to simplify the figure somewhat, the lines connecting the generated, y_1-, y_2-, and $\bar{y}_2$- signals to the input AND gates have been omitted.)

It appears at first that this circuit should behave in accordance with our flow table, and if it could be realized in an ideal manner, it would. However, there is an implicit assumption buried in our discussion thus far that is *never* physically realizable, namely, that there are no delays in the logic elements or in the wiring. When this unrealistic assumption is removed, then several kinds of malfunction become possible.

Consider, for example, the transition resulting when, with the system in 2-00 (see Table 1.5*a*), x_1 is turned on. This transition would make the total

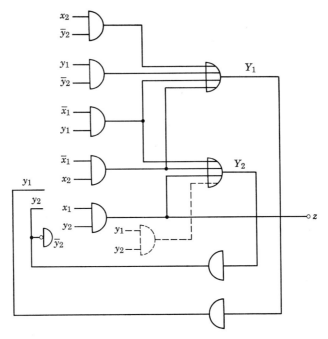

Figure 1.2   Circuit derived from Table 1.5.

state 2-10, and the output of the $\bar{x}_1 y_1$ gate (Fig. 1.2) that was keeping Y_1 and Y_2 on would then go to 0. *At the same time*, the output of the $x_1 y_2$ gate would go on, to hold Y_2 at 1. Hence, if this situation actually occurred the net result would be that Y_1 would go off and Y_2 would stay on, so that the next state would be 3-10 as specified. But now suppose that there were a relatively large delay in the output of the $x_1 y_2$ gate. Then Y_2 would *also* go to 0, and if the interval during which the $\bar{x}_1 y_1$ gate *and* the $x_1 y_2$ gate were both off were sufficiently long, y_2 would go to zero and the state of the system would then be 1-10. Here the $x_1 y_2$ gate would cease to receive inputs tending to turn it on, and the system would be stable.

An analysis of this situation, which is made in general terms in Chapter 4, indicates that the difficulty lies in the transient behavior of the combinational circuit generating Y_2. Although the steady-state output of this circuit is indeed 1, as specified, when $x_1 x_2 y_1 y_2$ is 0001 or 1001, it may go to 0 when the input is changing between these states. This type of transient error in a combinational circuit because of the presence of stray (unplanned) delays is said to be the result of a *combinational hazard*.

Combinational hazards associated with changes in one input signal at a time can always be eliminated by modifications of the logic circuit (in this case, for example, by adding the output of an AND gate generating y_1y_2 to the Y_2 OR gate as indicated by the dotted portion of Fig. 1.2). Such a solution may not be possible when several inputs are changed simultaneously.

In any event, transient false signals can always be filtered out by the action of delay elements with the inertial property discussed earlier. Thus, in our example, if the delay between Y_2 and y_2 were inertial and of sufficient magnitude, the x_1y_2-signal would go on before y_2 went off, thus suppressing the consequences of the temporarily false Y_2-signal. Here then is one important reason for the delay elements in the y-branches.

In the above discussion, it is shown how a transient error in a combinational circuit could, when that circuit is part of a sequential circuit, lead to a steady-state error. Now we illustrate how stray delays may cause trouble in a still more subtle manner. Referring again to Table 1.5a, and the circuit of Fig. 1.2, this time with the y_1y_2 gate (represented by the dotted lines) added, consider the *same* transition discussed above. When x_1 goes on (recall that the initial total state is 2-00), the $\bar{x}_1y_1$ gate goes off, turning off Y_1, but this time the Y_2-signal is held on by the y_1y_2 gate. Assume once more that there is a large delay in the output of the x_1y_2 gate. Then *only* the y_1y_2 gate is holding Y_2 on at this point. Since Y_1 is now 0, after some delay, assumed now to be *less* than the x_1y_2-delay, y_1 goes off. This in turn switches off the y_1y_2 gate *and* the signal that was trying to penetrate the x_1y_2-delay. Hence, Y_2 is switched off, and ultimately the system ends up in 1-10.

The possibility of the occurrence of the essential aspects of this sequence of events could have been predicted from an inspection of the flow matrix, without reference to the circuit. What happened was that the x_1-change caused (properly) a change in internal state from 2 to 3, but at the Y_2 terminal the internal-state change was seen *before* the input change because of the delay in the logic. Hence, at the Y_2 terminal, the system was seen as being in state 3-00, where Y_2 is unstable. Hence, Y_2 changed to 0 and when y_2 followed suit, the system ended up in 1-10.

The above argument suggests that altering the logic circuit may not be sufficient to solve the problem. As is seen in Chapter 4, not only is this true, but even altering the *state assignment* does not help. The only remedy lies in making certain that the various delays in the circuit are not so related as to lead to this kind of malfunction. This can always be achieved by inserting adequate delay elements in the y-branches, although in practice even rough estimates of the various stray delay values often make it evident that such delay elements are unnecessary. The flow-table configuration that causes the problem under discussion is called an *essential hazard* and is present when there is a total state T and an input x such that, if the system is initially in T and x is changed once, the total state reached is *not* the same as the one reached if x is changed two more times.

The effects of various assumptions regarding stray delays (particularly with respect to *where* they appear), restrictions on input changes, types of delay elements, etc., are treated in Chapter 4.

1.5 Feedback

An inspection of Fig. 1.2 indicates that there are several feedback loops present in this sequential circuit. This fact is evident from the algebraic expressions derived for Y_1 and Y_2. They contain terms that are positive functions of y_1 and y_2, respectively. Since y_i is always derived directly from Y_i (perhaps through a delay), feedback is obviously implied.

One may wonder if these circumstances are peculiar to this particular circuit. In fact, as is seen later, only a relatively small class of flow tables can be realized by circuits without feedback. For a large and significant class of sequential functions, each Y_i generated in an appropriate realization depends in part on y_i.

An important consequence of the kind of feedback involved here is the need for amplification in the feedback paths. In cases where logic is being implemented by physical devices that do not inherently provide gain (diode gates, for example), amplifiers must be provided explicitly.

The existence of feedback also serves to complicate fault location. Hence it may be desirable to provide special circuitry for breaking feedback paths in order to facilitate certain maintenance and diagnostic procedures.

The above considerations lend significance to the use of the *feedback index* as a measure of the amount of feedback in a circuit. The index is defined as the minimum number of wires that must be cut in order to eliminate all feedback loops. The number of amplifiers needed and the number of break points needed are clearly both equal to the feedback index.

An examination of the synthesis process shows that the number of state variables is necessarily an upper bound on the feedback index, since if the path from Y_i to y_i is interrupted for every i, there will be no closed loops left. In the example of Fig. 1.2, this number (2) *is* the feedback index. The obvious next question is, "Can the feedback index ever be *less* than the number of state variables?" The answer is "yes," and in Chapter 5, where the subject of feedback in sequential circuits is treated in a thorough manner, a method is described for synthesizing minimum feedback circuits for a broad class of sequential functions.

1.6 Modes of Operation

The example that has been carried through thus far is typical of a large and important class of sequential circuits. However, many variations of its particular subclass exist, and a number of significantly different modes of operation are possible. In this section we indicate the characteristics that distinguish various classes of circuits. First, for purposes of contrast, an example is displayed of a type of circuit distinctly different from the one already presented.

Consider the circuit of Fig. 1.3 with inputs x_1, x_2, and CP, and output z.† The *clock-pulse* (CP) input consists of a sequence of pulses generated by an independent source. The individual pulses are such that, when passed through the AND gates, they are suitable for driving the τ-FF's. Although the word "clock" suggests regular, periodic operation, this is not essential, as long as successive pulses are separated by a minimum time interval. However, it is usual for the spacing to be regular.

The x_1- and x_2-inputs are binary signals of the type discussed earlier except that they are constrained so as never to change while CP = 1. Each time CP goes on, the current input state is processed by the circuit. In between clock pulses, no cognizance is taken of the input. This constitutes the key distinction in the mode of operation of this circuit as compared with that of the circuit of Fig. 1.2.

The behavior of the system can now be described as follows:

The FF's are initially set to specify some internal state y_1y_2. The CP generator is then turned on and the total state of the system, defined by $x_1x_2y_1y_2$, is processed by the combinational circuit to generate the next internal state (by means of the τ_1- and τ_2-signals) and to produce a pulse (or no pulse) on the z-terminal. The clock pulse goes off *before* the new y_1- and y_2-values can get back to the AND gates, and the input signals are then permitted to change. The clock pulse then goes on again and the process is repeated.

Suppose now we are told that, in this example, the input x_1x_2 is to be regarded as an integer ranging from 1 to 3, written as a binary number; that is, $x_1x_2 = 01$ represents 1, $x_1x_2 = 10$ represents 2, and $x_1x_2 = 11$ represents 3, with $x_1x_2 = 00$ never occurring. Furthermore, the initial internal

† The τ-flip-flop (henceforth to be abbreviated as τ-FF) which serves as the memory element operates as follows: In the *set* state, $y = 1$ and $\bar{y} = 0$; whereas in the *reset* state $y = 0$ and $\bar{y} = 1$. After the application of a pulse of appropriate width, shape, and magnitude to the τ-terminal, the state of the FF changes. Thus, if a pulse is applied with the FF reset, it changes to the set state, and vice versa. In the absence of τ-pulses, the FF will remain quiescent in its current state. Such devices are easily realized, usually with a pair of transistors as the active elements.

τ-flip-flop

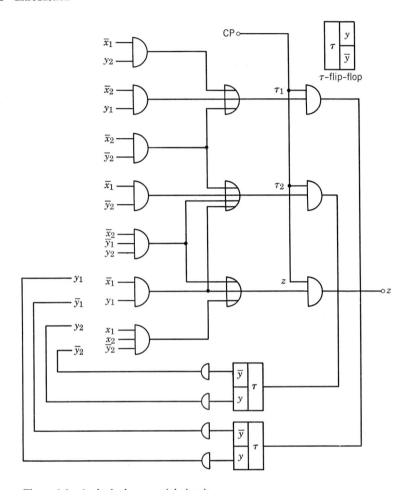

Figure 1.3 A clocked sequential circuit.

state is $y_1y_2 = 00$. Then an analysis of the circuit might proceed as follows: An inspection of the circuit yields the expressions (ignoring the clock pulse)

$$z = \bar{x}_2\bar{y}_1y_2 + \bar{x}_1y_1 + x_1x_2\bar{y}_2,$$

$$\tau_1 = \bar{x}_1y_2 + \bar{x}_2y_1 + \bar{x}_2\bar{y}_2,$$

$$\tau_2 = \bar{x}_2\bar{y}_2 + \bar{x}_1\bar{y}_2 + \bar{x}_2\bar{y}_1y_2 + \bar{x}_1y_1.$$

They in turn yield the maps shown in Table 1.6*a*, *b*, and *c*. It is now a straight-forward matter to construct the flow matrix shown as Table 1.6*d*. Note, for example, that in total state 2-01 $\tau_1 = 1$ and $\tau_2 = 0$. Hence y_1 will change,

Table 1.6

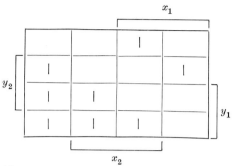

(a) z-map.

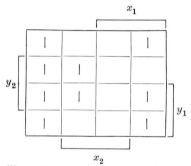

(b) τ_1-map.

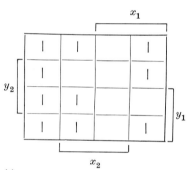

(c) τ_2-map.

	x_1x_2					
	00	01	11	10	y_1	y_2
1	3, 0	2, 0	1, 1	3, 0	0	0
2	4, 1	3, 0	2, 0	1, 1	0	1
3	1, 1	1, 1	3, 0	2, 0	1	1
4	2, 1	3, 1	4, 1	2, 0	1	0

(d) Flow matrix.

	n_1	n_2	n_3
1	2, 0	3, 0	1, 1
2	3, 0	1, 1	2, 0
3	1, 1	2, 0	3, 0

(e) Flow table.

while y_2 remains constant. Since y_1y_2 is currently 01, in the *next state*, y_1y_2 will be 11. This latter y-state corresponds to row 3; hence the next-state entry for 2-01 is 3. The output entries are obtained directly from Table 1.6a.

Now observe that, since $x_1 = x_2 = 0$ never occurs and the internal state is initially 1, there is no way to reach state 4. Hence, the flow table describing the normal behavior of the circuit need not include row 4, as shown in Table 1.6e (the 00 column has been deleted and the other columns relabeled and ordered in accord with the given interpretation of the input states.) The external behavior of the circuit is now precisely and compactly described by the derived flow table. (Note that stable states are no longer singled out by special marking, since they are not particularly significant for this type of circuit.) With 1 as the initial internal state, we can easily determine the output sequence that results from any input sequence. Suppose the input sequence is $n_3n_2n_1$, for example. The first input yields a 1-output (corresponding to total state 1-n_3) and the next state is 1. The n_2-input produces a 0-output and sends the system to state 3, where the n_1-input generates a 1-output and changes the internal state back to 1. Finding a clear, concise, verbal description that is equivalent to a given flow table is difficult at best, and usually impossible. However, in this case, after some careful study of the table, one can see that the output z becomes 1 whenever the current input brings the cumulative arithmetic sum of all inputs to a multiple of 3.

Observe that several of the transitions involve what appear to be critical races, in that both y_1 and y_2 are required to change (see, for instance, total state 1-10). Critical races are not a problem with *clocked systems* of the type under discussion, since the clock pulse will go off before any FF can change its state and have that change pass through the delay element to cause a change at the input to the combinational circuit. Thus the only requirement for the validity of a row assignment is that no code be assigned to two different rows. This easing of the row-assignment problem, and the fact that the hazard problem is virtually eliminated, motivates the use of such systems. However, a price is paid in terms of speed or reliability because the constraints on the clock pulses must be set to allow for "worst cases" of stray delays and manufacturing tolerances. Many variations of the model illustrated here are possible, and there are also important advantages to be gained by using two or more synchronized clock-pulse generators operating in different phases. Some of the timing problems involved with clocked, or synchronous, systems are discussed in Chapter 6.

An alternative representation of the information contained in Table 1.6e is shown in Fig. 1.4, which is known as a *state diagram*. The states are depicted by numbered nodes, and the transitions by arcs labeled with the inputs and outputs. Although some people argue that such graphs present their information in a more "intuitive" form, the author has found that this advantage tends to disappear rapidly as the number of states increases beyond 5 or 6. State diagrams have some advantage in describing systems with many input states but in which only a few input states are valid for each internal state. In such cases, the corresponding flow table would have many columns, but most entries would be "don't cares."

Thus far, we have introduced two principal kinds of restrictions on input signals. The first, illustrated by the traffic-light example, required only that there be a minimum time interval between successive changes. Circuits operating in this manner are referred to as *Huffman circuits*, after D. A. Huffman who developed most of the fundamental concepts involved in their analysis and synthesis.

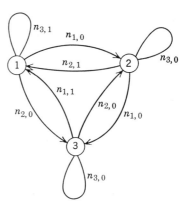

A closer examination of the physical situation indicates that, associated with such a circuit, there must really be *two* critical periods δ_1 and δ_2, where $\delta_1 > \delta_2$. If two signals change within a time interval *less* than δ_2, then they are considered as having changed simultaneously. If the changes occur *more* than δ_1 units apart, then the circuit reacts as though two *separate* input state changes have occurred. If the interval falls *between* δ_1 and δ_2, then we cannot be sure what the circuit will do. In our example, in which there are no con

Figure 1.4 State diagram equivalent to Table 1.6e.

straints on the relative timing of x_1- and x_2-changes, it is not critical whether two input changes, involving first one variable and then the other, are treated as having occurred simultaneously or consecutively. In many situations, however, it is natural to add the restriction that each change in the input state involve only one changing variable.

The general requirement that changes in the input state be minimally separated in time is very similar to the definition of *fundamental mode operation*, which can be stated as "the inputs are constrained so as to change only when the memory elements are all in stable conditions ($Y_i = y_i$ for all i)." However, this definition is more restrictive in that it would exclude systems in which a stable flow-table state corresponds to an oscillation among several y-states.

The second principal type of input constraint, illustrated by the circuit of Fig. 1.3, restricts input changes to intervals defined by externally generated clock signals. Only the *net* input change occurring during each interval is processed. A closely related constraint would be to require the input signals to go on only at the start of periods defined by clock signals and to be off whenever the clock signals are off. Given inputs meeting the former constraint, it is easy to obtain corresponding signals satisfying the latter one by simply passing each input (and its complement) through an AND gate controlled by the clock signal. Signals satisfying the latter constraint also meet the former constraint. The essential feature of *synchronous*, or *clocked*, systems is the introduction of an independently generated signal that defines the periods during which input changes are permitted.

A third class of input restrictions involves the generation of a "ready" signal by the sequential circuit. Input changes are permitted only when the ready signal (which may be though of as an *internally* generated clock pulse) is on. The advantage here is that, if the circuit can be made to generate the ready signal as soon as it has "digested" the previous input *and* if it is possible to arrange matters so that the input states can be fed to the circuit "on demand," then the average rate at which the circuit can process input changes may be significantly greater than is possible in either of the modes discussed earlier. Since basic theory of circuits operating under such constraints was developed largely by D. E. Muller, such circuits are referred to here as *Muller circuits* (the term *speed independent circuits* is also used).

A fourth category of circuits based on input constraints involves the requirement that there be a distinct input terminal for each input state, with a pulse appearing on the appropriate terminal to designate the input state (naturally, only one terminal at a time may be pulsed). The pulse widths are bounded both above and below, and a minimum time interval must elapse between successive pulses. Although no clock signals are involved, circuits of this type, which we refer to as *pulse-mode circuits*, are usually designed in virtually the same manner as synchronous circuits are. The same form of flow table is used, with the same interpretation; the row-assignment problem is the same, and the same sort of components are used.

Both Muller and Huffman circuits may be classified as *asynchronous circuits* to distinguish them from synchronous or pulsed circuits, which require the inputs to be synchronized with an external signal or pulse.

Further subdivision of circuit types can be made on the basis of the nature of the outputs. Outputs of synchronous or pulse-mode circuits can be pulses synchronized with the clock signal (as in Fig. 1.3) or with the input pulse. It is also possible to make the outputs of such circuits functions of only the internal states, without reference to the clock signals.

Outputs of asynchronous circuits may be classified with respect to the possible number of changes in the output state that may follow a single change in the input state. Probably the most important class consists of those circuits in which the output state may change at most once after a single change in the input state. Flow tables for sequential functions having this property can always be constructed so that each unstable state leads directly to a stable state with the same output state. Table 1.2 describes a function of this type, which we call a *single-output-change* (SOC) function. When the restriction that only one input variable at a time may change is added and when operation is in fundamental mode, the term *normal fundamental mode* is often used.

A broader class would include functions in which the output state may change more than once, but no more than some fixed number of times,

Table 1.7

	$x_1 x_2$			
	00	01	11	10
1	①, 00	2 , 10	①, 00	4 , 10
2	②, 10	3 , 00	②, 01	3 , 11
3	1 , 01	4 , 11	③, 01	③, 10
4	④, 10	④, 01	3 , 00	④, 01

(*a*) Multiple output changes.

	A	B	C
1	①, 0	2 , 0	4 , 0
2	1 , 0	1 , 1	4 , 0
3	1 , 1	③, 0	③, 1
4	④, 0	3 , 0	④, 1

(*b*) Unbounded number of output changes, stable states determined.

	A	B	C
1	①, 00	2, 01	①, 00
2	②, 01	3, 11	3 , 01
3	③, 11	1, 10	③, 11

(*c*) Unbounded number of output changes, stable states not determined.

following a single change in the input state. An example of such a *multiple-output-change* (MOC) function is described by Table 1.7*a*. If, with the system in 1-00, where the output state $z_1 z_2$ is 00, the input is changed to 01, the successive total states passed through will be 1-00, 1-01, 2-01, 3-01, 4-01, with outputs 00, 10, 00, 11, 01. Output z_1 changed four times, and z_2 changed twice. Note that, in this table no input change can cause any output signal to change more than four times.

Table 1.7*b* describes a function in which the output may change an *unbounded* number of times following a single input change. We refer to them as *unbounded-output-change* (UOC) functions. Thus, if, with the system in 1-*A*, the input state changes to *B*, the system will oscillate between 1-*B* and 2-*B* indefinitely until the input is changed again. This causes the output z to oscillate between 0 and 1. The number of oscillations is a function of the length of time that input state B is maintained and of the time constants of the circuit. However, once the oscillation is halted, the *next* stable state will be 1-A or 4-C, depending on whether the input state is changed to A or C, respectively, *regardless* of whether the internal state is 1 or 2 at the time of this change. Thus, the sequence of *stable* states for the flow table can always be predicted given the initial state and the input sequence.

Such is *not* the case for Table 1.7c, in which an input change from B to A may lead to any of *three* stable states, depending upon which part of the column-B cycle the system happens to be in when the change occurs.

It is sometimes useful to consider the class of functions in which no single output signal changes more than once for any one change in the input state. This class properly contains the SOC functions. For example, if a system has three output terminals, a single input change that causes the output state to go through the sequence $000 \rightarrow 100 \rightarrow 110 \rightarrow 111$ would *not* be a SOC function, but it could belong to the broader class.

Most of the material in the succeeding chapters is concerned with asynchronous circuits. Only those aspects of synchronous circuits (timing problems) are dealt with that call for techniques similar to those used in asynchronous problems. Within the area of asynchronous circuits, the emphasis is on Huffman systems; concerning which there now exists a substantial body of knowledge, particularly with reference to the synthesis problem. Much less exists in the way of formal synthesis techniques for Muller circuits. However, Chapters 4 and 6 include material on recent work which relates the two kinds of circuits by using some of the techniques developed for Huffman circuits to synthesize Muller circuits. It must be noted though that no attempt is made here to deal comprehensively with the material developed by the Muller school. The reader is, at appropriate points, referred to other sources.

1.7   Applications

Asynchronous sequential circuits of various kinds appear in a wide variety of situations, ranging from automatic elevators to interplanetary space vehicles. Some which are simple have their specifications derived fairly directly from the functions of the system in which they are embedded, as in the traffic-light example; others—some simple and some quite complex—have their specifications generated rather indirectly as part of a much larger synthesis procedure, as in the case of control circuits of general-purpose digital computers. Even when the basic systems are designed for synchronous operation, asynchronous circuits often play a part in interface situations, for example, in circuits controlling interactions between high-speed digital computers and slower peripheral units.

Often Huffman-type circuits can be designed which are faster and more reliable than synchronous or pulse-mode circuits that perform essentially the same functions, but usually the price is the use of more circuit elements. Such circuits are illustrated in Chapter 7. The frequency with which designers are finding the price to be a worthwhile expenditure seems to be increasing, and the advent of low-cost, inherently high speed, integrated circuits is likely to accelerate this trend considerably.

The rapid evolution of new components and circuit techniques and the pressure of new applications have often resulted in switching theory failing to supply answers to the problems confronting the design engineer at any given time. In part, the failure may be due to the relatively recent origins of the entire subject, combined with the multiplicity of criteria which practical designs must satisfy. It seems likely that the gap between theory and practice will diminish, since from a theoretical point of view, many apparently new component and design problems may be analogous to situations encountered earlier. For example, much of the theory pertinent to the design of relay contact networks, which are obsolete as far as high-speed systems are concerned, may be relevant to the design of logic circuits that use field effect transistors, or perhaps cryotrons.

It is the nature of engineering science that theory provides starting points for designs, indicates limits in various directions, points out critical factors, highlights the effects of certain parameters, and may provide specific solutions to particular subproblems. One should not expect to find theoretical approaches that generate complete solutions to complicated problems in systems synthesis. Thus, although switching theory may provide methods for realizing a given flow table with a minimum number of amplifiers, it does not follow that a designer should use such a technique in a rote manner, *even* if amplifiers are very expensive in the technology being used. It is almost invariably necessary to seek a design that strikes a balance among a number of different factors. The "pure" synthesis procedure that optimizes one factor is useful in establishing a limit on how far one can go in a particular direction, and it may be used to find an initial design that can then be perturbed so as to accommodate other considerations.

A number of algorithms in the field of switching theory have been programmed on digital computers, and no doubt this practice will become standard. Furthermore, one can expect the development of integrated packages of programs that the designer can conveniently use in conjunction with one another. Experience with programs of this sort indicates that the use of a computer by no means eliminates the need for a thorough understanding of the subject involved or for the development of *efficient* algorithms. The combinatorial nature of the problems arising in the design of switching circuits generally causes computation time to rise so swiftly with the size of the problem when enumerative algorithms are employed that relatively little is gained as compared with hand computation. Thus, although computerized design methods are not discussed explicitly in the succeeding chapters, it should be understood that they are in the background and do not substantially affect the significance of the material presented.

SOURCES

Detailed references to the sources of the results mentioned in this chapter are made in the subsequent chapters in which these topics are discussed more fully. An early work treating asynchronous sequential circuits as well as combinational switching theory, with the emphasis on relay circuit realizations, is by Keister, Ritchie, and Washburn [KE-1]. The foundation for the modern approach to the subject was laid by D. A. Huffman [HUF-1]. Good introductory treatments can be found in the books by Caldwell [CAL-1], McCluskey [McC-4], and Miller [MLR-1], with the last including an introduction to Muller circuits. Two other basic papers on sequential-switching theory are by Mealy [ME] and Moore [MO-1]. The terms "fundamental mode" and "normal fundamental mode" were introduced by McCluskey [McC-1]. Pertinent papers on automated design are by Smith, Tracey, Schoeffel, and Maki [SMI-1], and by Tan [TA-4]. An interesting application of the concepts presented here to parallel digital processes (in hardware and software) is by Bredt and McCluskey [BRE].

PROBLEMS

‡1.1 Assuming that only one input variable at a time may change and that the initial state is 1–00, write a concise word description of the function specified by the primitive flow table (Table P1.1).

Table P1.1

	x_1x_2				
	00	01	11	10	z
1	①	5	–	7	0
2	②	6	–	7	0
3	③	6	–	7	1
4	2	④	10	–	0
5	3	⑤	10	–	0
6	3	⑥	10	–	1
7	1	–	11	⑦	0
8	1	–	12	⑧	0
9	1	–	12	⑨	1
10	–	4	⑩	8	0
11	–	4	⑪	9	0
12	–	4	⑫	9	1

‡ Solutions are supplied at the end of the book to all problems marked with ‡ or *

1.2 Write a minimal *primitive* flow table for a sequential function having two inputs, x_1 and x_2, and one output z to conform to the following requirements:

(a) Whenever x_1 changes from 0 to 1, z changes three times.

(b) Whenever x_2 changes from 0 to 1, z changes twice.

(c) At all other times, z remains constant.

(d) Assume that x_1 and x_2 never change simultaneously and that input changes are spaced far enough apart so as never to occur while z is changing.

(e) In state 1–00, $z = 0$.

1.3 A seldom-used one-lane stretch of road is traversed occasionally by autos and trucks, *which may be going in either direction.* We wish to design a system that will detect trucks going from *left* to *right.* This will be done by placing a pair of photocell detectors x_1 and x_2 at a point on the road as shown in Fig. P1.3. They are separated

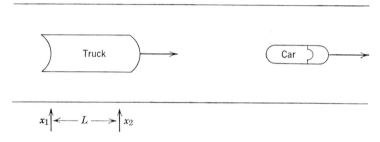

Figure P1.3

by a distance L, and each emits a constant voltage signal as long as any part of any vehicle is in front of it. All trucks exceed L in length and are shorter than $2L$, and all nontrucks are shorter than L. Assume that, in the vicinity of the photocells, no two vehicles ever come closer together than $2L$.

Specify a primitive flow table for an asynchronous function with inputs x_1 and x_2 that causes an output Z to go on once for each truck headed rightward.

‡**1.4** Construct a primitive flow table for a sequential circuit that will generate clock pulses C_1 and C_2 (for a system with a two-phase clock) as follows:

The input to this circuit is a train of pulses with minimum width w and minimum spacing between pulses s. A C_1-pulse is to be followed by a C_2-pulse after an interval no less than s, and the same minimum interval should elapse after a C_2-pulse prior to the next C_1-pulse. Pulse widths of C_1 and C_2 should approximate w. In effect, we wish to distribute the input pulses alternately to the C_1 and C_2 terminals.

1.5 In a pulsed, synchronous system, we wish to resynchronize a signal x at a given location. At this terminal, x, if it appears at all, will be on at time t. However, because of stray delays, we are uncertain about how long prior to t_1 its leading edge may appear. In order to remove this uncertainty, we plan to generate a new signal z that will have its leading edge at t and that will have duration w if x is on at t. The plan is to be accomplished by means of a retiming signal k which goes on at t and off at $t + w$. Specify a primitive flow table for a circuit that will generate z from x and k.

1.6 Consider a synchronous sequential function of one variable x which emits a 1-output whenever the number of 1-inputs up to that time exceeds the number of 0-inputs. Otherwise the output is 0. If possible, write a flow table for such a function. Otherwise discuss briefly the difficulty.

CHAPTER 2

Flow-table Reduction

There are several reasons for wishing to reduce the number of rows in a flow table. One is that the more compact form may be easier to understand. Redundant states may obscure the operation of the system being described. A second reason is that reducing the number of states may lead to a reduction in the number of state variables needed to encode the table. This in turn means a savings in those components (perhaps, delay elements, amplifiers, or flip-flops) that are associated with each state variable. A savings in logic may also result since fewer state-variable excitation functions will have to be realized and since the remaining state-variable and output functions may have fewer arguments. Even if the number of state variables is not reduced, logic savings may result from the introduction of additional "don't care" rows in the flow matrix. Note that when any of the above-mentioned economies are realized, they are accompanied by increased reliability and reduced maintenance and wiring costs (fewer parts to fail, inspect for failure and replace, or wire, respectively).

None of the advantages mentioned are infallibly associated with state reduction. It is possible to display cases in which a reduced table is *less* comprehensible than an equivalent version with more states, and there are tables that cannot be realized without more complex logic than that required in realizing an equivalent table with more rows coded with more state variables. However, on the average, in the absence of knowledge to the contrary, complexity can be expected to decrease with the number of states. It is quite unlikely that a nonminimal table, as originally constructed, will just happen to be in the form leading to an optimal solution. The designer should be able to eliminate the inadvertant redundancy present in the given table and *then* in a systematic manner perhaps expand the table to force it into some desirable form.

In the course of exploring the flow-table reduction problem, various covering and equivalence relations are developed that are potentially useful in manipulating flow tables for purposes other than the elimination of superfluous states.

The approach to the flow-table reduction problem that is taken here is quite general in that it is applicable to flow tables representing synchronous as well as asynchronous functions, and to incompletely specified tables. In fact, the basic theory to be developed in the first five sections deals with synchronous functions, and the aspects of the problem peculiar to asynchronous functions are postponed until Section 2.6.

2.1 General Concepts

Consider the function described by Table 2.1a. It is assumed that the system described is always in some internal state (row) and that, when an input occurs, the resulting output and next internal state are given by the

Table 2.1

	A	B	C	D
1	2, 0	–, 1	3, –	2, 0
2	3, 0	5, 1	2, 0	–
3	3, 0	4, 1	–	5, 0
4	–	1, 1	2, –	–
5	–	–	1, 1	–

(*a*) Incompletely specified sequential function.

	A	B	C	D
t	*t*, –	*t*, –	*t*, –	*t*, –

(*b*) Trap row.

appropriate table entries. Thus, if, with the system initially in row 1, the input sequence *AAABB* is applied, the system will pass through the states 2, 3, 3, 4 and end up in state 1, emitting the output sequence 00011.

The dashes in the table indicate unspecified entries. If, with the system initially in state 3, the input sequence *BCC* is applied, the resulting output sequence is 1–0. The interpretation of the dash is that we *don't care* what output symbol is emitted at that time. A circuit would be considered to meet the specifications for this condition regardless of whether it generated a 0 or a 1 in the position of the dash, and it is *not* necessary that the generated output corresponding to a particular dash in the flow table always be the same. This is a key point since it means that we cannot always reduce a table with don't cares by filling in the dashes in all possible ways and then reducing each of the resulting fully specified tables (see Problem 2.2).

If, starting in state 4, the input sequence BB is applied, then the sequence of internal states that results is 1 –, and the output sequence is 11. Here, since an unspecified next-state entry is encountered, the internal state becomes and remains unspecified from that point on; hence, regardless of what inputs are applied after the BB, the outputs will all be unspecified. The effect of unspecified next-state entries can be obtained by adding to the table a "trap" row t (Table 2.1b), all of whose next-state entries are t and outputs unspecified. All unspecified next-state entries are then filled in with t's. It is not necessary to resort to this technique in applying the methods to be discussed here.

A state s_A of a flow table A is said to *cover* a state s_B of a flow table B if, for every finite input sequence, the output from A when started in s_A is the same as the output from B when started in s_B whenever the latter is specified. For example, if s_A covers s_B and there is some input sequence generating 0–1—0 from s_B, then the same input sequence might generate 001–00 from s_A.

A flow table A is said to *cover* a flow table B if every state of B is covered by at least one state of A. If table A covers table B, then table A is a satisfactory replacement for table B in that any circuit conforming to A will conform to the specifications of B. The flow-table reduction problem is that of finding a flow table with a minimal number of rows that covers the given table. Note that the covering relation (both for states and for tables) is reflexive and transitive, but *not* symmetric.

Flow tables A and B are said to be *equivalent* if A covers B *and B* covers A. For fully specified flow tables, it is easy to show (see Section 2.4) that if A covers B, then B covers A, so that two fully specified tables must be equivalent if one covers the other. The definition of equivalence is a simple generalization of the definition stated in terms of fully specified tables. Two tables are *trivially equivalent* if they are the same except for a relabeling of the rows.

In cases in which the initial state is restricted to a proper subset of all the states, then obviously states not accessible from any initial state may be deleted immediately. It is assumed subsequently that any such deletion has already been made before our procedures are applied. Incidentally, a *strongly connected* flow table is one for which, given any two states i and j, there exists some input sequence that takes the system from i to j.

2.2   Compatible States

If a table B can be covered by a table A with fewer rows, then there must be sets of rows of B that can be covered by single rows of A. This suggests the definition of two states of a flow table as being *compatible* if they are both covered by a single row of some flow table A. A set of states of a flow table which is covered by a single state of some flow table is referred to as a *compatible set* or simply as a *compatible*. Determining the compatibles of a flow table is a key step in the reduction process. Before proceeding, however, we first introduce some notation that is useful both here and later on.

Given input and internal states I and s, respectively, we define $N(s, I)$ and $Z(s, I)$, respectively, as the next-state and output entries, if specified, for the total state s-I. Furthermore, if $\mathscr{I}$ is a *sequence* of input states, we define $Z(s, \mathscr{I})$ as the *last* member of the output sequence, if specified, when $\mathscr{I}$ is applied with the system initially in s. Similarly, $N(s, \mathscr{I})$ is defined as the state that the system is taken to by $\mathscr{I}$, if specified, when started in s.

Referring now to Table 2.1a, we ask whether rows 2 and 5 can be covered by a single state s_{25} of any table? If so, then what should the output entries be for s_{25}? In column A, a 0 is needed if 2 is to be covered, and this is also satisfactory for 5, since $Z(5, A)$ is unspecified in this column. Similarly, a 1-output is required for the B column. For the D-input, since the outputs are not specified for 2 or 5, the s_{25} output in this column may also be left unspecified. In order to cover 2 for the input sequence consisting of C, $Z(s_{25}, C)$ must be 0. But then s_{25} does not cover 5, which has a 1-output for this sequence. Hence, no single row can cover 2 and 5 because their outputs are specified to be different in column C. Thus 2 and 5 are incompatible.

In general, a necessary condition for the compatibility of two rows is that, in each column where outputs are specified for both, the specifications should be the same. This condition is referred to more concisely as *output compatibility*.

The pair of rows 1 and 3 meet the above condition. Hence, in attempting to construct a row s_{13} that covers both of them, there is no problem in specifying the output entries. In each column I, $Z(s_{13}, I)$ is set equal to $Z(1, I)$ or to $Z(3, I)$ (whichever is specified); $Z(s_{13}, I)$ is left unspecified if $Z(1, I)$ and $Z(3, I)$ are both unspecified. (Reading from left to right the s_{13} outputs are 0, 1, –, 0.) This assignment ensures that the covering definition will be satisfied for all input sequences of unit length. Consider, however, the problem of filling in the next-state entries of s_{13}, with particular reference to column D. In order for s_{13} to cover 1, $N(s_{13}, D)$ must specify a row that covers 2, which is $N(1, D)$. This requirement is necessary since, if $\mathscr{I}$ is an arbitrary input sequence, then (where $D\mathscr{I}$ is the sequence that consists of D followed by $\mathscr{I}$)

$$Z(s_{13}, D\mathscr{I})$$

must be the same as $Z(2, \mathscr{I})$, wherever the latter is specified. Similarly, $N(s_{13}, D)$ must also correspond to a row covering 5, which is $N(3, D)$. But this means that there must be a single state covering both 2 and 5, a pair of rows previously shown to be incompatible. Hence there is no possible satisfactory value for $N(s_{13}, D)$; therefore s_{13} cannot exist, so that rows 1 and 3 are also incompatible. Let us write $a \sim b$ if a and b are compatible and $a \nsim b$ otherwise.

The above argument may be summarized by saying that $1 \sim 3$ implies $2 \sim 5$, and since $2 \nsim 5$ it follows that $1 \nsim 3$.

In general we say that a set Q *implies* the set R if R is the set of next-state entries for Q under some particular input. The preceding example can easily be generalized to show that, if p and q are compatible, then so is every pair of rows implied by pq. This generalization prepares the ground for the following lemma:

LEMMA 2.1 *Q is a compatible iff Q is output compatible and Q does not imply an output incompatible set through any sequence of implications.*

PROOF. (*a*) First consider the "only if" part. If Q is not output compatible, it is clearly incompatible, since there would be no way of specifying output entries for a covering state. Suppose Q implies an output incompatible set Q_m through a sequence of sets $Q, Q_1, \ldots, Q_m$ such that each member of the sequence implies the next member. Then Q_{m-1} must be incompatible, since for any state purported to cover Q_{m-1} there can be no satisfactory next-state entry for the input under which Q_{m-1} implies Q_m. The argument can now be carried backward through the sequence to establish the incompatibility of Q.

(*b*) For the "if" part, we assume that Q satisfies the hypothesis. Then a table B can be constructed with a state s_Q such that if $q_1 \in Q$ and I is an input such that $Z(q_1, I)$ is specified, then $Z(s_Q, I) = Z(q_1, I)$. Now let R be the set implied by Q under some input J. Then clearly R too satisfies the hypothesis. Hence if $N(s_Q, J)$ is specified as s_R in table B, the outputs for s_R can be selected to satisfy the outputs of the members of R in the same sense that the s_Q outputs were chosen to satisfy the outputs of the members of Q. Furthermore, the next-state entries of s_R can be generated in the same manner as those for s_Q. Iterating this process yields a state of B for each set of states directly or indirectly implied by Q. (It is a finite process, since there can only be a finite number of such sets.) But now it is easy to see that for every input sequence $\mathscr{I}$, and every state $q \in Q$, $Z(q, \mathscr{I})$ when specified must equal $Z(s_Q, \mathscr{I})$, hence s_Q covers Q. This establishes Q as a compatible.

It is now possible to specify a simple recursive procedure for finding all *incompatible* pairs of a flow table and hence indirectly detecting all compatible pairs.

PROCEDURE 2.1 *Finding Incompatible Pairs*

1. List all pairs that are output incompatible.
2. Add to the list all pairs that imply pairs already on the list.
   Repeat this step until no new pairs can be added.

In our example, step 1 yields only the pair 25. Repeated application of step 2 then successively adds to the list of incompatible pairs 13, 15, and 24.

All other state pairs are compatible, namely, 12, 14, 23, 34, 35, and 45. We note at this point that compatibility although a reflexive (x is clearly compatible with x) and symmetric ($a \sim b$ is equivalent to $b \sim a$) relation, is *not* transitive. Thus in our example, although $1 \sim 2$ and $2 \sim 3$, it is *not* true that $1 \sim 3$.

Procedure 2.1 can be organized for more efficient implementation with the aid of a *pair chart* as shown in Table 2.2a. There is a unique position in the

Table 2.2

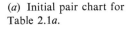

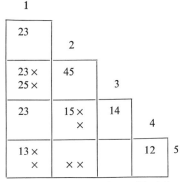

(a) Initial pair chart for Table 2.1a.

(b) Final pair chart for Table 2.1a.

chart for each pair of states. If a pair of states is output incompatible, then an × is entered in its position (see 25 in our example). Otherwise all the pairs implied by pair ij are entered in position ij. Thus, for example, since 13 implies 23 and 25, these two pairs are entered in the 13 position. The situation in which ij implies ij is of no consequence and is ignored. Two states that are output compatible and imply no other pairs are obviously compatible; this circumstance is indicated by a blank in the chart (see 35 in the example). Now we start from the ×-cells and trace backwards to add other incompatibles to the list. Select an ×-cell (25 is the only one in the example at the start) and place ×'s in all cells that have its coordinates as entries. In the example (see now Table 2.2b) this leads to an × being placed in 13. Then place a second × in the initial ×-cell to signify that it need not be considered any further. Repeat this process until no cells with single ×'s remain. In the example we next select 13, place an × in 15, add a second × to 13, and so forth. As a final check, we ascertain that all implications in cells without ×'s refer to other cells without ×'s. This case is shown in Table 2.2b, which is referred to as the *final pair chart*. The cells with ×'s correspond to incompatibles, and the other cells correspond to compatibles. This is an efficient process that can be carried out effectively for fairly large tables.

Having found the compatible pairs, we would now like to find larger sets of states that can be covered by single states of some table. In fact we would like to be able to find *all* of the compatibles. First observe that, if S is a compatible, then any subset of S is certainly a compatible since a state covering S also covers every subset of S. Let us define a *maximal compatible* (abbreviated MC) for a given flow table as a compatible that is not a subset of any larger compatible. Then given the set of all MC's it is easy to determine all other compatibles, which are of course the subsets of the MC's. Hence our next step is to develop a procedure for finding the MC's, given all of the compatible pairs. First we need the following lemma:

LEMMA 2.2   *A set of states S is a compatible iff every pair of states in S is a compatible.*

PROOF.   (*a*) Any subset of a compatible, hence any pair of states of a compatible, must also be a compatible, since any state covering a set clearly must also cover all of its subsets.

(*b*) Suppose that every pair of states of S is a compatible. Then it follows easily that S must be output compatible. If R is a set implied by S then every pair of states of R is implied by a pair of states of S. A corollary of Lemma 2.1 is that every set implied by a compatible set is also a compatible. Hence every pair of states of R is a compatible, so that R also satisfies the hypothesis. Hence, by an inductive argument, it follows that no sequence of implications starting with S can lead to an output incompatible set. Therefore, by Lemma 2.1, S must be a compatible.

The problem of finding MC's corresponding to a given set of compatible pairs is one that arises in a number of contexts other than the one under study here. Problem 2.15 illustrates one such situation, and another one is given in Chapter 3. Two different solution algorithms are developed here and a third one sketched. The first works directly with the compatible pairs as presented in the final pair chart, building up the compatibles step by step.

PROCEDURE 2.2   *Finding MC's from Compatible Pairs*

1. Initiate a compatible list (*c*-list) with the compatible pairs in the rightmost column having at least one non-× entry.
2. Proceed to the left, column by column. Let S_i be the set consisting of all states whose entries in the current column i have no ×'s. Intersect S_i with each member of the current *c*-list. Whenever such an intersection has more than one member, add the set consisting of the union of i and that intersection to the list. At the end of this process for column i, delete any duplicated entries and entries that are contained in other entries. Also,

add pairs consisting of i and any members of S_i that did not appear in any of the intersections.

3. The final c-list, plus any one-member sets consisting of states not in any other member of the c-list are the MC's.

As an example, consider the pair chart of Table 2.3, where blank entries signify compatible pairs. Starting at the right with column 8, we find that S_i

Table 2.3   Example for Finding MC's

```
        1
      ┌───┐
      │ × │ 2
      ├───┼───┐
      │   │   │ 3
      ├───┼───┼───┐
      │   │ × │   │ 4
      ├───┼───┼───┼───┐
      │ × │   │ × │   │ 5
      ├───┼───┼───┼───┼───┐
      │   │ × │   │ × │   │ 6
      ├───┼───┼───┼───┼───┼───┐
      │   │   │ × │   │   │   │ 7
      ├───┼───┼───┼───┼───┼───┼───┐
      │   │   │   │ × │   │ × │ × │ 8
      ├───┼───┼───┼───┼───┼───┼───┼───┐
      │ × │ × │   │   │ × │   │   │   │ 9
      └───┴───┴───┴───┴───┴───┴───┴───┘
```

and the c-list after the indicated column has been processed are as shown below:

First step: $c = \{89\}$,
$S_7 = 9$: $c = \{89, 79\}$,
$S_6 = 79$: $c = \{89, 679\}$,
$S_5 = 78$: $c = \{89, 679, 57, 58\}$,
$S_4 = 5679$: $c = \{89, 4679, 457, 58\}$,
$S_3 = 4689$: $c = \{389, 4679, 3469, 457, 58\}$,
$S_2 = 3578$: $c = \{389, 238, 4679, 3469, 457, 257, 258\}$,
$S_1 = 34678$: $c = \{389, 138, 238, 4679, 1467, 3469, 1346, 457, 257, 358\}$.

It does not seem necessary to prove the validity of this method, as it is quite straightforward. The next method, though not particularly efficient as it stands, has a more sophisticated basis. It operates with the *incompatible* pairs.

Consider $\mathcal{K}$, the set of compatibles corresponding to the final pair chart of Table 2.2*b*, where the incompatible pairs are 13, 15, 24, and 25. No member of $\mathcal{K}$ can contain 1 and 3, or 1 and 5, or 2 and 4, or 2 and 5. The set of states *missing* from each member of $\mathcal{K}$, which we refer to as its *complementary set*, must include 1 or 3, and 1 or 5, and 2 or 4, and 2 or 5. Expressing this algebraically, we see that the complementary set for each member of $\mathcal{K}$ must satisfy the Bolean expression

$$A = (1 + 3)(1 + 5)(2 + 4)(2 + 5).$$

(A set "satisfies" A if $A = 1$ when only those elements of A belonging to the set are set equal to 1.) Thus every product term p of A corresponds to a compatible, which can be obtained by taking the set of elements *not* in p, and every compatible c corresponds to a product term of A, obtainable by taking the set of elements not in c.

Consider now a *maximal* compatible. Its complementary set is of *minimal* size, and since the minimal product terms of a function are its prime implicants, it follows that a product term of A corresponding to the complementary set of a maximal compatible is a prime implicant. Conversely, if p is a prime implicant of A, then the corresponding compatible is maximal, since nothing can be added to its complementary set. Hence the MC's are simply the complementary sets of the prime implicants of A. This then gives us our second procedure for finding MC's.

PROCEDURE 2.3 *Finding MC's from Incompatible Pairs*

1. Form a Boolean product-of-sums expression A, with each sum term composed of the members of an incompatible pair and in which every such pair appears exactly once.
2. Find the prime implicants of A.
3. Generate an MC from each prime implicant by taking the set of states *not* represented in the prime implicant.

Applying this method to the example of Table 2.2*b*, we start with

$$A = (1 + 3)(1 + 5)(2 + 4)(2 + 5).$$

It is convenient to apply the distributive law to obtain

$$A = (1 + 35)(2 + 45).$$

Multiplying out yields

$$A = 12 + 145 + 235 + 345.$$

Since A is always a monotone increasing function (no complemented terms are involved), the only processing of the sum-of-products expression required is to eliminate terms subsumed by other terms (the absorption law). Since there are no such redundant terms in the above expression, it follows that each of its terms is a prime implicant. (Incidentally, the reduced sum form of a monotone increasing function—or any unate function—consists of the sum of *all* of its prime implicants.) Applying step 3, we then obtain the MC's, 345, 23, 14, and 12.

For a large table, finding the prime implicants of A may be somewhat messy, and it is very desirable to develop efficient techniques tailored to the characteristics of the problem as it appears here. An obvious minor step is to combine at the outset the terms derived from each column, by using the distributive law of Boolean algebra. For the problem in Table 2.3 we get:

$$A = (1 + 259)(2 + 469)(3 + 57)(4 + 8)(5 + 69)(6 + 8)(7 + 8).$$

A good appreciation of the computational complexity of Procedure 2.3 may be attained by completing the solution of this problem.

A third procedure for finding the MC's is mentioned briefly. It is in a sense dual to Procedure 2.2 in that it involves using the *incompatible* pairs, working from left to right in the pair chart, and decomposing sets (instead of building them up) to obtain the MC's. For the example in Table 2.3, we start in column 1 with the two sets that are consistent with the incompatibles of that column, one set consisting of all elements *except* for 1 (23456789) and the other consisting of all elements except those incompatible with 1 (134678). Proceeding leftward, each current set is similarly decomposed—if necessary—into two sets on the basis of the incompatibles in the current column. The final collection of sets consists of the MC's.

For hand computation, the author prefers Procedure 2.2, although it would not be easy to justify such a choice. Any of the procedures discussed can be programmed for computer execution, and such programs have been written for them, as well as for procedures not mentioned here.

As far as the flow-table reduction problem is concerned, it becomes evident in the next section that finding the MC's is *not* the most difficult part of the problem.

2.3 Closed Sets of Compatibles

After having found the MC's for a given flow table, one might feel that all that remains is to select from among them a set that covers all of the states and then to proceed to construct the reduced table. In the example of Table 2.1*a*, this approach might lead to the choice of 12 and 345. Suppose that we attempt to form a two-row table covering Table 2.1*a*, in which rows 1 and 2 of the new table cover the sets of rows 12 and 345, respectively, of the old table, as shown in Table 2.4. (To the right of each row of the reduced table is a listing

Table 2.4   An Attempt to Use the MC's 12 and 345

	A	B	C	D	
1	?, 0	2, 1	?, 0	1, 0	12
2	2, 0	?, 1	1, 1	2, 0	345

of the rows of the old table covered by this row. We follow this practice consistently in this chapter.)

There is no difficulty in filling in the output entries, since the grouped states are of course output compatible. In column D, the next-state entries of the original table for rows 1 and 2 are 2 and –, respectively; hence in the new table, the column-D entry for the row covering 1 and 2 (row 1) must correspond to a row covering 2. Thus a 1 is entered. The column-C entries for the old table in rows 3, 4, and 5 are –, 2, and 1; hence in Table 2.4 we need a next-state entry corresponding to a row covering 1 and 2 in position 2-C. Again a 1 suffices. In a similar manner, next-state entries can be found for positions 2-A, 1-B, and 2-D. What about 1-A? Here, the states covered are 1 and 2, and in Table 2.1a the next-state entries for these rows in column A are 2 and 3, respectively. But no single state of Table 2.4 covers *both* 2 and 3, and so no acceptable entry can be made. Similar situations arise in the other total states labeled with question marks in Table 2.4; for example, a row covering 1 and 4 is necessary in position 2-B.

Thus we see that despite the fact that 12 and 345 are compatible sets covering all of the rows of the original table, they are not sufficient to form the basis of a covering table.

The missing rows are those that would cover compatible sets implied by the compatibles selected for use; that is, 12 implies 23, and 345 implies 14. If rows covering these two sets are added and if they in turn do not imply any other compatibles not covered by the incremented set, then a covering table can be completed. Since 12, 23, 14, and 345 constitute the *complete* set of MC's, one would not anticipate any difficulty in filling in the next-state entries. In fact Table 2.5 has been constructed in just this manner to cover Table 2.1a. Not only was it possible to fill in the next-state entries, but in a number of cases, choices existed. For example, the entry in 2-A is required to

Table 2.5   A Table Covering Table 2.1

	A	B	C	D	
1	3, 0	2, 1	3, 0	1/3, 0	12
2	2/3, 0	4, 1	1, 1	2, 0	345
3	2/3, 0	2, 1	1/3, 0	2, 0	23
4	1/3, 0	1/4, 1	3, –	1/3, 0	14

refer to a row covering row 3 of the old table. But both rows 2 and 3 of the new table do this; hence either a 2 or a 3 would be a satisfactory entry. In order to preserve this option, which may be exercised to advantage later in the synthesis procedure, the entry 2/3 is made. Similar options are indicated elsewhere in the table.

In general, a set of compatibles can be used in the construction of a covering flow table only if both:

1. Every row of the original table is covered by at least one of the compatibles.
2. The set is *closed* in the sense that any set of rows implied by any compatible in the set is a subset of at least one compatible of the set.

The set of all MC's always meets these requirements; hence the number of MC's constitutes an upper bound on the number of rows of the minimal-covering table. However, since the number of MC's often exceeds the number of rows in the given table, it is often a rather useless bound.

There is no reason to restrict the choice of compatibles for the covering set to the MC's. In fact, it can be shown that in certain cases, such a restriction would preclude finding a minimal-row solution. Hence our problem is to select a closed set of compatibles covering all states and having a minimal number of members. This set is referred to henceforth as a *minimal closed covering*. Unfortunately there is no known simple, efficient algorithm for solving the problem in its most general form. Solutions for some important special cases are discussed in the next section, and in the remainder of this section some general principles are enunciated, and a useful heuristic technique are presented.

In building a minimal closed covering, compatibles are added or enlarged in order to cover previously uncovered states of the original table or to cover compatibles implied by previously selected members. The enlargements of a compatible may introduce implications not previously present, perhaps requiring additional expansion of the set. The introduction of new compatibles, in addition to the possibility of enlarging the implication burden, also increases the number of states in the solution table. Merging two compatibles into one larger one may also introduce new implications, but it reduces the number of states in the solution. Splitting a compatible, of course, produces the inverse effects.

If a maximal compatible uniquely covers a row of the original table and does not imply any compatible that is not one of its subsets, then it must be a member of some minimal closed covering. A compatible c_1 may always be substituted for a compatible c_2 without danger of missing a minimal solution if c_1 includes c_2 and if every compatible implied by c_1 is included in a compatible implied by c_2.

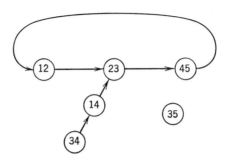

Figure 2.1 Implication graph.

The structure of implications among the two-member compatibles is so crucial that it can serve as an excellent basis for constructing a solution. An effective technique for displaying and utilizing this structure is now presented, and illustrated by finding a minimal closed covering for Table 2.1a.

After having found the maximal compatibles (12, 14, 23, and 345), we construct an *implication graph* from the final pair chart for the table (Table 2.2b) as follows. Each compatible pair is represented by a node, and if pair p_1 implies pair p_2, then an arc (directed branch) is drawn from the node representing p_1 to the node representing p_2 (see Fig. 2.1).

Now we proceed to select pairs to include in our closed covering. Since 35 implies nothing else, it can be selected, without incurring any further obligations. If we stop there and choose 1, 2, and 4 as the other members of the closed covering, we then have another four-row solution. In order to do any better, some other pair must be chosen. But now we note from the figure that every other pair implies (in general, indirectly) the three pairs 12, 23, and 45. Hence we might as well start out by choosing these. Since they imply no other pairs and cover all states, they constitute a three-member closed covering. No two of them can be combined, since two of them are MC's; hence no better solution exists. The corresponding minimal-row solution for our example is shown in Table 2.6. Note that 45 is not maximal and that 12 and 23 overlap.

In general, the implication graph is used to select pairs with minimal implications and to guide the combination process (here the MC's indicate

Table 2.6 Minimal-row Solution

	A	B	C	D	
1	2, 0	3, 1	2, 0	1/2, 0	12
2	2, 0	3, 1	1/2, 0	3, 0	23
3	—	1, 1	1, 1	—	45

the possibilities) so that whatever additional pairs are needed do not imply large numbers of previously unselected pairs. The general idea is to start at the terminal ends of the graph (with nodes that imply few or no other nodes) and work back up as necessary. Note that the graph can often be simplified by deleting arcs that parallel other paths. Implication graphs can also be constructed with nodes representing larger compatibles, but these may become too unwieldy.

Although the MC's and the pairwise implications are valuable guides in constructing a solution, they may lack necessary information in some cases, namely, implications among multiple-member compatibles. For example, if *abc* implies *def*, it follows that the pairs *ab*, *bc*, and *ac* imply the pairs *de*, *df*, and *ef* (not necessarily in this order), but the converse may or may not be true. Hence, after finding a solution using the implication graph, it is necessary. to verify that all implications among multiple-member compatibles are satisfied. If the ostensibly closed set of compatibles can be used to construct a flow table, then this condition must have been satisfied. In fact, the successful construction of a flow table from a collection of sets of states always serves as a check on the fact that collection is indeed a closed set of compatibles. In problem 2.8 at the end of this chapter, the significance of multimember compatible implications is illustrated.

A sometimes useful *lower* bound on the size of the smallest closed set of compatibles is the cardinality of the largest maximal *incompatible*. The latter can be found from the pair chart by applying any of the techniques for finding MC's to the *incompatible* pairs.

A rather difficult state-reduction problem is now solved, namely, that of reducing Table 2.7a, for which the final pair chart and MC's are shown in Table 2.7b, and the implication graph in Fig. 2.2. (After making a rough sketch of the latter, it was redrawn with some arcs deleted or rerouted so as to retain the essential structure in a neater form.) The following discussion

Table 2.7 a   A Difficult Table

	A	B	C	D
1	2, —	4, —	—	3, —
2	6, —	9, —	—	—
3	—	—	7, —	8, —
4	2, —	1, —	6, —	5, —
5	—	—	—	6, —
6	1, 0	—	2, —	—, 1
7	5, 1	2, —	—	—
8	5, —	—	—	1, 0
9	5, —	3, —	—	—

Table 2.7b   Pair Chart and MC's

1	2	3	4	5	6	7	8	9	mc's
26 49	**2**								45789 4569
38		**3**							23789
35× ×	19× 26×	58× 67×	**4**						2369
36		68× ×	56	**5**					25789
12	16	27	12 26		**6**				2569
24× 25×	29 56		12 25		× ×	**7**			1238
13 25	56	18	15 25	16	× ×		**8**		1236
25× 34×	39 56		13 25		15	23		**9**	1258
									1256

does not include every detail of the solution process in that only a few of the "dead-end" paths are mentioned.

First we observe that the states included in compatibles without implications are 2, 3, 5, 6, 7, 8, and 9. They can best be covered by using four compatibles, such as, 9, 23, 56, and 78. None of the compatibles involved can be combined (without bringing in pairs with implications), and so the best that can be done with implication-free compatibles is a six-member solution. Now we try to improve on this by working our way up some chain in the graph. Starting with the 25 at the bottom of one chain, we see that the next step up adds the loop consisting of 13, 18, and 38; these three have no other implications and can be combined to give us 138. Thus another six-member solution consists of {25 , 138, 4, 6, 7, 9}. But moving up the chain one more step enables us to combine the 4 and 9, which yields {25, 138, 49, 6, 7}, a five-member solution. Moving up still another step brings in the set 12, 26, and 16 which can be combined to permit the 6 in our solution to be replaced by 126. This replacement does not immediately reduce the number of compatibles in our set, which is now {25, 138, 49, 126, 7}, but it does permit us to add other pairs that imply 12, 26, and 16. The possibility of combining two of the

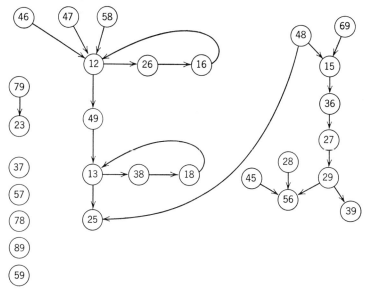

Figure 2.2 Revised implication graph.

compatibles in the current set is now investigated. A number of possibilities, such as merging 25 and 138, can be discarded at once by inspection of the MC's. Although 1256 is an MC, we do not pursue the possibility of merging 25 with 126 because it requires the pair 15, which a glance at the implication graph tells us would require the addition of many new pairs. The same reason, in slightly weaker form, discourages us from trying to merge 25 and 7.

The next possibility is to form 479 from 4 and 7. This requires us to satisfy the implications of 47 and 79. The former is already covered, and the latter requires us to include one new pair, namely, 23. If we do this, we obtain {25, 138, 126, 479, 23}. Combining 23 and 138 requires the addition of 56, an implication of 28, yielding {25, 126, 479, 1238, 56}. But now 25 and 56 can be merged without further obligation, giving us {126, 479, 1238, 256}, a four-member solution. Observe that the step-by-step transformations are carefully selected so that each requires a minimum additional burden of implied pairs.

At this stage, or perhaps after some attempts to reduce further the set, we suspect that four may be the minimum. The only two-member set of compatibles covering all nine rows are the MC's 1236 and 45789, and they do not form a closed set (36, for example, implies 27 which is not in the set). Hence no two-member solution exists, and there remains only the question of whether there is a three-member solution.

First we attempt to find one by splitting a member of {1236, 45789} in order to get rid of implications not in the set. However, *both* compatibles would have to be split, since 45 implies 56, which is not in the set. Hence any three-member solution would have to involve compatibles that are subsets of *three* different MC's.

There are 21 three-member sets of MC's that cover the nine states, and no closed covering can be found generated from any of them by taking one subset of each member. (Splitting a member would of course mean a solution with four or more members.) We spare the reader the entire enumeration and simply select one case at random, namely, {4569, 23789, 1238}, to illustrate

Table 2.8   A Minimal-row Table Covering Table 2.7a

	A	B	C	D	
1	1, 0	2, –	1/3/4, –	3, 1	126
2	4, 1	3, –	1/4, –	4, –	479
3	4, –	2, –	2, –	3, –	1238
4	1, 0	2, –	1/3/4, –	1/4, 1	256

the nature of the process. The states 4 and 6 each appear only once in this set and hence cannot be deleted from the first member, which contains both of them. But, an inspection of Fig. 2.2 indicates that the pair 46 indirectly implies 16, which is not a subset of any number of {4569, 23789, 1238}; hence no three-member closed covering is derivable from this candidate.

Thus, Table 2.7a cannot be reduced to less than four-rows, and we have found one such solution, namely, Table 2.8, based on the closed covering developed earlier. There may very well be other four-row solutions unrelated to Table 2.8.

The methods discussed here, although partially enumerative and heuristic, nevertheless have been found to be effective for flow tables with as many as fifteen rows. It would be interesting to see how sucessfully they could be implemented on a digital computer.

In the next two sections some important special cases are treated for which efficient reduction algorithms exist. Partial reductions are also discussed.

2.4   Equivalence, Fully Specified Tables, and Partial Mergers

Consider a state p of a fully specified flow table. If q is a state of the same or some other table and q covers p, then it must also be true that p covers q. This follows because for *every* input sequence $\mathscr{I}$, $Z(p, \mathscr{I})$ is specified and $Z(q, \mathscr{I})$ must equal $Z(p, \mathscr{I})$. Thus the covering relation is symmetric and hence is an equivalence relation when a fully specified table is involved (as is pointed out in Section 2.1, the covering relation in general is reflexive and transitive). It now follows that, if a fully specified table T_1 is covered by a table T_2, then T_2 (assuming it has no extraneous states not reachable from the states covering T_1) must also be fully specified, and furthermore T_1 covers T_2. Hence T_1 and T_2 are equivalent in the sense defined in Section 2.1.

Now suppose that p and r are compatible states of a fully specified flow table. Then some state q covers both of them. Hence p and r are equivalent to q, and therefore they are equivalent to one another. Thus for fully specified tables, compatibility becomes an equivalence relation. This means that all the states of a fully specified table can be partitioned into mutually disjoint sets, within each of which all members are equivalent. These sets are none other than the MC's, which therefore constitute a unique minimal closed covering. This fact leads directly to a minimal-row solution that is unique within trivial relabelings of the names of the rows. Furthermore, finding the MC's given the compatible pairs is particularly simple. We summarize the procedure for reducing fully specified flow tables as follows:

PROCEDURE 2.4   *Reduction of Fully Specified Flow Tables*

1. Find the two-member compatibles as in Procedure 2.1.
2. Find the MC's as follows:
   2.1. List as the first MC the set consisting of row 1 and all states compatible with row 1 as indicated by the entries in column 1 of the final pair chart.
   2.2. Having listed the first $j - 1$ MC's, add to the list as the jth MC the set consisting of k, the smallest number corresponding to a state not yet included in any member of the list, and all of the states compatible with k as indicated by the entries in column k of the final pair chart. Repeat this step until all states have appeared in some MC. It may be necessary to add some one-member MC's corresponding to states incompatible with all other states.
3. From the reduced table form the closed covering consisting of all the MC's as in Section 2.3.

As an example of the application of the above process, consider Table 2.9a, a fully specified table, with final pair chart Table 2.9b, MC's (listed in the order found) 135, 24, 6, and minimal-row equivalent Table 2.9c.

In many cases when an incompletely specified flow table is to be reduced, there may be a number of pairs of rows that are obviously compatible and that imply no other pairs of rows or imply only pairs that are obviously compatible. One may then be tempted to carry out some preliminary row mergers before applying the general row-reduction procedure in the hope of

Table 2.9

x

	0	1
1	3, 0	2, 1
2	1, 1	6, 0
3	5, 0	2, 1
4	5, 1	6, 0
5	5, 0	4, 1
6	2, 0	1, 1

(a) Fully specified table.

1					
× ×	2				
35	× ×	3			
× ×	15	× ×	4		
35 24	× ×	24	× ×	5	
12× 23×	× ×	12× 25×	× ×	14× 25×	6

(b) Final pair chart.

x

	0	1	
1	1, 0	2, 1	135
2	1, 1	3, 0	24
3	2, 0	1, 1	6

(c) Reduced table.

reducing the overall amount of computation. For example, an inspection of Table 2.10a indicates that we could immediately merge the sets of rows 1236 and 45 since each set implies only a subset of the other. This leads to Table 2.10b which cannot be reduced any further since no two of its rows are compatible. A less ambitious preliminary step would be to merge 123 and 45 to obtain Table 2.10c. The techniques discussed earlier in this chapter then lead at once to a further reduction to Table 2.10d which has *fewer* rows than Table 2.10b. Hence we see a case where the wrong kind of preliminary merger leads to a "dead-end" table that cannot be further reduced. (Note that, if rows 1 and 3 of Table 2.10c are merged—surely an "obvious" merger—then the same impasse is reached.)

The point here is that, since covering is not, in general, a symmetric relation, it is possible to find a table B that covers a table A *and* a table D that covers A but *not* B. If B is the result of a preliminary merger, and D a minimal-row table covering A, then it may be that neither D nor any other minimal-row table covering A also covers B so that the preliminary merger

Table 2.10

	A	B	C
1	1, 0	2, –	5, 0
2	2, 0	3, –	4, 0
3	2, 0	1, –	4, 0
4	–	2, –	7, 1
5	–	1, –	7, 1
6	1, –	2, –	5, 0
7	1, 1	2, 1	8, 0
8	6, 0	3, 0	6, 1

(a) Table to be reduced.

	A	B	C	
1	1, 0	1, –	2, 0	1236
2	–	1, –	3, 1	45
3	1, 1	1, 1	4, 0	7
4	1, 0	1, 0	1, 1	8

(b) The wrong kind of preliminary mergers.

	A	B	C	
1	1, 0	1, –	2, 0	123
2	–	1, –	4, 1	45
3	1, –	1, –	2, 0	6
4	1, 1	1, 1	5, 0	7
5	3, 0	1, 0	3, 1	8

(c) A useful preliminary merger.

	A	B	C	
1	1, 0	1, –	2, 0	1
2	3, 0	1, 0	3, 1	25
3	1, 1	1, 1	2, 0	34

(d) Minimal-row table covering (a) and (c).

precludes finding the desired solution. If, however, preliminary mergers are made only when the resulting table is equivalent to the given table, then this risk is eliminated. Thus, if the preliminary merger yields a table C that is equivalent to A, then any table covering A also covers C; hence the smallest table covering C is also the smallest table covering A. We now indicate how to restrict preliminary mergers so as to achieve this effect.

Define two states as being *I-equivalent unless*:

1. They are output incompatible, or
2. In some column the next-state or output entry of one of them is unspecified while the corresponding entry for the other *is* specified, or
3. They imply a pair of rows that are not *I*-equivalent because of (1), (2), or (3).

This definition reduces to the standard definition of equivalence (discussed earlier) for fully specified tables. If we apply this definition to incompletely specified tables, it amounts to treating dashes as specific outputs or next states, and it is not hard to show that two states are *I*-equivalent if and only if they cover one another. If a table C is obtained from a table A by merging *I*-equivalent states (this is how Table 2.10c was derived from Table 2.10a), then C and A will be equivalent, as desired. Since finding the minimal-row *equivalent* of a given table is much simpler than finding the minimal covering (Procedure 2.4 is essentially applicable if we use *I*-equivalence instead of compatibility), it may be computationally advantageous to use the two-stage process illustrated by Table 2.10. The reversible nature of the process of reduction to an equivalent table, as opposed to the generally irreversible nature of reductions to covering tables, may also be significant under certain circumstances.

2.5 Restrictions on Input Sequences

A common source of optional (don't care) entries in flow tables are restrictions on the kinds of input sequence permitted. In particular, when the optional entries result from the knowledge that certain consecutive pairs of input signals cannot occur, the reduction problem is significantly simplified in that all sets of MC's that cover every row are closed.

First some definitions are necessary to make the concepts more precise:

An ordered pair of input symbols $\mathscr{F}$ is a *forbidden pair* (for some flow table) if for all states s, $N(s, \mathscr{F})$ and $Z(s, \mathscr{F})$ are undefined. A flow table is defined as *pair restricted* if for every state s, $N(s, I_1I_2)$ and $Z(s, I_1I_2)$ are both defined *unless* (a) I_1I_2 is forbidden, or (b) there is an input I_0 such that I_0I_1 is forbidden and a state t such that $N(t, I_0) = s$. If either (a) or (b) is true, then *both* $Z(s, I_1I_2)$ and $N(s, I_1I_2)$ are undefined.

Roughly speaking, a pair-restricted table is one in which all of the optional entries can be accounted for by the existence of one or more disallowed two-member input sequences. As an example of a pair-restricted table, consider Table 2.11a. No matter what state we start in, applying either CA or DB leaves the final output and state unspecified. Furthermore, no total

Table 2.11 *a*   A Pair-restricted Flow Table

	A	B	C	D
1	6, 0	1, 0	2, 0	4, 0
2	—	6, 0	2, 0	4, 0
3	—	1, 0	3, 0	4, 0
4	5, 1	—	2, 0	4, 0
5	5, 1	5, 0	3, 0	4, 0
6	1, 0	6, 0	3, 0	4, 0

Table 2.11*b*   Covering Table

		States					
		1	2	3	4	5	6
	45				1	1	
MC's	234		1	1	1		
	1236	1	1	1			1

state for which the next-state and output entries are optional can be reached by any two-member sequence other than CA or DB. It is not difficult to test an arbitrary flow table for this property.

The following lemma is now necessary to establish that compatibility is transitive under certain conditions for a pair-restricted flow table:

LEMMA 2.3 *If a flow table is pair restricted and has an input I_0 and states i, j, k, p, and q such that $i \sim j$, $j \sim k$, $N(p, I_0) = i$, and $N(q, I_0) = j$, then $i \sim k$.*

PROOF.   (By contradiction.) Suppose $i \nsim k$. Then for some input sequence $\mathscr{L}$, $Z(i, \mathscr{L})$ and $Z(k, \mathscr{L})$ are both defined and unequal. Let $I_0\mathscr{L}$ be the sequence consisting of I_0 followed by $\mathscr{L}$. Then since $N(p, I_0) = i$, it follows that $Z(p, I_0\mathscr{L})$ is defined; hence $I_0\mathscr{L}$ does not contain a forbidden pair. Now we show that $Z(q, I_0\mathscr{L}) = Z(j, \mathscr{L})$ is defined. It follows from the definition of pair restriction that, since $I_0\mathscr{L}$ does not contain a forbidden pair, the only way $Z(q, I_0\mathscr{L})$ could be undefined would be if there existed a state r and an input I such that II_0 were forbidden and $N(r, I) = q$. But then $N(q, I_0)$ would be undefined, which is not the case $[N(q, I_0) = j]$. Hence, $Z(q, I_0\mathscr{L}) = Z(j, \mathscr{L})$ must be defined. Since $j \sim k$, $Z(j, \mathscr{L}) = Z(k, \mathscr{L})$, and since $\mathscr{L}$ was chosen so that $Z(i, \mathscr{L}) \neq Z(k, \mathscr{L})$, it follows that $Z(i, \mathscr{L}) \neq Z(j, \mathscr{L})$, contradicting the hypothesis of the lemma and thus completing the proof.

Now the desired theorem can be proved:

THEOREM 2.1 *For any pair-restricted flow table, every set of MC's that covers every state is closed.*

PROOF.   Suppose that C is a compatible implied by some member of such a set. Let c_1 be any state in C and M a maximal compatible of the set such that c_1 belongs to M. We shall show that *every* member of C must be in M. Let c_i be an arbitrary state of C and m an arbitrary state M. We then have $c_i \sim c_1$ and $c_1 \sim m$. Since C is implied by some set of states of the table, it follows that c_1c_i must be implied by a subset of that set say pq; hence for some input I_0, $N(p, I_0) = c_1$ and $N(q, I_0) = c_i$. Thus the conditions of Lemma 2.3 are satisfied, and it follows that $c_i \sim m$. Since m was arbitrarily chosen, it follows that c_i is compatible with *every* member of M; hence, by definition of an MC, c_i must be a member of M. Finally, since c_i is an arbitrary member of C, *every* member of C must belong to M. Hence C is a subset of M, and since this argument is valid for *any* compatible implied by any member of this set of MC's, it follows that the set is closed, as was to be shown.

The theorem can now be used as follows: Given a pair-restricted flow table, find the set of all MC's (using the techniques of Section 2.2) and then choose the smallest set of MC's that includes every state. This is the same covering problem that arises in the minimization of combinational functions and can be expressed in the form of a covering table (usually called a prime-implicant table). A number of methods of solution can be found in the literature (for example, see [McC-4] and [GIM-1]). Theorem 2.1 assures us that the resulting set is closed and can therefore be used to construct a flow table covering the given one. There may be other equally small closed coverings, but none with fewer members. This is easily seen by letting $\{c_1, c_2, \ldots, c_n\}$ be an arbitrary closed covering of our table. Each c_i is contained in at least one MC which we can label M_i. Then the closed set $\{M_1, M_2, \ldots, M_n\}$ contains no more members than the original set (perhaps fewer if some MC contains 2 *different* members c_i and c_j), and it could have been obtained by our procedure.

Table 2.12 Reduced Version of Table 2.11

	A	B	C	D	
1	1, 0	1, 0	1, 0	2, 0	1236
2	2, 1	2, 0	1, 0	2, 0	45

The reader may verify that the MC's of Table 2.11a are $\{45, 234, 1236\}$. Although certainly not necessary in this case, a covering table for this set is shown in Table 2.11b, in which a 1 appears in each position in which the row MC includes the state represented by the column. The problem is to choose a minimal set of rows such that for every column there is at least one member of the set with a 1 in that column. In this case $\{1236, 45\}$ obviously is such a set and hence, by our theorem, is a closed covering, resulting in the reduced Table 2.12. (It is interesting to note that Table 2.11a happens to be vulnerable to attack via the preliminary reduction method discussed in Section 2.4.)

Restrictions on allowable input sequences may be expressed in a form other than an incompletely specified flow table. One may be presented with a fully specified flow table (or a flow table with unspecified entries because of other reasons) and then told that certain finite subsequences cannot be included in any input sequence. We shall discuss this situation only briefly with the aid of an example.

Suppose that Table 2.13a is given with the stipulation that ABA will never be part of any input sequence and that we are asked to find a minimal-row table that satisfies the specifications of the given table for all allowed inputs. Note first that the given table is irreducible as it stands. There are several approaches to this problem, and we present one, namely, the expansion of the given table into a form in which unspecified entries express the input constraints, and then the reduction of this table by standard procedures.

In the example, the expanded version is shown in Table 2.13b which is

Table 2.13a Given Table

	A	B	C
1	3, 0	4, 0	2, 0
2	4, 0	4, 0	2, 0
3	3, 1	1, 0	1, 0
4	3, 1	4, 0	1, 0

Table 2.13 b Expanded Table with Forbidden Sequence ABA

	A	B	C	
1	5, 0	4, 0	2, 0	1
2	6, 0	4, 0	2, 0	2
3	5, 1	1, 0	1, 0	3
4	5, 1	4, 0	1, 0	4
5	5, 1	7, 0	1, 0	3(A)
6	5, 1	8, 0	1, 0	4(A)
7	—	4, 0	2, 0	1(AB)
8	—	4, 0	1, 0	4(AB)

Table 2.13 c Reduced Table

	A	B	C	
1	2/3, 0	3, 0	1, 0	1278
2	2/3, 1	1, 0	1, 0	356
3	2/3, 1	3, 0	1, 0	45678

developed as follows: The first four rows correspond to the given table (the corresponding rows are shown to the right), with identical output entries, and identical next-state entries in all columns (B and C) except for those (A) which represent initial symbols of forbidden sequences. In these columns the next-state entries refer to new rows which are labeled on the right to indicate the corresponding row of the given table and the prefix of the forbidden sequence that led to the row. Thus, in the example, if an A is applied with the system in state 1, the next state in the expanded table is 5, which corresponds to 3 in the given table, and is labeled 3(A) to indicate that it can be reached *only* after the input A, which is a prefix of forbidden sequence ABA. Row 6 is similarly related to row 4. Output entries in the added rows are the same as those in the corresponding rows of the given table. Next-state entries in the columns that received special treatment as above are treated similarly. In addition, in a row with a prefix label x, the entry in column I for which xI is a prefix of a forbidden sequence must be to a row labeled xI. Thus, the next-state entry for total state 5-B is 7, which is labeled 1(AB) to indicate that it corresponds to row 1 of the given table *and* can be reached only following input sequence *AB*. The entries for a row that is labeled with an input sequence consisting of all but the final symbol of a forbidden sequence are handled as above, except for those in the column corresponding to that final symbol, which are left unspecified. Thus total state 7-*A*, which can be reached only via forbidden sequence *ABA*, has unspecified entries.

Once the expanded table has been obtained, it can be reduced to a minimal form by using the techniques described earlier. (In our example this leads to Table 2.13*c*.) Note that, in order to mirror the original specifications, it is necessary always to start the system in a state covering one of the original rows (that is, in the example, a row covering one of the first four rows of Table 2.13*b*) in order that the outputs specified by the given table be obtained for all allowed input sequences. If we were to start in state 5, for example, the allowed input sequence *BA* would lead to unspecified behavior of the system.

The expanded table resulting when the forbidden sequences are all of length 2 is always a pair-restricted table so that the technique described earlier in this section is applicable. We could generalize our definition of pair restriction to characterize the broader class of expanded tables, but it is not known whether the reduction problem can be simplified for this class.

2.6   Asynchronous Flow Tables

The application of the ideas discussed earlier in this chapter to the reduction of flow tables for asynchronous functions is the subject of this section. It will become apparent that, for SOC functions,† only a minimal accommodation is necessary, whereas the situation is somewhat more complex for MOC functions.

There are two basic reasons why asynchronous functions cannot be treated the same way as pulsed or synchronous functions:

1. The assumption that the input state can change only when the system is in a steady-state condition corresponding to a stable state of the flow table or, in the case of UOC functions, an oscillation among a set of states.

2. The fact that when examining an output sequence we are usually concerned with the *order* in which the output states occur, without reference to any time scale, so that it is meaningless to refer to the same output state as being repeated several times in succession. (An exception to this will be discussed at length.)

We begin by considering the SOC case, since it is somewhat simpler, more important, and better understood. Table 2.14*a* describes a function of

---

† See page 23 for definitions of SOC, MOC, and UOC functions.

Table 2.14

	A	B	C
1	①,0	2,0	3,0
2	②,0	②,1	3,0
3	1,0	③,0	③,0

(a) Table with delayed output change.

	A	B	C	
1	①,0	①,1	2,0	12
2	1,0	②,0	②,0	3

(b) Reduced version of (a).

this type, and if the methods of Section 2.2 are applied, then it might quickly be concluded that there are no compatible pairs of rows and hence that the table is already in minimum-row form. However, some of the incompatibilities are a consequence of the fact that the output in state 1-B a transient state, is specified as being different from the output for the succeeding stable state 2-B. But in no case would the sequence of output *changes* be altered if $Z(1, B)$ were made equal to $Z(2, B)$, and if this is done, then states 1 and 2 become equivalent and the table can be reduced to Table 2.14b. In general, for functions of the class under consideration, it it obvious that the sequence of output states can never be altered by setting outputs for unstable states equal to the outputs for the corresponding next states. Furthermore, it will become evident shortly, that although this may make compatible rows that were previously incompatible, it can never have the opposite effect.

A second key point is illustrated by Table 2.15a, which also has no compatible pairs as it stands. In particular, rows 1 and 2 are incompatible because, under input B, 12 implies 23. This in turn is due to the fact that $N(1, B) = 3$, and the effect of this entry is to cause the transition from 1-B to 2-B to take place in two steps (via 3-B), without any output changes occurring. If $N(1, B)$ is changed to a 2, thus eliminating the redundant step, the function is not changed in any essential way, but rows 1 and 2 become compatible, permitting a reduction to Table 2.15b.

A flow table for an asynchronous SOC function may be put in *standard form* by altering the entries for the unstable states, where necessary, according to the following procedure:

Table 2.15

	A	B	C
1	①,0	3,0	①,0
2	②,0	②,0	1,0
3	③,1	2,0	1,0

(a) Table with redundant transition.

	A	B	C	
1	①,0	①,0	①,0	12
2	②,1	1,0	1,0	3

(b) Reduced version of (a).

PROCEDURE 2.5   *Transforming SOC Flow Tables into Standard Form*

If u is a state that is unstable in column I and s is the stable state ultimately reached from u when the input is held at I, then:
1. Set $N(u, I) = s$ and
2. Set $Z(u, I) = z(s, I)$.

An SOC flow table T is said to be *A-covered* by a table V if, for every stable state p_t of T, there is a stable state p_v of V such that whenever the same input sequence is applied to the two tables starting in p_t and p_v, respectively, the output sequence from V is essentially equivalent to that generated by T, whenever the latter is specified. (As mentioned earlier, output sequences are essentially equivalent for this type of function if they describe the same sequence of changes. Thus, 0101, 01101, 01001, 01–001, and 0–10–1 are all essentially equivalent.) It is not difficult to see that the standard form of a flow table A-covers it, and vice versa.

For SOC flow tables, the state-reduction problem amounts to that of finding a minimal-row table that A-covers the given table. We now show that a solution can be found by applying the procedures developed earlier in this chapter to the standard form of the given table.

THEOREM 2.2   *Suppose T is an arbitrary SOC flow table, T^* is a standard form of T, and T_m is a minimal-row covering of T^*. Then T_m is a minimal-row A-covering of T.*

PROOF.   Since covering clearly implies A-covering, T_m A-covers T^* But T^* A-covers T, and so by transitivity T_m A-covers T. Now to prove minimality of T_m, let T_A be any table that A-covers T, with T_A^* a standard form of T_A. Then T_A^* A-covers T, which in turn A-covers T^* (any table A-covers its standard form). Hence T_A^* A covers T^*. But if a standard-form table A-covers another standard-form table, it also covers it. Hence T_A^* covers T^*. Then T_A^* has at least as many rows as T_m (a *minimal*-row covering of T^*), and since T_A has no fewer rows that T_A^*, it follows that T_A has at least as many rows as T_m, which completes our argument that T_m is a minimal-row A-covering of T.

A related result is that if, in an arbitrary SOC flow table, for every unstable state s-I, $N(s, I)$ corresponds to a stable state in column I and $Z(s, I)$ is unspecified, with all other entries specified, then the minimal-row table covering this table could have been obtained by reducing the table obtained by specifying the $Z(s, I)$ entries to conform to our definition of a standard-form table. The proof depends on the fact that the compatible pairs and implications of the transformed, fully specified table are the same as those for the given table.

Turning now to MOC flow tables, we assume that the system always starts out in a total state that is stable. Thus if there is a row in the flow table that has *no* stable states, its entries can serve only as intermediate steps in multistep transitions and can be reached *only* via such intracolumn transitions. The consequence of this assumption is that such *unstable* rows need not be covered by rows of covering flow tables.

Two basic interpretations of MOC flow tables are considered here. Under the *time-independent* interpretation, which is more in the spirit of the preceding discussion, it is assumed that only the *order* in which various output states appear is significant. Under the *time-dependent* interpretation it is

Table 2.16

	x				x		
	0	1			0	1	
1	①, 0	2, 0		1	①, 0	2, 0	1
2	1, 1	3, 1		2	1, 1	3, 1	23
3	2, 1	4, 1		3	2, 0	③, 0	4
4	3, 0	④, 0					

(a) MOC flow table.   (b) Reduction of (a) under time-independent interpretation.

assumed that the duration of transient output states is indicated in the table by the number of internal-state transitions for which that output persists. Thus, in the case of Table 2.16a, under the time-dependent intepretation, it is assumed that after x is turned on with the system initially in 1-0, z is to remain at 0 for 1 unit of time (the unit being the time it takes for an internal-state change to occur), then to switch to 1 for 2 units (while in states 2 and 3) of time, and then to go to 0. Under the time-independent interpretation, all that is specified under these circumstances is that z is to change to 1 and then revert to 0.

If we apply the general definition of compatibility, then Table 2.16a has no compatible pairs and is hence irreducible. Under the time-independent interpretation, Table 2.16b is clearly equivalent to Table 2.16a. But it is *not* equivalent under the time-dependent interpretation, since the 1-pulses last only for 1 unit of time. (We would consider the two tables as being equivalent if we were concerned only with the *relative* durations of the output states.) If a table covers another under the time-dependent intepretation, then it also covers it under the time-independent interpretation, but the reverse is not always true.

First we consider the time-dependent case. In Table 2.17a, rows 1 and 4 are incompatible, because they imply 25 under input B, and this pair is output incompatible because of input A. The basis for this argument is that, starting in 1 and 4, respectively, and applying input sequence BA would produce two different output sequences, namely, 01 and 00. But this is only for synchronous operation and is *not* so if the table is interpreted as representing an asynchronous function. The B-input would have to be left on long enough to let the system reach the next stable state, which in our example is 3 for *both* starting states. The output sequence produced in both cases during the transition is 010. In order to take this into account, we must modify the flow table to show that the intermediate state following 1-B is one in which the next input

Table 2.17

	A	B	C
1	①, 0	2 , 0	2 , 0
2	②, 1	3 , 1	②, 0
3	1 , 0	③, 0	5 , 0
4	④, 0	5 , 0	2 , 0
5	4 , 0	3 , 1	⑤, 0

(*a*) Given table.

	A	B	C
1	①, 0	6 , 0	2 , 0
2	②, 1	3 , 1	②, 0
3	1 , 0	③, 0	5 , 0
4	④, 0	7 , 0	2 , 0
5	4 , 0	3 , 1	④, 0
6	—	3 , 1	—
7	—	3 , 1	—

(*b*) Expansion.

	A	B	C	
1	①, 0	2 , 0	2 , 0	14
2	②, 1	3 , 1	②, 0	267
3	1 , 0	③, 0	4 , 0	3
4	1 , 0	3 , 1	④, 0	5

(*c*) Reduced table.

can *only* be a B (and similarly for the state following 4-B). The modification can be accomplished (Table 2.17*b*) by expanding the table to introduce new states 6 and 7 that have next-state entries only in the B column. The modified table now incorporates in its general structure, with the aid of don't care entries, the constraints imposed by the mode of operation and can therefore be reduced by our basic procedure to obtain Table 2.17*c*. In general, if in the original table $N(s, I) = t$, where t-I is unstable, then in the expanded table a new state t' is introduced with don't cares in all columns except I, $Z(t', I) = Z(t, I)$, and $N(t', I) = N(t, I)$. We also change $N(s, I)$ to t'. If $N(t, I)$ is unstable in I, then another new row must be added, and so forth, until every unstable state leads directly to a stable state or to a total state that is the only state in its row with specified entries. The resulting table covers the given table under the assumptions we have made, including the one about starting the system in a stable state.

The time-dependent interpretation is a plausible one in many circumstances in which one wishes to place rough bounds on the absolute or relative durations of output pulses generated by an asynchronous system. It should be realized that in such a case the row assignment must also be such as to preserve these quantities (see Subsection 3.3.5), and of course the variability of interstate transition times is also dependent on the delays in the feedback loops.

As an example of how a table may be reduced under the time-independent assumption, consider Table 2.18a. An obvious first step is to expand the

Table 2.18

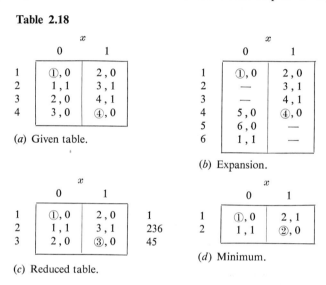

(a) Given table.

(b) Expansion.

(c) Reduced table.

(d) Minimum.

table in the same manner as that for the last case, thus obtaining Table 2.18b. (Again we assume that we always start the system in a stable state. Note, for example, that no row of the new table covers row 3, an unstable row, of the old table.) Now we must use a modified definition of compatibility to reduce this table. Two states p and q are said to be *B-compatible* if for every input I:

1. By appropriate filling in of dashed elements, the output sequence generated when I is applied with the system in p can be made essentially equivalent (in the sense discussed above) to that obtained if q had been the initial state, and

2. The *stable* states *ultimately* reached when I is applied are B-compatible when the initial states are p and q, respectively.

In the example, this definition gives us the maximal B-compatibles $\{1, 235, 236, 45\}$. Implications are only in terms of the ultimate stable states, and in the example there is none. Thus we are led to the choice of $\{1, 236, 45\}$ as the minimal closed covering, and this in turn generates Table 2.18c.

However, one can easily see that the two-row table shown in Table 2.18d is the actual minimum-row covering of the given table (and of Table 2.18b and c). Yet this table cannot be obtained by our procedure; therefore the procedure obviously is not a complete solution to the minimization problem for the time-independent case. The factor that has not been taken into account in our example is the possibility of omitting the first output state from the sequence occurring after the new input has been applied, when it happens to be the same as the output for the initial stable state.

Table 2.19

	x				x		
	0	1			0	1	
1	①, 0	2, —		1	①, 0	2, 1	123
2	—	3, 1		2	1, 1	②, 0	45
3	—	4, 1					
4	5, —	④, 0		(b) Solution.			
5	1, 1	—					

(a) Expansion.

A possible approach, which at least seems to take care of the kind of situation illustrated here, is to convert the expanded table into primitive form with appropriate don't care entries to account for the initial outputs in transient sequences. Thus in our example, Table 2.18b would be converted to Table 2.19a, which has the maximal B-compatibles $\{123, 235, 45\}$, with no implications from any compatible. A minimal closed covering is therefore $\{123, 45\}$, which gives us the minimum-row solution Table 2.19b. The generalization of this approach and a proof that it produces minimal-row solutions remain to be made.

State reduction of UOC functions has not been considered in detail, although the problems would seem to be similar to those for the bounded-length case discussed here.

SOURCES

Solutions for the problem of reducing fully specified flow tables were first presented by Huffman [HUF-1], Moore [MO-1], and Mealy [ME-1]. Ginsburg [GIN-1, 2, 3] first constructed examples indicating that the techniques for reducing fully specified tables can not always reduce incompletely specified tables; he proposed some new methods and first proposed the lower bound based on the largest incompatible. The general approach to reduction presented here is due to Paull and Unger [PA-1, UN-4], and the implication graph method was developed from ideas in the former reference by Unger [UN-5]. The "trap row" concept of Section 2.1 is due to Narasimhan [NA-1], and Procedure 2.3 for finding MC's was developed by Marcus [MAR-2]. The discussion of partial merging is based on work by Unger [UN-4]. McCluskey [McC-2] proved Theorem 2.1, on pair-restricted tables, for the special case in which the tables represent SOC asynchronous functions and are in primitive form. It was then generalized to the form presented here by Unger [UN-4]. The material in the latter part of Section 2.5 dealing with flow tables accompanied by a list of forbidden input sequences is due to Paull [PA-3]. Paull and Waldbaum [PA-2] formally introduced Procedure 2.5 for putting SOC tables in standard form before reduction. A formal proof that, in the above-mentioned class of tables, the outputs for unstable states can be set to the values at the next stable states without spoiling any chances for mergers was presented by Reed [RE-1], who credits Huffman [HUF-1] for having stated it originally. The material on reduction of time-dependent MOC flow tables is due to Friedes [FRD-1]. Paull and Waldbaum [PA-2] considered the problem of reducing time-independent MOC flow tables (but without our assumption about stable starting states) and introduced what is referred to here as *B*-compatibility. An interesting approach to finding minimal closed coverings by casting the problem in the form of a modified prime-implicant table has been presented by Grasselli and Luccio [GR-1, 2]. This method, not discussed here, is not attractive for hand computation, but seems suitable for use with a computer. They also discuss the application of integer programming to the problem. Grasselli and Luccio [GR-3] have also considered the question of reducing the number of *columns* in a flow table, along with the number of rows. Other approaches to state-table reduction not discussed here include the work of Beatty and Miller [BE-1, 2, MI-1]. An interesting application to a scheduling problem of the concepts of compatibles and maximal compatibles, as well as a discussion of the problems involved in programming algorithms for finding MC's is due to Hall and Acton [HAL-3].

PROBLEMS

2.1 Construct a flow table with no more than four input columns for which Table P2.1 is the implication table.

Table P2.1

1			
	2		
23 ×	×	3	
×	12	24	4

*2.2   Obtain from Table P2.2 two different tables by fitting in the unspecified output entry first with a 0 and then with a 1. Reduce each table. Can you find a table covering Table P2.2 that has fewer rows than either of those generated above?

Table P2.2

	x	
	0	1
1	1, –	2, 0
2	3, 0	1, 0
3	2, 1	1, 0

2.3   Find the maximal compatibles corresponding to Table P2.3.

Table P2.3

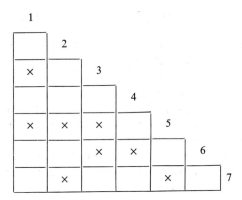

2.4   Find the minimal-row flow table equivalent to Table P2.4.

Table P2.4

	$x_1 x_2$			
	00	01	11	10
1	2, 0	3, 0	5, 0	7, 0
2	2, 0	1, 0	4, 0	5, 0
3	3, 0	2, 0	3, 0	6, 0
4	3, 0	2, 0	1, 0	5, 1
5	7, 0	3, 0	6, 0	2, 0
6	7, 0	3, 0	1, 0	2, 0
7	2, 0	5, 0	4, 0	6, 0

2.5   Reduce Table P2.5 to a minimal covering table.

Table **P2.5**

	x	
	0	1
1	3, 00	4, —
2	2, —	5, —
3	1, 01	5, 10
4	1, 11	—, —
5	2, —	3, 11

‡**2.6**   Reduce Table P2.6 to a minimal covering table.

Table **P2.6**

	$x_1 x_2$			
	00	01	11	10
1	3, 0	1, –	–	–
2	6, –	2, 0	1, –	–
3	–, 1	–	4, 0	–
4	1, 0	–	–	5, 1
5	–	5, –	2, 1	1, 1
6	–	2, 1	6, –	4, 1

2.7   Reduce Table P2.7 to a minimal covering table. (This is a difficult problem.)

Table **P2.7**

	$x_1 x_2$			
	00	01	11	10
1	6, –	–	–	7, –
2	3, –	2, –	–	7, 0
3	2, –	7, –	–	–
4	8, –	10, –	4, 0	8, –
5	–	–	9, –	–
6	–	6, 0	–	4, 1
7	7, 0	6, 1	4, –	5, –
8	8, –	–, 1	–, 1	10, –
9	10, 1	1, –	4, –	–
10	–, 0	–	–	3, –

*2.8   Find minimal-row flow tables covering Tables P2.8a and P2.8b, respectively.

Table P2.8

	A	B	C	D
1	2, 0	4, 0	–	6, 0
2	3, 0	5, 0	5, 0	–
3	–, 0	–, 0	6, 0	4, 0
4	1, –	–, 1	–, 1	–
5	3, –	1, 1	–	7, 0
6	–, 1	2, 1	–	–
7	–, 0	–, 1	8, –	–
8	–, 1	–	9, 0	–
9	–, 1	–	–, 1	1, 1

(a)

	A	B	C	D
1	2, 0	4, 0	–, 0	7, –
2	3, 0	5, 0	–, 0	–
3	1, 0	6, 0	–, 0	–
4	–	2, 1	–, 1	1, –
5	–	–	–, 1	3, 0
6	2, 1	–	–, 1	–
7	–, 0	–, 1	8, –	–
8	–, 1	–, 0	9, –	–
9	–, 1	–, 1	–	1, 1

(b)

2.9   Find the minimal-row flow table that is *equivalent* to Table P2.10.

Table P2.9

1	2, 0	–, 1	3, –	2, 0
2	8, 0	5, 1	2, 0	–
3	3, 0	6, 1	–	5, 0
4	–	7, 1	2, –	–
5	–	1, 1	1, 1	–
6	–	1, 1	2, –	–
7	2, 0	–, 1	8, –	2, 0
8	3, 0	4, 1	–	5, 0

2.10   Are Tables P2.10a and P2.10b equivalent?

Table P2.10

	$x_1 x_2$			
	00	01	11	10
1	1, 0	2, 1	3, 0	3, 0
2	1, 1	4, 0	3, 0	2, 0
3	4, 0	3, 1	1, 0	1, 0
4	2, 1	1, 0	4, 0	3, 0

(a)

	$x_1 x_2$			
	00	01	11	10
1	2, 0	1, 1	3, 0	3, 0
2	4, 1	3, 0	2, 0	1, 0
3	3, 0	4, 1	1, 0	1, 0
4	3, 1	2, 0	1, 0	4, 0

(b)

2.11   ‡(a) Does Table P2.11a cover Table P2.11b?
(b) Does Table P2.11b cover Table P2.11a?

Table P2.11

	A	B	C
1	3, –	2, –	1, 0
2	3, –	1, 0	1, 0
3	1, 1	2, 1	3, 0

(a)

	A	B	C
1	2, –	2, 0	1, 0
2	3, 1	3, 1	2, 0
3	2, –	3, –	1, 0

(b)

2.12   Find a minimal-row flow table that covers *both* Table P2.12*a* and Table P2.12*b*.

Table P2.12

	A	B	C
1	2, –	–	1, 0
2	1, 1	3, 1	2, 0
3	2, –	1, 0	1, 0

	A	B	C
1	2, 1	2, 1	1, 0
2	1, –	2, –	3, 0
3	1, –	1, 0	3, 0

2.13   Find a minimal-row flow table that covers Table P2.13 under the assumption that no input sequence contains *ABB* or *BC* as a subsequence.

Table P2.13

	A	B	C
1	2, 0	3, 0	2, 0
2	2, 0	4, 0	4, 1
3	3, 0	2, 0	3, 0
4	3, 0	1, 0	4, 0

2.14   Under the time-dependent assumption, find the smallest flow table that covers Table P2.14.

Table P2.14

	$x_1 x_2$			
	00	01	11	10
1	①, 0	2, 1	4, 0	①, 0
2	②, 1	5, 0	–	②, 0
3	③, 1	5, 0	③, 1	③, 1
4	1, 0	④, 1	④, 0	2, 0
5	3, 1	⑤, 1	⑤, 0	6, 1
6	1, 0	3, 1	4, 0	⑥, 0

*2.15   Midterm exams are to be scheduled on Monday, Tuesday, Wednesday, and Thursday at 3:00 P.M. Ten classes *A, B, C, D, E, F, G, H, J, K* must each be given a different exam. It is desirable to avoid conflicts for *all* students involved, even though some students are in more than one class. Show how this can be done, given that the following pairs of classes are the *only* ones with *no* overlapping membership:

AG, CH, EK, AD, CJ, GH, AF, DE, BE, DF, BK.

CHAPTER 3

The State-assignment Problem

As indicated in Section 1.3, the state-assignment problem (also referred to as the row-assignment problem) is that of assigning states of binary-valued state variables to the rows of a flow table so that no internal transition is dependent for its successful conclusion on the relative values of the delays associated with the state variables. Within this fundamental constraint there are secondary objectives which may include using a minimal number of state variables, minimizing the number of state variables that must change in sequence for any one transition, minimizing the amount of logic needed, simplifying the design process, and minimizing the average load on the power supply.

The fundamental nature of the state-assignment problem has led to the development of a variety of solutions tailored to satisfy different criteria. Some of the methods to be discussed here yield *universal assignments* valid for arbitrary flow tables with a given number of rows; whereas others generate assignments to fit particular flow tables. Some upper bounds are presented on the number of state variables necessary for certain classes of row assignments as functions of the number of rows.

3.1 Connected Row Sets

Let us try to code Table 3.1, a four-row table, with the minimum possible number of state variables, namely two. This means that each of the four-states of the two y-variables must be assigned to one row of the table. Suppose, we start by assignment 00 to row 1. No loss in generality is thereby entailed, since if a row assignment is valid, then so are all the assignments obtained from it by complementing any combination of the y-variables.

Since there is a transition from row 1 to row 2 (in column B) and this transition cannot be routed through any other state [the $3 \rightarrow 1$ transition in column C, for example, can be routed through row 2 by changing $N(3, C)$ to a 2], it is necessary that the state assigned to 2 be adjacent (differ in only one variable) to that assigned to row 1. Let us use 01 for this purpose, again

Table 3.1

	A	B	C	D
1	①, 0	2 , 0	①, 0	①, 0
2	3 , 0	②, 0	1 , 0	②, 0
3	③, 0	4 , 1	1 , 0	1 , 0
4	1 , 0	④, 1	1 , 0	④, 0

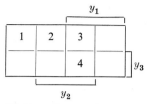

(a) Given table.

(b) Part of row assignment.

without loss in generality, since permuting the columns of a valid row assignment yields another valid assignment. Since the y-state for 2 must be adjacent to that for 3, because of the $N(2, A)$ entry, we *must* assign 11 to row 3. But now a critical race exists for the transition beginning in 3-D between rows 3 and 1. Thus there is *no* valid two-variable assignment for this table.

Suppose we allow a larger number of state variables, but restrict ourselves to using one y-state per row and require that each inter-row transition be direct and involve a single y-change. Then we must find three y-states s_1, s_2, s_3 that are mutually adjacent, because of the existence of transitions $1 \to 2$, $2 \to 3$, and $3 \to 1$. This too is impossible, since if each of the preceding transitions is carried out in turn, then the system would begin and end in state 1 with three y-changes having occurred. Thus at least *one* y-variable would have undergone a net change in value, which contradicts the condition that only *one* y-state be assigned to row 1.

In order to solve this problem we relax the conditions that each row be assigned a single y-state and that each transition take place in one step. Furthermore, a third y-variable will be allowed. Let us define a *row set* R_i as a set of y-states assigned to row i of the flow table. No y-state occurs in more than one row set. When the system is in a y-state of R_i and the input is I_j, the output will be $Z(i, I_j)$, and if $N(i, I_j) = k$, then the y-excitations will be such as to lead to a state of R_k either directly or via a series of transitions through y-states in R_i.

We construct our row sets so that:

1. If t and u are y-states in some set R_i, then there is a path linking t and u through mutually adjacent states of R_i. (Such a set R_i is said to be *connected*.)

2. If in the flow table there is an unavoidable transition from row i to row j, then the sets R_i and R_j are *adjacent* in that a member of R_i is adjacent to a member of R_j.

In our example the pairs of rows that must have adjacent y-states are $(1, 2)$, $(2, 3)$, $(3, 4)$, $(1, 4)$, and $(1, 3)$. We shall endeavor to construct connected row sets with the necessary linking, though it should be pointed out at the outset that there is no nonenumerative algorithm for accomplishing this. The purpose of this exercise is to give the reader some intuitive grasp of the problem, to illustrate that in practice it can be solved without too much difficulty, and to introduce a class of universal row assignments of the connected row-set type.

It is useful to plot our assignment on a Karnaugh map (K-map) with the y-variable values as coordinates. We begin by assigning 000 to row 1, 010 to row 2, 110 to row 3, and 111 to row 4. These choices satisfy the requirements

Table 3.1 (continued)

	y_1		
$1a$	2	3	$1b$
		$4a$	$4b$

y_3

y_2

(c) Completed row assignment.

	A	B	C	D	y_1	y_2	y_3
$1a$	$\textcircled{1a}$, 0	2 , 0	$1b$, 0	$\textcircled{1a}$, 0	0	0	0
$1b$	$\textcircled{1b}$, 0	$1a$, 0	$\textcircled{1b}$, 0	$\textcircled{1b}$, 0	1	0	0
2	3 , 0	$\textcircled{2}$, 0	$1b$, 0	$\textcircled{2}$, 0	0	1	0
3	$\textcircled{3}$, 0	$4a$, 0	$1b$, 0	$1b$, 0	1	1	0
$4a$	$4b$, 0	$\textcircled{4a}$, 0	$1b$, 0	$\textcircled{4a}$, 0	1	1	1
$4b$	$1b$, 0	$\textcircled{4b}$, 0	$1b$, 0	$\textcircled{4b}$, 0	1	0	1

(d) Flow matrix.

imposed by the first three adjacency pairs listed above, and they are plotted in Table 3.1b. It is now necessary to add y-states so as to make R_1 adjacent to R_3 and R_4. We select one of the several possible ways of doing this, namely, expanding R_1 to make it adjacent to R_3 and then expanding R_4 to make it touch R_1. This solution is shown in Table 3.1c, in which the added members are $1b$ and $4b$.

In Table 3.1d, the flow matrix corresponding to this assignment and the specific transitions that must be made between y-states are shown. For example, if the system is in $1b$-B, it is not possible to go directly to 2-B since a critical race would ensue (involving y_1 and y_2). Hence a transition is first made *within* the R_1 set to $1a$, the member adjacent to R_2. Various options are available in filling in the next-state entries of the flow matrix, particularly with respect to the stable states. For example, $1a$ or $1b$ could be assigned to $N(1a, A)$ or $N(1b, A)$, giving us four possibilities including $N(1a, A) = 1b$ and $N(1b, A) = 1a$, which would cause y_1 to oscillate for the stable state corresponding to 1-A of the flow table. These options may be exercised so as to achieve such goals as simplifying the logic circuits. Note that the two unassigned y-states 001 and 011 introduce two rows of don't care entries in the flow matrix (they do not appear explicitly in Table 3.1d).

In general, the process used to obtain the row assignment of Table 3.1d is one of trial and error. After satisfying some of the constraints, one may find that the others cannot be satisfied, and it may be necessary to alter the initial steps. A certain facility may be acquired after some practice, but, in general, even the number of state variables necessary for a given table cannot easily

Table 3.2 $2S_0$ **Assignment for Eight-Row Tables**

1	1	1	1	5	6	7	8
2	2	2	2	5	6	7	8
3	3	3	3	5	6	7	8
4	4	4	4	5	6	7	8
1	2	3	4	5	5	5	5
1	2	3	4	6	6	6	6
1	2	3	4	7	7	7	7
1	2	3	4	8	8	8	8

be determined. What can be done however, is to construct universal n-state row assignments that are valid for *any* n-row table. Of course such a "store-bought" assignment cannot in general be expected to be as good as one that is tailored to fit a particular table.

The basic idea is to construct connected row sets that are *intermeshed* in the sense that, given any i and j, R_i is adjacent to R_j. It then follows that, regardless of what transitions are called for by the flow table, they can always be carried out by a sequence of single-step (or noncritical-race) transitions within the row set of the initial state, followed by a final single-step transition across the "border" into the row set of the destination state.

Table 3.2 is a K-map representation of a six-variable, intermeshed, connected row-set assignment for eight-row flow tables. It is convenient to think of the map in terms of quadrants designated by variables y_1 and y_2 (10 is the upper right quadrant, etc.). The variables with odd subscripts specify columns in the map, and the even-subscripted variables designate rows. Consider the codes assigned to 2, a typical flow-table state. In the 00 quadrant, all of the y-states in the row for which $y_4y_6 = 01$ (henceforth to be referred to as the 01 row) are assigned to R_2. These y-states clearly constitute a connected subset that includes all states with $y_1y_2y_4y_6 = 0001$ (y_3 and y_5 taking on all four possible sets of values). In general, within each quadrant, the rows and the columns each constitute a connected subset. The column for which $y_3y_5 = 10$ (the 10 column) in the 01 quadrant is also assigned to R_2. Since the 01 row in the 00 quadrant naturally includes a member of the 10 column (the y-state 001001), it follows that the two subsets of R_2 are connected; hence R_2 is a connected row set. A similar argument applies to each of the other row sets.

The demonstration that the two components of R_2 are adjacent can also be generalized to show that each of the rows of the 00 quadrant is connected to each of the columns in the two neighboring quadrants (01 and 10). Thus, for example, the 01 row of quadrant 00 is adjacent to each of the columns in the 01 quadrant, which, reading from left to right, have been assigned to R_1, R_2, R_3, and R_4, respectively. This same row is also adjacent to each of the columns of quadrant 10, which belong to R_5, R_6, R_7, and R_8. Of course, because of symmetry, the columns are similarly connected to each row of each adjacent quadrant. It therefore follows that the row sets are intermeshed so that we do indeed have a universal assignment for all eight-state tables. Note that, although each row set is connected, the connectivity between the column and row subsets comprising it is not utilized since *each* subset is adjacent to a member of a subset of every row set. (An extreme example of an assignment with intermeshed, but *disconnected* row sets is presented in Subsection 3.3.1.)

The scheme depicted in Table 3.2 can easily be generalized to flow tables with 2^n rows, where n is any positive integer. Consider the case $n = 4$, where twice as many row sets are needed as in our example. The same basic structure is retained, but the number of rows and columns in each quadrant is doubled. This change requires an additional odd-subscripted y-variable to specify the column, and another even-subscripted variable to help specify the row. Precisely the same arguments apply in showing the connectedness of rows and columns of neighboring quadrants. Letting $S_0 = \lceil \log_2 r \rceil$ (see Section 1.3), one can see that the number of y-variables used in this type of assignent for an an r-row table is $2S_0$; hence it is generally referred to as the $2S_0$ assignment.

If we define a *transition time* as the maximum amount of time necessary for any y-variable to change value, then if a $2S_0$ assignment is used, any inter-row transition in the flow table can be made in no more than two transition times. In Table 3.2, for example, a transition from y-state 001001 (a state in R_2) to a y-state corresponding to row 5 can be made in two stages. First there could be a noncritical race within the 01 row of the 00 quadrant to the state (000011) adjacent to R_5. Transitions within a row (or column) subset of a row set can always be made via noncritical races, since only the column (or row) variables change, and all intermediate states are hence in the same row set and can be assigned the same Y-excitations. The time required for this step is one transition time, since all the y-variables that must change are given new Y-values simultaneously. The second step entails a change in a quadrant variable (y_1 in our example) to take the system into the new row set. In some cases only one step is necessary, such a change from any member of R_2 to a member of R_3 or when the initial y-state happens to be on the border of the destination row set.

We see then that, with a $2S_0$ assignment, *any* flow table can be coded without critical races using $2S_0$ y-variables and with no transition requiring more

Table 3.3 $2S_0 - 1$ Assignment for Sixteen-row Tables

1	1	1	1	5	6	7	8	9	9^a	9	9^b	9^c	10	11	12
2	2	2	2	5	6	7	8	10	10	10	10	9	10	11	12
3	3	3	3^e	5	6	7	8	11	11	11	11	9^d	10	11	12
4	4	4	4	5	6	7	8	12	12	12	12	9	10	11	12
1	2	3	4	5	5	5	5	13	14	15	16	13	13	13	13
1	2	3	4	6	6	6	6	13	14	15	16	14	14	14	14
1	2	3	4	7	7	7	7	13	14	15	16	15	15	15	15
1	2	3	4	8	8	8	8	13	14	15	16	16	16	16	16

Row/column bracket labels: y_1, y_7, y_6, y_4, y_2, y_5, y_3

than two transition times. Next it is shown that the $2S_0$ figure can be cut to $2S_0 - 1$, but at the price of doubling the maximum time for an inter-row transition.

In the $2S_0 - 1$ assignment the quadrants of the $2S_0$ assignment are replaced by octants, and transitions are sometimes necessary between the subset rows and columns assigned to each flow-table state. A seven-variable assignment with sixteen intermeshed connected row sets is shown in Table 3.3. The variables y_1, y_2, and y_3 specify the octant, y_5 and y_7 indicate the column within an octant, and y_4 and y_6 designate the row within an octant. Each row set consists of a row and a column in neighboring octants (so that they are connected), and if a particular row (column) subset is not adjacent to a member of some destination row set, then its associated column (row) subset is. For example, if the system is initially in the y-state of R_9 marked with an a in Table 3.3, and a transition to a state in R_3 is to be made, the transition cannot be made directly from the 00 row containing the initial state. First the 01 column of the 100 octant must be reached via a race from a to b, followed by a change of octant variable y_3 to get the system into the state labeled c. A race within the new octant to d is followed finally by a change in octant variable y_1 to bring the system to the R_3-state labeled e. This typifies the worst-case transition, which requires four transition times.

Once again, doubling the number of row sets is accomplished by doubling the number of rows and columns in each octant, which requires two additional y-variables. Going the other way, for a four-row table we find each octant contains just *one* row and *one* column, being dedicated to a single flow-table state. It is left to the reader to construct the universal three-variable assignment for four-row tables.

There is, incidentally, a class of $2S_0 + 1$ assignments related to those discussed above, but with the K-map partitioned into just *two* sectors (see Problem 3.3). One might be encouraged to think that by *increasing* the number of sector (sixteen would be the logical next step) the number of state variables needed would be progressively reduced. This is not the case however, and it has been conjectured, though not proved, that a universal assignment based on intermeshed row sets requires $2S_0 - 1$ variables.

If the number of rows of the given flow table is not a power of 2 and satisfies the relation $2^{S_0-1} < r \leq (3/4)2^{S_0}$, then there is an intermeshed connected row-set assignment requiring only $2S_0 - 2$ state variables. Such an assignment is shown for twelve-row tables in Table 3.4. The left half

Table 3.4 $2S_0 - 2$ Assignment for Twelve-row Tables

1	1	3	4	9	9	9	10
2	2	3	4	10	10	9	10
1	2	3	3	11	12	11	11
1	2	4	4	11	12	12	12
5	5	5	6	11	11	9	10
6	6	5	6	12	12	9	10
7	8	7	7	11	12	9	9
7	8	8	8	11	12	10	10

(with overhead bracket labels y_1, y_3; bottom label y_5; side labels y_4, y_6, y_2)

of this table is precisely the map for a $2S_0 - 1$ assignment for eight states, and the right half takes care of half that many states in such a manner as to make their row sets adjacent to one another *and* to each of the row sets represented in the left half.

These assignments are interesting because they establish certain bounds very neatly and may suggest forms that can be applied in particular cases. It is unlikely, however, that one of the universal assignments would prove to be efficient for a particular flow table.

3.2   Shared-row State Assignments

Whereas in the preceding section each y-state used in a row assignment is assumed to be associated with a particular flow-table state, a more flexible approach is taken here. A single y-state is assigned to each row, and other y-states are used as necessary to bridge transitions between rows whose y-states are not adjacent. A "bridging" state, which appears as a supplementary row of the flow matrix, may be used in different columns to bridge transitions between different pairs of rows, hence the term *shared rows*.

Table 3.5   Given Flow Table

	A	B	C	D
1	①,0	①,0	4,0	6,0
2	1,0	②,0	5,0	②,0
3	6,0	4,0	③,0	③,0
4	6,0	④,0	④,0	5,0
5	⑤,0	1,0	⑤,0	⑤,0
6	⑥,0	7,0	⑥,0	⑥,0
7	⑦,1	⑦,0	3,0	2,0

A useful concept is that of a *destination set*. Corresponding to every stable state q-I there is a *destination set* D_{Iq} consisting of *all* rows in column I that have q as the next-state entry; that is, $D_{Iq} = \{p \mid N(p, I) = q\}$.

The flow table in Table 3.5 is used to illustrate the method, which is similar in its heuristic nature to that discussed early in Section 3.1. The first step is to list the destination sets for each input column. In column A of our example, an option exists because of the three-member destination set $(3, 4, 6)$. We may find it convenient to alter the table by changing $N(3, A)$ to 4 or $N(4, A)$ to 3, thereby making one of the transitions indirect without changing the function. (This operation is in a sense inverse to the first step of Procedure 2.5 for standardizing flow tables.) The effect is to give us a choice of replacing the pair of transitions $3 \to 6$, $4 \to 6$ by either of two other pairs if such a change would help us to find a state assignment. The destination sets for our example are (one-member sets are omitted):

$$A: (2, 1) (3, 4, 6)$$
$$B: (3, 4) (5, 1) (6, 7)$$
$$C: (1, 4) (2, 5) (7, 3)$$
$$D: (1, 6) (4, 5) (7, 2).$$

First we informally demonstrate that no three-variable assignment exists based on the row-set concept. Since the flow table has seven rows, only one of the row sets can have as many as two members. Consider now the transitions between members of the pairs $(1, 2)$, $(1, 4)$, $(1, 5)$, $(2, 5)$, and $(4, 5)$. They dictate that the row sets for the four states involved be mutually adjacent to the extent shown by the graph of Fig. 3.1a (row sets connected by an edge must be adjacent). Suppose each of the row sets involved consisted of a single y-state, then since each edge of the graph must correspond to a change in one y-variable, it would be possible to go from R_1 to R_2 to R_5 and back to R_1 while making exactly three y-variable changes. Clearly this is impossible, as is the similar odd loop involving R_1, R_4, and R_5. In order to break *both* odd loops, a second state must be added either to R_1 or to R_5. Making the first choice (the argument is the same in either case), we would obtain a graph involving the y-states for rows 1, 2, 4, and 5 as shown in Fig. 3.1b. But it is not possible to assign a y-state to each node of this graph such that adjacent nodes have adjacent codes. This is because given two y-states differing in two variables there are only two other y-states that are each adjacent to both of them. But in Fig. 3.1b, 2, 1B, and 4 are each adjacent to both 1A and 5; hence, we have reached an impasse.

Now let us see if a three-variable solution can be found using the shared-row approach. Each destination set must be connected, by adding supplementary states if necessary. Since a single y-state is available for use as a shared row, and since row 1 belongs to four destination sets, it is essential

Figure 3.1

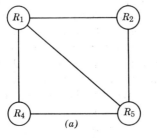 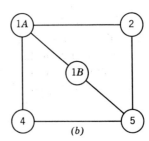

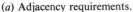

(a) Adjacency requirements.   (b) One way to satisfy (a).

Table 3.6

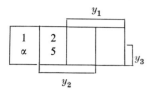

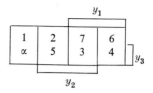

(a) Initial assignment map.

(b) Final assignment.

that the state assigned to the shared row (which we designate as α) be adjacent to that assigned to row 1. Since 2 and 5 must be linked and since 1 must be linked to each (we use the term linked to mean mutually adjacent or each adjacent to α), we might make them adjacent to one another by putting one adjacent to α and the other adjacent to 1. This arrangement gives us the partial assignment shown in Table 3.6a. Now it is necessary to place 4 so that it is linked to both 1 and 5. This is possible *only* by assigning to it the remaining y-state neighboring α. It is now necessary to assign to 6 the remaining y-state linked to 1. Since 7 must be linked to both 2 and 6, it must be assigned the only vacancy adjacent to both. Thus we have one remaining y-state, which goes to the last row, namely, 3. Checking the resulting assignment as shown in Table 3.6b against the transition list, we see that in column A, the $(3, 4, 6)$ set is connected by the adjacencies of 3 to 4 *and* 4 to 6. In $B\,(1, 5)$ is connected by a link through α. Similar uses of the shared row connect $(1, 4)$ of C and $(4, 5)$ of D. All other transitions are satisfied by direct adjacencies; hence the assignment is valid. Note that, in any one column, the shared row can be used for more than one transition only if they all have the same destination state. The flow matrix for the assignment found is shown in Table 3.6c, in which various next-state entries have been modified to set up the indirect transitions referred to in the discussion.

Table 3.6 (continued)

	A	B	C	D	y_1	y_2	y_3
1	①, 0	①, 0	α, 0	6, 0	0	0	0
2	1, 0	②, 0	5, 0	②, 0	0	1	0
3	4, 0	4, 0	③, 0	③, 0	1	1	1
4	6, 0	④, 0	④, 0	α, 0	1	0	1
5	⑤, 0	α, 0	⑤, 0	⑤, 0	0	1	1
6	⑥, 0	7, 0	⑥, 0	⑥, 0	1	0	0
7	⑦, 1	⑦, 0	3, 0	2, 0	1	1	0
α	—	1, 0	4, 0	5, 0	0	0	1

(c) Flow matrix for Table 3.5.

The preceding example confirms the presumption that the shared-row type of assignment is generally more efficient than the row-set method in terms of the numbers of y-variables needed. A very interesting and more significant confirmation is the four-variable row assignment shown in Table 3.7*a*, which is valid for *all* eight-state SOC sequential functions. For any column of such a table it is possible to use the eight unassigned y-states as shared rows in a nonconflicting manner to bridge all transitions between nonadjacent states. A row-set assignment for this class of tables requires five state variables.

Table 3.7*a* Universal Assignment for Eight-Row Tables

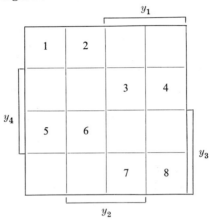

This four-variable assignment was discovered by means of a search algorithm executed on a computer. Its validity has since been established in a more conventional manner by grouping the y-states into adjacent pairs, considering all combinations of interpair transitions that can occur in a column (taking symmetry into account to reduce the number), and showing that the bridging states are adequate in each case.

The assignment of Table 3.7*b*, valid for all twelve-row SOC tables and employing five state variables (as opposed to six needed for the $(2S_0 - 2)$ row-set assignment), was discovered in a similar manner, but has not been verified by an independent proof. The fact that the universal row-set assignments of Section 3.1 are valid for MOC and UOC as well as SOC flow tables should not be overlooked.

Thus far the universal shared-row assignments have not been generalized to cover tables with other than eight or twelve rows (although of course the eight-row assignment is valid for seven-row tables). However, it has been established that a valid shared-row assignment of the *form* of Table 3.7*c* can be found for every five-row SOC table having fewer than fifteen columns.

Table 3.7*b*   **Universal Assignment for Twelve-Row Tables**

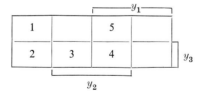

1	2			9	10		
		3	4				
5	6						
		7	8			11	12

In particular, the assignment shown is valid for any SOC flow table that does *not* have a column with destination sets (1, 4) *and* (2, 5). For such a table, we may simply interchange the *y*-states assigned to states 4 and 5. But this does not work if (1, 5) and (2, 4) are destination sets in some column; in such a case another permutation is needed. There are fifteen possible columns of the form in questions, and only if a table contains one of each is it impossible to find a satisfactory permutation of the assignment of Table 3.7*c*.

Table 3.7*c*   **A Form Good for All**
Five-Row Tables with Fewer Than
Fifteen Columns

1		5	
2	3	4	

Clearly there are some interesting open questions concerning the problem of realizing flow tables with a minimum number of state variables. In the following sections we give top priority to some other criteria.

3.3   Single-transition-time Assignments

Speed of operation is often an important consideration in the design of switching circuits, and it is not unusual to pay for it with significant increases in the number of components used. A key factor influencing the speed of operation of asynchronous sequential circuits is the maximum number of transition times required for an interstate transition. As seen in the previous section, this number can always be held to 2 if a $2S_0$ state assignement is used. It is now shown that there are several techniques for halving this figure. Row assignments for which a single transition time is always sufficient for any transition are called *single-transition-time* (STT) *assignments*.

The first STT assignments to be presented, the one-*shot* assignments, have the added property that only a single state variable changes state for each inter-row transition, and the solution presented is in the form of a class of universal assignments. The one-shot feature is significant if some price must be paid when a variable changes state, perhaps in energy, heat dissipation, component deterioration, or risk of malfunction. Such an assignment might also have value as a tool in coping with certain theoretical questions.

A less restricted class of STT assignments, referred to as *noncritical race* (NCR) *assignments* may involve simultaneous changes in several state variables for certain transitions, with the outcomes independent of the order in which the y-variables actually change. These assignments are specific to particular flow tables and are, as might be expected, usually more efficient than the one-shot assignments. Certain properties of these assignments also make them valuable for other purposes, as is seen in the next two chapters. Some bounds on the number of state variables needed to realize STT assignments are developed in this section.

3.3.1   The One-shot Assignment

A universal one-shot assignment for an r-row flow table must employ at least $r - 1$ state variables, since from a y-state representing row i it must be possible to reach any of $r - 1$ other states by changing a single variable. The shared-row concept has no application here since there are no intermediate states; all transitions must be direct from initial to final state. This leads us then inevitably to the intermeshed row-set approach, although since the direct nature of the transitions precludes intraset steps, there is no reason for making the row sets connected.

These points are nicely illustrated by Table 3.8, which depicts a three-variable universal one-shot assignment valid for all four-row flow tables (flow table rows are numbered from 0 to $r - 1$ in this subsection for reasons that become evident shortly). Each row set has two members, located as far apart as possible, and each state in R_i is adjacent to a member of R_j for every $j \neq i$. The number of state variables is $r - 1$ and in this case, it is also the minimum number required to code all four-row tables even for assignments not of the STT variety. Hence this assignment is interesting and useful apart from its

Table 3.8 A Universal One-shot Assignment for Four-Row Flow Tables

0	2	3	1
3	1	0	2

y_1 spans the top. y_3 labels the right side. y_2 labels the bottom.

illustrative value. The generalization of this assignment to larger tables, with $r = 2^n - 1$ is now presented. (For the benefit of those familiar with the Hamming single-error correcting codes [HAM-1], it may be stated at once that the y-states assigned to R_0 are those corresponding to Hamming code words with no errors and that, for $i > 0$, R_i consists of those words with errors in position i.) Some formal notation is necessary. Let the jth digit from the right in the binary representation of the nonnegative integer I ($I \leq 2^n - 1$) be designated as $b_j(I)$, so that

$$I = \sum_{j=1}^{n} b_j(I)2^{j-1}.$$

Thus, for example, $b_1(6) = 0$, $b_2(6) = 1$, and $b_3(6) = 1$. Let the set of non-negative integers whose binary representations have a 1 in position j be designated as p_j. Thus $p_j = \{I \mid b_j(I) = 1\}$, and as examples we have $p_1 = \{1, 3, 5, 7, \ldots\}$, $p_2 = \{2, 3, 6, 7, \ldots\}$, and $p_4 = \{8, 9, 10, 11, 12, 13, 14, 15, 24, 25, \ldots\}$. For $\underline{y}$, a binary n-vector $(y_n, y_{n-1}, \ldots, y_1)$, and $\oplus\Sigma x_k$ representing summation modulo-2, define $C_k(\underline{y}) = \oplus \sum_{j \in p_k} y_j$. Thus $C_1(1101) = 0$ and $C_2(1101) = 1$. (These correspond to parity check equations.)

Now we can define the row-set R_I as $R_I = \{\underline{y} \mid C_k(\underline{y}) = b_k(I)$ for $k = 1, 2, \ldots, \lceil \log_2 n \rceil\}$. For example, in the case of an 8-row table, R_0 includes 0000000, 0110011, and 1010010, while R_5 includes 0010000, 0100011, and 1101000.

In order to establish the intermeshed nature of the row-sets another definition is useful. Let $I(+)J = \sum_{k=1}^{n} [b_k(I) \oplus b_k(J)]2^{k-1}$. This amounts to specifying $I(+)J$ as the number whose binary representation has a 1 in each position where the binary representations of I and J *differ* and is equivalent to:

$$b_k(I(+)J) = b_k(I) \oplus b_k(J) \qquad \text{for } k = 1, 2, \ldots, n.$$

Thus $3(+)5 = 6$, and $12(+)7 = 11$. The following theorem indicates specifically which y-variables must be changed in order to switch between a given pair of row-sets.

THEOREM 3.1 *If y^* differs from y in just the $I(+)J$ component and if $y \in R_I$, then $y^* \in R_J$.* (Thus if y belongs to R_3 and if we change the value of y_6, the resulting vector y^* will be in R_5).

PROOF.   1. $b_k(I) \neq b_k(J)$ iff (if and only if) $b_k[I(+)J] = 1$, as indicated by the second form of the definition of $(+)$.
2. $b_k(I) \neq b_k(J)$ iff $I(+)J \in P_k$. This follows from step 1 and the definition of P_k.
3.   Since, by hypothesis, $y \in R_I$, $C_k(y) = b_k(I)$ for $k = 1, 2, \ldots$, n, and it follows from step 2 that $C_k(y) \neq b_k(J)$ iff $I(+)J \in P_k$.
4.   If y_m is changed, then *just* those C_k for which $m \in P_k$ will change, as can be seen from the definition of C_k. Thus if $y_{I(+)J}$ is changed, then just those C_k will change for which $I(+)J \in P_k$.
5.   But it then follows from steps 4 and 3 that a change in $y_{I(+)J}$ results in changes in *just* those C_k for which $C_k(y) \neq b_k(J)$. Hence, if y is changed to y^*, we have $C_k(y^*) = b_k(J)$ for all k and therefore $y^* \in R_J$, as was to be proved.

The Hamming one-shot assignment described above requires $2^{S_0} - 1$ state variables, so that the number of state variables needed increases linearly with the number of rows as contrasted to the assignments of Section 3.1 which require the number of state variables to increase only with the logarithm of the number of rows.

A rather special type of one-shot assignment that is sometimes useful is the *reflected Gray-code* assignment. It is directly applicable to 2^n-state flow tables where the interstate transitions are between states i and $i + 1$ ($1 \leq i < 2^n$) or between 2^n and 1. (Other transitions are also admissible, as will become evident.)

One y-state is assigned per row, and n y-variables are used. The codes assigned to states i and $i + 1$ ($1 \leq i < 2^n$) differ in exactly *one* y-variable, as do the codes assigned to 1 and 2^n. We define the assignment recursively:

1. Assign to row 1 the code $000 \cdots 0$ and to row 2 the code $100 \cdots 0$.
2. Assume that for some $k \geq 1$, rows 1 through 2^k have been assigned codes with $y_i = 0$ for all $i > k$. Then assign codes to rows $2^k + 1$ through 2^{k+1} as follows: For all of these rows, set $y_{k+1} = 1$ and set $y_i = 0$ for all $i > k + 1$. For each row $(2^k + j)(1 \leq j \leq 2^k)$, set $y_i(i \leq k)$ equal to the value of y_i in row $(2^k + 1 - j)$.

The term "reflected" stems from the fact that the states of the variables $y_1, y_2, \ldots, y_k$ are symmetric about a line separating rows 2^k and $2^k + 1$.

An eight-state code is shown below:

row	y_1	y_2	y_3
1	0	0	0
2	1	0	0
3	1	1	0
4	0	1	0
5	0	1	1
6	1	1	1
7	1	0	1
8	0	0	1

3.3.2 Unicode STT Assignments for SOC Functions

In this subsection we consider a class of STT assignments in which transitions may occur by means of noncritical races among all of the variables distinguishing the initial and final states. Only SOC functions are treated here, and the assignments are restricted to those with one y-state per row, which we refer to as *unicode* assignments. The abbreviation USTT is used to denote unicode STT assignments. (Generalizations are discussed in Subsections 3.3.4 and 3.3.5.) The techniques to be discussed here generate assignments specific to particular flow tables, and since y-states not assigned to rows may occur as intermediate states in different transitions occurring in different columns, they may be classified among the shared-row assignments. It is assumed that the given flow tables are in the standard form generated by Procedure 2.5.

Letting $\mathscr{S}$ be a set of y-states, we define $T(\mathscr{S})$, the set of states *spanned* by $\mathscr{S}$, to be those y-states comprising the smallest subcube that contains every member of $\mathscr{S}$. This set consists of just those y-states with 0's in every position where every member of $\mathscr{S}$ has a 0, and 1's in those positions where every member of $\mathscr{S}$ has a 1; for example, $T(00110, 10010, 00111)$ consists of those y-states for which $y_2 = 0$ and $y_4 = 1$, namely,

$$\{00010, 00011, 00110, 00111, 10010, 10011, 10110, 10111\}.$$

A convenient way to describe such a subcube set is to write a single y-state indicating the values of the fixed y's and leaving dashes in positions corresponding to the remaining y's. In our example this gives us –0–1–, which can be expanded to obtain the indicated set by filling in the dashes with 0's and 1's in all of the possible 2^3 ways.

Suppose that a unique y-state $\underline{y}^i$ is assigned to each row i of a given flow table and that in some column there is an $i \to j$ transition. If $\underline{y}^i$ and $\underline{y}^j$ differ in more than one variable, then depending on the distribution of delay values in the circuit, the y-variables that distinguish i from j may change in *any* order. Those y-variables that have the *same* values in y^i and y^j do not change at all. Hence, during the transition, the system may pass through any state in $T(\underline{y}^i, \underline{y}^j)$. [Henceforth, when no confusion will result, we shall write $T(i,j)$ for $T(\underline{y}^i, \underline{y}^j)$.] If $\underline{y}^i$ and $\underline{y}^j$ differ in only *one* y-variable, then there are no intermediate states, as indicated by the fact that $T(i,j) = \{\underline{y}^i, \underline{y}^j\}$. When i is stable in the column involved so that $i = j$ (the transition becomes the trivial one, $i \rightarrow i$), then $T(i,j) = \{\underline{y}^i\}$.

If in a given flow table $N(i, I) = j$, then in the corresponding flow matrix, for every s whose y-state is in $T(i,j)$, $N(s, I)$ must equal j in order for the resulting circuit to be STT and free of critical races. Hence, if $i \rightarrow j$ and $k \rightarrow m$ are transitions in the same column of a flow table and $m \neq j$, then it follows that $T(i,j)$ and $T(k,m)$ must be disjoint. Otherwise, the two transitions would impose contradictory requirements on the flow matrix entries for the common y-states. But if there are no such contradictions in any column, then it clearly is possible to assign next-state values for all intermediate states in each column which ensure the proper outcome of each transition. This establishes the following lemma:

LEMMA 3.1   *A row assignment for a SOC flow table has no critical races iff, for every pair of transitions $i \rightarrow j$ and $k \rightarrow m$ that appear in the same column such that $j \neq m$ and $i \neq j$ or $k \neq m$, the sets $T(i,j)$ and $T(k,m)$ are disjoint.*

Our next step is to establish conditions on the state variables that are necessary and sufficient to satisfy Lemma 3.1.

Letting U and V be disjoint subsets of the flow-table rows, we define a *partial state dichotomy* (which is hereafter referred to simply as a *dichotomy*) as the unordered pair (U, V). Given a pair of transitions $i \rightarrow j$ and $k \rightarrow m$, where i and j are each different from k and m, we say that the *associated dichotomy* is (U, V), where $U = \{i,j\}$ and $V = \{k, m\}$. This dichotomy is generally written as (ij, km). In cases in which one of the transitions is degenerate (say $i = j$), we obtain a dichotomy such as (i, km), and if both transitions are degenerate, the associated dichotomy reduces to (i, k). A state variable y_i in a particular row assignment is said to *cover* a dichotomy (U, V) if $y_i = 0$ for every state in U and $y_i = 1$ for every state of V (or vice versa). We can now state the following theorem:

THEOREM 3.2   *A row assignment for a SOC flow table is a valid USTT assignment iff, for every pair of transitions $i \rightarrow j$ and $k \rightarrow m$ that appear in the same column and such that $j \neq m$, the associated dichotomy (ij, km) is covered by at least one y-variable of the assignment.*

PROOF.   If (ij, km) is covered by a y-variable y_c, then $y_c = 0$ for every member of $T(i,j)$ and $y_c = 1$ for each member of $T(k, m)$ (or vice versa) so that these sets are disjoint. If this is true for every dichotomy formed as in the hypothesis of Lemma 3.1, then it follows from that lemma that there are no critical races. Given any two rows i and j such that for some input I_k, $N(i, I_k) \neq N(j, I_k)$, there will be a column I_k dichotomy separating i and j. The covering y-variable will distinguish the y-states assigned to these rows. If no such I_k exists, then i and j are compatible with no implications. [A dichotomy (i, j) can be added if in this latter case there is some reason to have distinct codes for i and j.]

To prove the "only if" part, we must consider the conditions under which two transition sets can be disjoint. As indicated earlier, such a set can be specified by giving the values of the *fixed* y-variables, those that have the same values at the initial and final states. A particular y-state belongs to a given transition set iff the fixed variables have the same values in this state as in the set. Two transition sets obviously cannot contain a common member if some y-variable is fixed in both sets but at opposite values. Suppose, on the contrary, that each y-variable is either fixed at the same value in both sets or not fixed in at least one of the sets. (Such a pair of transition sets is 010–0– and 0–010–.) Then there exists a nonempty intersection of these sets with fixed variables wherever *either* set has fixed variables. (In our example the intersection is 01010–.) It follows then that, if two transition sets are disjoint, there must be a variable fixed at 0 in one set and at 1 in the other set. Such a variable covers the associated dichotomy.

Thus, if, for every pair of transitions $i \to j$ and $k \to m$ as described in the hypothesis, the corresponding transition sets $T(i, j)$ and $T(k, m)$ are disjoint, it follows that the dichotomy (ij, km) must be covered by some y-variable; hence the proof of the theorem is complete.

For any SOC flow table we can derive a set of dichotomies (sometimes referred to as *Tracey* conditions); the remaining part of the problem is to assign the y-variables so as to cover every member of this set. Since there are obviously many ways of doing this, the goal is usually to do so with a minimal number of variables. First we make some preliminary observations that are helpful in cutting down the magnitude of the problem. If U^* contains U and if V^* contains V, then we say that the dichotomy (U^*, V^*) *covers* the dichotomy (U, V), and since any y-variable covering the former must also cover the latter, we need not include (U, V) explicitly in our list of dichotomies. This means, among other things, that, if $i \to j$ is a transition in some column, we need never consider $j \to j$ as a transition in that column, since any dichotomy employing the latter is covered by a dichotomy involving the former. Furthermore, a dichotomy (i, km) generated in one column may be deleted from our list if (ij, km) is generated in some other column.

Table 3.9 is now used to illustrate the above concepts and subsequent

Table 3.9   SOC Flow Table

	A	B	C	D
1	①, 0	①, 0	4 , 0	5 , 0
2	3 , 0	②, 0	②, 0	5 , 0
3	③, 0	③, 0	4 , 0	③, 0
4	5 , 1	④, 0	④, 0	3 , 0
5	⑤, 1	⑤, 0	2 , 0	⑤, 0

steps in the synthesis procedure. The column-A transitions are $1 \to 1$, $2 \to 3$, and $4 \to 5$, resulting in the dichotomies (formed by taking all pairs of transitions) (1, 23), (1, 45), and (23, 45). Column B contributes only the ten dichotomies of the form (i, j), all of which are covered by larger dichotomies in the other columns. Column C has transitions $1 \to 4$, $3 \to 4$, and $5 \to 2$, resulting in (14, 25) and (25, 34), and column D contributes (15, 34) and (25, 34), the latter appearing for the second time. Neither (1, 23) nor (1, 45) is covered by any of the larger dichotomies, and so no deletions can be made.

At this point we could assign a distinct y-variable to cover each of the six dichotomies and arrive at a six-variable assignment. However such an assignment would clearly be wasteful since it is not hard to find pairs of dichotomies in the set that can be covered by the same y-variable. [For example, (1, 45) and (23, 45), or (14, 25) and (25, 34)]. If two dichotomies can both be covered by the same y-variables, it must be possible to form a larger dichotomy (that is, one in which at least one of the two component sets is increased) which covers both. Thus, in our example, (134, 25) covers both (14, 25) and (25, 34). The problem can be formulated as being that of finding a minimal set of dichotomies such that every dichotomy in the list is covered by at least one member of this set. It is then a trivial matter to specify a y-variable for each of the members of the minimal covering set.

The problem is reminiscent of one encountered earlier in Section 2.2, namely, that of finding maximal compatibles. At first one may be tempted to define two dichotomies as being compatible if they can be covered by a single dichotomy, and then proceed to find the MC's by methods already described. However this procedure is not quite workable, as can be seen by noting that, since the three dichotomies (1, 23), (1, 45), and (23, 45) are pairwise compatible, we would expect, from Lemma 2.2, to find that there is a single dichotomy covering all of them. But none exists, because in order to cover (1, 23) *and* (1, 45), a y-variable would have to have the *same* value for every member of {2, 3, 4, 5}, and in this case it would not cover (23, 45).

The situation can be remedied by replacing each dichotomy (U, V) by a pair of *ordered dichotomies*, $[U, V]$ and its *complement* $\overline{[U, V]} = [V, U]$. We refer to U and V as the *left* and *right sets*, respectively, of $[U, V]$. Two ordered dichotomies are defined as being *compatible* if no state appears in the left set of one and the right set of the other. It is not difficult to show that compatible ordered dichotomies can be covered by a single y-variable and that Lemma 2.2 is applicable in that a set of ordered dichotomies can be covered by a single ordered dichotomy iff the members of the sets are pairwise compatible. The MC's can then be found by one of the methods of Section 2.2 and a minimal subset of them selected such that a representative of each dichotomy (one of the ordered dichotomies corresponding to it) is covered by at least one member of this set. There are, of course, no implications among the dichotomies, and so the latter part of the problem can be dealt with as a covering problem of the prime-implicant type. Finally, a covering y-variable is generated for each of the selected MC's and the flow matrix formed, with appropriate entries in the members of every transition set. Before illustrating the process, a useful simplification is presented.

It is usually possible to represent many of the original dichotomies by only *one* ordered dichotomy, thereby greatly reducing the amount of computation needed to find the MC's. The following theorem establishes this technique:

THEOREM 3.3 *Let D be a set of ordered dichotomies derived from some set of unordered dichotomies. For some state s, label as p_1, p_2, etc., the members of D having s in their left sets, and label as q_1, q_2, etc., the members of D that do not contain s in either set. Then a minimal set of MC's covering each member of D or its complement can be found by considering only the ordered dichotomies labeled as p's or q's. (The complements of the p's can be ignored.)*

In the example of Table 3.9 (whose six dichotomies have been listed earlier) we might choose $s = 5$. (This is a good choice since 5 appears in a maximal number of dichotomies, and so the number of ordered dichotomies that can be ignored is maximized.) The theorem states that instead of considering twelve ordered dichotomies, we need consider only 7, namely, the q dichotomies [1, 23] and [23, 1] and the p dichotomies [45, 1], [45, 23], [25, 14], [25, 34], and [15, 34].

PROOF.   If two ordered dichotomies a and b are compatible, then so are $\bar{a}$ and $\bar{b}$. Hence, if every member of some MC is complemented, the result is also an MC, and it covers the same *unordered* dichotomies. Also note that given any i and j, no MC of D can include p_i and $\bar{p}_j$ (since by definition all p's have s in their left sets and all $\bar{p}$'s have s in their right sets). Now suppose we have a minimal covering of D. If any MC in that covering contains $\bar{p}$ dichotomies, we can replace it by an MC with no $\bar{p}$ dichotomies obtained by complementing all of its members, and we still have a minimal covering. But this then gives us a minimal covering with only p's and q's, which could have been found directly had we ignored the $\bar{p}$'s.

Table 3.10a   Pair Chart for Finding MC's

a
(1, 23)

X	$\bar{a}$ (23, 1)				
X		b (45, 1)			
	X		c (45, 23)		
X		X	X	d (25, 14)	
X	X	X	X		e (25, 34)
	X	X	X	X		f (15, 34)

To complete our example, we form the pair chart of Table 3.10a from the seven selected ordered dichotomies (they are shown with letter tags that are used in manipulating them). The incompatible pairs can be found easily, column by column, as follows: Run down a column placing X's in all rows where the left set of the row dichotomy contains a member of the right set of the column dichotomy. (In column a this places X's in the $\bar{a}$, d, and e rows.) Then repeat the process interchanging left and right. (This adds an X in row b.) Having filled in the X's as shown in the table (blank entries represent compatible pairs), we now generate the MC's using a method such as Procedure 2.2 to obtain ef, de, bc, $\bar{a}b$, $\bar{a}d$, ac, af. Although it is not hard in this case to find a minimal covering by inspection, the covering table shown in Table 3.10b is often useful. The columns are labeled with letters representing the *unordered* dichotomies, and the rows with the MC's. The 1-entries for each row appear in just those columns whose dichotomies are covered by the MC of that row. A minimal set of rows such that every column has a 1-entry in at least one member of the set is $\{ef, \bar{a}d, bc\}$ (another such set is

Table 3.10b   Covering Table

		Unordered dichotomies					
		a	b	c	d	e	f
	ef					1	1
	de				1	1	
	bc		1	1			
MC's	$\bar{a}b$	1	1				
	$\bar{a}d$	1			1		
	ac	1		1			
	af	1					1

Table 3.11 Flow Matrix for Table 3.9

	A	B	C	D	y_1	y_2	y_3
1	①, 0	①, 0	4 , 0	5 , 0	0	1	1
2	3 , 0	②, 0	②, 0	5 , 0	0	0	1
3	③, 0	③, 0	4 , 0	③, 0	1	0	1
4	5 , 1	④, 0	④, 0	3 , 0	1	1	0
5	⑤, 1	⑤, 0	2 , 0	⑤, 0	0	0	0
α_1	5 , 1	—	4 , 0	5 , 0	0	1	0
α_2	5 , 1	—	4 , 0	3 , 0	1	0	0
α_3	—	—	4 , 0	3 , 0	1	1	1

$\{af, de, bc\}$). Note that it is *not* necessary to include in our set MC's covering a and MC's covering $\bar{a}$.

Corresponding to the first solution, we have the dichotomies [125, 34], [235, 14], and [45, 123] which result in the flow matrix of Table 3.11, in which the states α_1, α_2, and α_3 can be entered only in the course of races. In column A, for example, α_1 and α_2 are members of $T(4, 5)$; hence, since they may be entered during a $4 \rightarrow 5$ transition, they must have the same entries as the destination state 5.

The method described above may be summarized as:

PROCEDURE 3.1 *Finding Minimal y-variable USTT Assignments for SOC Flow Tables*

(We refer to this procedure as the *Tracey* method.)
1. In each column list the transitions, including transitions $i \rightarrow i$ in columns in which i is stable and is not the destination of any other transition. (No special attention need be paid to states with unspecified next-state entries, since if the row assignment conforms to Theorem 3.2, such a state never appears in transition sets with different destination states.)
2. For each column, form a dichotomy (ij, km) for every pair of transitions $i \rightarrow j$ and $k \rightarrow m$ where $j \neq m$.
3. Select a state s that appears a maximal number of times among the set of dichotomies constructed in 2. Form a list of ordered dichotomies consisting of the complementary pair generated by each dichotomy that does *not* contain s and, from each dichotomy containing s, the single ordered dichotomy with s in its left half.
4. Using a pair table and any of the methods in Section 2.2, find the MC's corresponding to the ordered dichotomies.
5. Using a covering-table approach if necessary, find a minimal set of the MC's that covers every dichotomy.

6. By taking unions of all left sets and of all right sets for the constituents of each MC of step 5 in turn, generate a set of covering dichotomies.
7. Form a flow matrix by associating a covering y-variable with each of the covering dichotomies. In each column, assign the same entries to every state within each transition set.

In step 7, it often occurs that some of the covering dichotomies do not refer to every state; for example, a covering dichotomy of a six-row flow table might be (12, 456). In this case the value of the covering variable could be specified as either 0 or 1 in row 3. This is because (12, 456) is covered by both (123, 456) and (12, 3456) so that either of these dichotomies can be used in its place. By placing a – in row 3 of the y-value column for this variable, we leave open an option that may be exploited later to help gain some other objective. We could also treat the dash as representing both 0 and 1 so that *several* y-states would in effect be assigned to row 3. Transitions to row 3 could then be made to any of these states, which again provides potentially useful options. (The assignment then of course ceases to be of the unicode type.)

The Tracey method leads to minimal y-variable USTT assignments (though a great deal of computation is often necessary), but it is useful to consider a second approach to the same problem, which we refer to as the *Liu method*. The Liu assignments are not always minimal in terms of the number of y-variables used, but they have features that are important in several contexts that arise in subsequent chapters.

Recall that the destination sets of each column partition the rows into disjoint sets based on the stable states of that column (see Section 3.2). The destination sets of column I_2 of Table 3.12, for example, are {12}, {356}, and {47}. The basic idea underlying the Liu method is to associate a subset V_i of the y-variables with each input column I_i, and a unique state of V_i with each destination set of I_i. Such an assignment is shown in Table 3.12, in which V_1, V_2, and V_3 are $y_1y_2y_3$, y_4y_5, and y_6y_7, respectively.

Table 3.12   SOC Flow Table

	I_1	I_2	I_3	Basic Liu assignment						
				y_1	y_2	y_3	y_4	y_5	y_6	y_7
1	①,0	2,0	①,0	0	0	0	0	0	0	0
2	3,0	②,0	5,1	1	0	0	0	0	0	1
3	③,0	6,0	③,0	1	0	0	0	1	1	0
4	④,0	7,0	3,0	1	1	1	1	0	1	0
5	⑤,0	6,0	⑤,1	1	1	0	0	1	0	1
6	4,0	⑥,0	5,1	1	1	1	0	1	0	1
7	⑦,1	⑦,0	1,0	0	1	0	1	0	0	0

If there are transitions $i \rightarrow j$ and $k \rightarrow m$ in column I_n, $j \neq m$, then i and j belong to D_{nj}, and k and m belong to D_{nm}. Since the state of the V_n-variables is not the same in D_{nm} as in D_{nj}, it follows that there must be some y-variable of V_n that covers (ij, km). Hence Theorem 3.2 is satisfied.

There are several refinements to the basic Liu method which make possible reductions in the number of state variables needed. First of all, it is not necessary that the sets V_j and V_k be disjoint for $j \neq k$, and so if y-variables in each of two V-sets have either the same values for every row or complementary values for every row, then only one such variable is necessary.

Suppose next that the number of destination sets for I_i is k, where k is *not* a power of 2. Then $\lceil \log_2 k \rceil = n$ state variables are necessary in V_i, but the number of states of the V_i-variables (2^n) exceeds the number of destination sets. It is therefore possible to specify only partially some of the variables of V_i. For example, in Table 3.12, there are three destination sets of column I_3 and so the 0-values assigned to y_7 in rows 3 and 4 (the members of D_{33}) could be changed to unspecified entries (dashes) since, whenever y_6 (the other member of V_3) is equal to 1, the destination set *must* be D_{33}. If this change is made, then y_1 satisfies the specifications for y_7 and hence can replace y_7 in v_3 as well as serve in v_1.

Another technique used to reduce the number of state variables in a Liu assignment is referred to here as *set lumping*. (In at least one application of Liu assignments, discussed in Section 5.4, it cannot be used.) Set lumping is based on the idea that Theorem 3.2 does not require that the V_i-variables distinguish among one-member destination sets of I_i. It is thus possible to merge (lump) all or some of the one-member destination sets of any column into a smaller number of larger sets before assigning V_i-states. In Table 3.12, for example, one might treat the sets D_{11}, D_{15}, and D_{17} as a single three-member set. This would mean an immediate reduction of V_1 to two members.

These ideas are applied in Table 3.13, in which, in the initial coding, V_1, V_2, and V_3 consist of y_1y_2, y_3y_4, and y_5y_6, respectively. The three one-member destination sets of I_1 are lumped into one set, which becomes the

Table 3.13 Simplified Liu Assignment

	I_1	I_2	I_3	y_1	y_2	y_3	y_4	y_5	y_6	y_1	y_2	y_3	y_4
				Initial coding						Merged assignment			
1	①, 0	2, 0	①, 0	0	–	0	0	0	0	0	0	0	0
2	3, 0	②, 0	5, 1	1	0	0	0	1	–	1	0	0	1
3	③, 0	6, 0	③, 0	1	0	1	–	0	1	1	0	1	0
4	④, 0	7, 0	3, 0	1	1	0	1	0	1	1	1	0	0
5	⑤, 0	6, 0	⑤, 1	0	–	1	–	1	–	0	–	1	1
6	4, 0	⑥, 0	5, 1	1	1	1	–	1	–	1	1	1	1
7	⑦, 1	⑦, 0	1, 0	0	–	0	1	0	0	0	1	0	0

largest set, and the state(s) 0– of V_1 assigned to it. (Assigning incompletely specified states to the largest destination sets is good strategy since it maximizes the number of dashes in the y columns and hence the chances of merging y columns.) In I_2, the V_2-states assigned to D_{22}, D_{26}, and D_{27} are 00, 1–, and 01, respectively. After completing the initial coding, which requires six y-variables, an attempt is then made to find single y columns that can replace two or more of the initial columns. For example, y_1 is the same as y_6 except when the latter has dashes, and it can therefore serve to replace the latter in V_3. Similarly, y_2 and y_4 are the same whenever both have no dashes; hence there is a single y column that can replace both of them. These two pairs have been replaced by y_1 and y_2, respectively, in the merged assignment, in which y_3 and y_5 have been copied as y_3 and y_4, respectively. The problem of finding a minimal set of columns covering all columns of the initial assignment is completely analogous to that encountered earlier in finding a minimal set of covering dichotomies. We must consider each column *and* its complement (Theorem 3.3 is applicable and eases this problem), defining columns to be compatible if they are not specified differently in any row. A single column replaces each MC of the minimal covering and is formed by setting its value in row i to a 0 (or 1) if any constituent is specified at 0 (or 1) in that row, or if all the constituent y's are unspecified in row i, then the replacement y is also left unspecified there.

Because of the various options available in assigning V-states to each D_{ij}, the above procedure does not always lead easily to minimal-variable Liu assignments. A *generalized Liu assignment* may be defined as one in which, for every input I_i and every pair of states p and q that are stable in I_i, the dichotomy (D_{ip}, D_{iq}) is covered by some y-variable. All Liu assignments obtainable using the above methods satisfy this condition, which of course also implies the satisfaction of the conditions of Theorem 3.2. Minimal-variable generalized Liu assignments can be found via Procedure 3.1, where dichotomies of the form (D_{ip}, D_{iq}) replace those generated in steps 1 and 2.

Although in general this approach leads to the use of fewer y-variables than required by the Liu methods discussed earlier, the number of variables associated with each input column may no longer be minimal, a drawback in certain situations (see Section 5.4).

A characteristic of all Liu assignments is that, for every input I_i and every state p that is stable in I_i, there is a unique y-space subcube that contains $T(D_{ip})$ and is disjoint from $T(D_{iq})$ for all other states q that are stable in I_i. This property, essential in certain applications (see Subsection 6.1.2), is not shared by all assignments satisfying Theorem 3.2, as is illustrated by the fact that in Table 3.11 the transitions to 4-C take place within two different, though overlapping subcubes of the y-space.

The magnitude of the computation involved to find minimal general Liu assignments is, in general, less than that required to follow the Tracey procedure, since the number of dichotomies that must be considered is often smaller and never larger. The price paid is that more y-variables may be needed because of a loss of freedom in the covering of certain dichotomies. Thus, for example, in the minimal USTT assignment found for Table 3.11, $(134, 25)$ is not covered and two different y-variables cover $(25, 34)$ and $(25, 14)$; whereas in any Liu assignment, $(134, 25)$ must be covered.

The question of how many state variables are necessary to realize the "worst" n-row SOC flow table with a **USTT** assignment is considered in the following subsection.

3.3.3 Bounds on the Number of State Variables Needed for USTT Assignments

The one-shot assignment of Subsection 3.3.1 sets a bound of $2^{S_0} - 1$ state variables for a universal STT assignment. It is shown here that this bound can be lowered substantially if the one-shot feature is dropped. First, an upper bound is established by a nonconstructive process, and then a constructive procedure is developed for producing universal USTT assignments requiring a number of state variables lying between the two bounds referred to above.

THEOREM 3.4 *There exists a universal n-variable, USTT assignment for SOC flow tables such that* $n = 21S_0 + 9$.

PROOF. We first determine the maximum number of n-variable row assignments that are *not* valid for every r-row table. An obvious consequence of Theorem 3.2 is that an assignment is valid for every r-row table iff it covers every dichotomy of the form (ij, km) where i, j, k, and m are distinct rows.

1. Consider first how many y columns *fail* to cover some particular dichotomy (ab, cd) of an r-row table. These are the columns that do *not* have the values 0, 0, 1, 1, or 1, 1, 0, 0 in the rows a, b, c, and d, respectively. Hence the number is $(2^4 - 2)2^{r-4} = 14 \times 2^{r-4} = (7/8)2^r$.

2. The *total* number of n-variable row assignments that can be constructed by selecting n such y columns (with repetition) is $[(7/8)(2^r)]^n = (7/8)^n 2^{rn}$.

3. The number of different (ij, km) dichotomies in an r-row table is $3\binom{r}{4}$.

4. The number of different n-variable row assignments that fail to cover at least one (ij, km) dichotomy must be less than (because of overlaps)

$$3\binom{r}{4}(7/8)^n 2^{rn}.$$

5. The total number of n-variable row assignments for r-row tables is $(2^r)^n = 2^{rn}$.

6. Hence the number of n-variable row assignments that cover *all* (ij, km) dichotomies and that are thereby valid for all r-row SOC flow tables

   exceeds $V = 2^{rn} - 3\binom{r}{4}(7/8)^n 2^{rn}$.

7. Then given any r and n, if V is nonnegative, there exists at least one n-row assignment of the type under discussion which is valid for every r-row SOC table. To obtain the desired bound, we must therefore find the smallest n, as a function of r, for which V is at least 0.

8. Setting $V \geq 0$, we obtain $2^{rn} - 3\binom{r}{4}(7/8)^n 2^{rn} \geq 0$, and canceling 2^{rn}

   yields $(7/8)^n \leq \left[3\binom{r}{4}\right]^{-1}$.

9. Taking logarithms (to the base 2) and solving for n yields

   $$n \leq \frac{\log_2 [3r(r-1)(r-2)(r-3)]}{\log_2 (8/7)}.$$

10. Replacing $r(r-1)(r-2)(r-3)$ by r^4 and approximating $\log_2 (8/7)$ by 0.193 and $\log_2 3$ by 1.59 gives us

    $$n \leq \frac{4 \log_2 r + 1.59}{0.193} \leq 21 \log_2 r + 9 = 21S_0 + 9$$

as was to be shown.

This is obviously not a tight bound, primarily because of step 4, and does not even get under the $2^{S_0} - 1$ bound until S_0 exceeds 8. Nevertheless it shows that bounds for USTT assignments go up linearly with S_0 (as do the bounds for general row assignments) rather than exponentially as does the bound for the one-shot assignments. No construction is as yet known for producing $21S_0 + 9$ assignments.

We now outline a constructive proof that $(S_0^3 + 5S_0)/6$ is also a bound for the same problem. The construction itself is of some interest, as is the fact that, for $S_0 \leq 11$, it undercuts the bound of Theorem 3.4.

We begin by defining a *separating system* $S_{i,j}(S_0)$ as a set of y-variables assigned to a set of states with 2^{S_0} members such that for any disjoint pair, P and Q, of subsets of these states, with i and j members, respectively, (P, Q) is covered by a y-variable of the set. The number of y-variables necessary in $S_{i,j}(S_0)$ is defined as $N_{i,j}(S_0)$. Note that a USTT assignment valid for any 2^{S_0}-state SOC flow table constitutes a separating system $S_{2,2}(S_0)$. We now demonstrate constructively that $N_{2,2}(S_0) \leq (S_0^3 + 5S_0)/6$.

Table 3.14   An $S_{1,2}(S_0)$ System

$$R = \begin{bmatrix} \begin{array}{cc|c} & & 0 \\ & & 0 \\ & & \cdot \\ A & B & \cdot \\ & & \cdot \\ & & 0 \\ \hline & & 1 \\ & & 1 \\ \bar{A} & B & \cdot \\ & & \cdot \\ & & 1 \end{array} \end{bmatrix}$$

Clearly $N_{1,1}(S_0) = S_0$, since we need S_0 variables to provide enough y-states to distinguish among 2^{S_0} system states [that is, to cover (i, j) for every distinct pair of states i and j]. Now we argue that $N_{1,2}(S_0) \le S_0(S_0 + 1)/2$ on the basis of the system shown as a partitioned matrix R of Table 3.14. The columns are the y's and the rows are the states. Submatrix A represents a separating system $S_{1,1}(S_0 - 1)$, $\bar{A}$ represents A with all elements complemented, and B represents a separating system $S_{1,2}(S_0 - 1)$. It must now be shown that given any three states i, j, and k, some column of R covers (ij, k). Let $m = 2^{S_0 - 1}$ and i^*, j^*, and k^* be equal to i, j, and k, respectively, modulo m. Then if i^*, j^*, and k^* are distinct, there is a column of B that covers $(i^* j^*, k^*)$, and the corresponding column of R covers (ij, k). Remaining are the cases in which $k = i$ (or j) modulo m, that is, in which k and i (or j) are in corresponding rows in the upper and lower halves of R. Without loss of generality, let us assume that k is in the lower half. Then we have essentially the following cases (in which i and j are less than m):

1. $(ij, i + m)$: covered by the rightmost column of R.
2. $(i(i + m), j)$: covered by the column of R corresponding to the B column that covers (i, j).
3. $(i(j + m), i + m)$: covered by the R column corresponding to the A column that covers (i, j).

Thus R does indeed describe an $S_{1,2}(S_0)$ separating system. We compute the value of $N_{1,2}(S_0)$ corresponding to R recursively as follows:

1. $N_{1,2}(1) = 1$ (One y-variable suffices for a two-row flow table)
2. $N_{1,2}(S_0) \le N_{1,2}(S_0 - 1) + N_{1,1}(S_0 - 1) + 1$,
   $N_{1,2}(S_0) \le N_{1,2}(S_0 - 1) + S_0$,   (by construction of R).

This leads to:

$$N_{1,2}(S_0) \le \sum_{i=1}^{S_0} i = \frac{S_0(S_0 + 1)}{2}.$$

Now, using a similar approach we construct an $S_{2,2}(S_0)$, again corresponding to the matrix R of Table 3.14, where this time A is an $S_{1,2}(S_0 - 1)$ system, $\bar{A}$ is its complement, and B is an $S_{2,2}(S_0 - 1)$ system. The validity of R is established as above by considering various cases, of which there are ten basic types. Here, the dichotomies to be covered are of the form (ij, pq).

1. If i^*, j^*, p^*, q^* are all distinct, then there is a B column that does the job.

The next six cases involve $i^* = q^*$. We indicate the covering column, leaving it to the reader to verify the details. (Let i, j, and p below all be less than m.)

2. $(pj, i(i + m))$: B column covering (pj, i).
3. $(p(j + m), i(i + m))$: B column covering (pj, i).
4. $(ij, p(i + m))$: A column covering (ij, p).
5. $(ij, (p + m)(i + m))$: rightmost column.
6. $(i(j + m), p(i + m))$: A column covering (i, jp).
7. $(i(j + m), (p + m)(i + m))$: A column covering (ip, j).

The last three cases involve only two distinct members of (i^*, j^*, p^*, q^*).

8. $(ij, (i + m)(j + m))$: rightmost column.
9. $(i(i + m), j(j + m))$: B column covering (i, j).
10. $(i(j + m), j(i + m))$: A column covering (i, j).

Clearly $N_{2,2}(1) = 1$, and by construction and our earlier result we obtain the recursive relation

$$N_{2,2}(S_0) \leq N_{2,2}(S_0 - 1) + N_{1,2}(S_0 - 1) + 1$$

$$N_{2,2}(S_0) \leq N_{2,2}(S_0 - 1) + \frac{S_0(S_0 - 1)}{2} + 1.$$

We then obtain

$$N_{2,2}(S_0) \leq 1 + \sum_{i=2}^{S_0} \left[1 + \frac{i(i - 1)}{2} \right] = \frac{S_0^3 + 5S_0}{6},$$

as was to be shown. Thus the following theorem is established:

THEOREM 3.5   *There is a constructive procedure for finding universal USTT assignments for SOC flow tables which require $(S_0^3 + 5S_0)/6$ state variables.*

This bound never exceeds the $2^{S_0} - 1$ bound and falls below it at $S_0 = 4$, remaining below it from then on. It is below the $21S_0 + 9$ bound when $S_0 \leq 11$. A more complex recursive process somewhat analogous to the one just described has been devised recently such that for various infinite sequences of values of S_0, $N_{1,2}(S_0) \leq S_0^{1.59}$ and $N_{2,2}(S_0) \leq S_0^2$.

Some miscellaneous additional results pertaining to small flow tables may be mentioned briefly. A straightforward application of the methods described earlier to the fifteen (ij, km) dichotomies possible for a five-row table shows that six state variables are necessary and sufficient for a universal USTT assignment for five-row SOC tables. A somewhat more sophisticated approach leads to the conclusion that seven state variables are necessary and sufficient for a similar universal assignment for six-row flow tables.

In the next subsection we see that by permitting multiple codings, both universal assignments and assignments for specific flow tables can be found requiring fewer state variables than the *best* unicode assignments for the corresponding cases.

3.3.4   Multicode STT Assignments

First consider the assignment shown in Table 3.15, where five state variables are used and a complementary pair of y-states is assigned to each of six rows. If i, j, k, and m are four distinct states, then the reader may verify that for each of the i-states, the smallest subcube in the map that contains that state and one of the j-states is otherwise empty and does not overlap the minimal subcube containing either k-state and the nearest m-state. Thus, regardless of which i-state the system is in, there is a j-state such that the corresponding $T(i, j)$ is disjoint from either $T(k, m)$ set. For example, a transition between 2-state 01100 and the nearest 5-state 01001 can be made without passing through the region involved in a $4 \rightarrow 6$ transition starting in either 00011 or 11100. Thus this assignment is a valid universal STT assignment for six-row SOC flow tables, and it requires two fewer variables than the best corresponding unicode assignment. An eleven-variable universal STT assignment

Table 3.15   A Five-Variable Universal Multicode STT Assignment for Six-Row SOC Flow Tables

Table 3.16a SOC Flow Table

	I_1	I_2	I_3	I_4	I_5
1	①, 0	①, 0	①, 0	4, 0	①, 0
2	1, 0	6, 0	3, 0	②, 0	②, 0
3	③, 0	1, 0	③, 0	4, 0	2, 0
4	3, 0	④, 0	1, 0	④, 0	④, 0
5	⑤, 1	⑤, 0	6, 0	⑤, 0	⑤, 0
6	5, 1	⑥, 0	⑥, 0	2, 0	⑥, 0

for fourteen-row flow tables has also been found; whereas the best corresponding unicode assignment *probably* requires more variables (this has not yet been proved). These assignments were obtained in a rather ad hoc manner and serve principally to illustrate the possibilities inherent in using more than one y-state per row.

Now let us turn our attention to Table 3.16a, which describes a SOC function. Applying the methods of Subsection 3.3.2 shows that at least four state variables are necessary for a USTT assignment in this case. However the three-variable coding shown in Table 3.16b, in which two y-states are assigned to row 1, is a valid STT assignment for Table 3.16a. A closer analysis of this example provides a clue that can serve as the basis for a general algorithm.

The dichotomies (12, 34) and (13, 26), resulting from transitions in columns I_1 and I_2, respectively, are clearly incompatible. But if we split row 1 into rows $1a$ and $1b$ and allow the $2 \rightarrow 1$ transition of column I_1 to become $2 \rightarrow 1a$ and the $3 \rightarrow 1$ transition of column I_2 to become $3 \rightarrow 1b$, then the aforementioned dichotomies become $(1a2, 34)$ and $(1b3, 26)$, and the corresponding ordered dichotomies $[1a2, 34]$ and $[26, 1b3]$ are compatible. This splitting has in effect been done in the multicode row assignment, where y_1 covers $[1a256, 1b34]$. The particular type of "row splitting" executed here is to allow a state that is stable in two columns to be assigned different codes in these columns.

In order to incorporate this idea into a general algorithm, we may begin by expanding the given table into a larger, equivalent table in which, if a

Table 3.16b Multicode STT Assignment

state i of the original table is stable in columns I_1 and I_2, with transitions in both columns leading to i, then the expanded table will have states i_1 and i_2 corresponding to i, each being stable in both I_1 and I_2, and with all transitions to i in column I_1 (or I_2) replaced by transitions to i_1 (or i_2). The expansion for our example is shown as Table 3.16c in which the image of state i in column I_k is ik. Procedure 3.1 is then applied to the table except that certain dichotomies are not used. In particular we treat states ij and ik as being equivalent (which they are); hence in column I_k we do *not* generate a dichotomy to force $T(p, ik)$ to exclude ij. Thus, in our example, $((12)(33), 11)$ is not listed as a dichotomy as would normally be the case because of column-I_2 entries. Hence a pair of rows such as ij and ik, derived from the same row i of the given table, might be assigned the same y-state, which would have the effect of retracing the expansion process to some extent. This effect occurs to a considerable degree in our example.

Each dichotomy of the original flow table gives rise to a set of mutually compatible dichotomies of the expanded table; hence any covering of the original table corresponds to a covering (with the same number of y-variables) of the expanded table. Of course, the converse is not true, as illustrated by the example. Thus, using the expansion procedure, the resulting assignment has no more, and may have fewer, state variables than the best unicode assignment for the original table. However, this method does not necessarily lead to the best multicode assignment. It does not, for example, take into account the possibility that it may be advantageous to allow some of the transitions to a stable state in some column of the expanded table to terminate in different equivalent states, instead of in just one state. It has been shown

Table 3.16c Expanded Table

	I_1	I_2	I_3	I_4	I_5
11	⑪,0	⑪,0	⑪,0	4 ,0	⑪,0
12	⑫,0	⑫,0	⑫,0	4 ,0	⑫,0
13	⑬,0	⑬,0	⑬,0	4 ,0	⑬,0
24	11 ,0	62 ,0	33 ,0	24 ,0	㉔,0
25	11 ,0	62 ,0	33 ,0	25 ,0	㉕,0
31	㉛,0	12 ,0	㉛,0	4 ,0	25 ,0
33	㉝,0	12 ,0	㉝,0	4 ,0	25 ,0
4	31 ,0	④ ,0	13 ,0	④ ,0	④ ,0
5	⑤ ,1	⑤ ,0	63 ,0	⑤ ,0	⑤ ,0
62	5 ,1	㉒,0	㉒,0	24 ,0	㉒,0
63	5 ,1	㉓,0	㉓,0	24 ,0	㉓,0

that this feature can lead to y-variable reductions not otherwise attainable. However, adding this feature greatly complicates the procedure, which is already inflated by the necessity of coping with the expanded table, and there is no assurance that an optimum result will always be achieved even so. Thus the problem of finding an algorithm leading to STT assignments with a minimum number of state variables remains open.

3.3.5   State Assignments for MOC Flow Table

Time-dependent MOC functions are introduced in Section 2.6, where they are treated with respect to state reduction. Since there is a nominal time assigned to each flow-table transition, it is necessary, in order to preserve this feature, that the row assignment be such that each transition takes about the same amount of time. This condition is satisfied by STT assignments. The universal one-shot assignment of Subsection 3.3.1 is valid for *any* type of flow table and hence can be applied at once to this problem. However, Theorem 3.2 which establishes the conditions under which a USTT assignment is valid applies only to SOC flow tables. In this section, we extend, in a rather informal manner the covering conditions of that theorem so that MOC functions can be treated.

If a flow table is not SOC only because of situations in which, for some input I_k and row i, $Z(i, I_k) \neq Z(N(i, I_k), I_k)$ (an instance of such a multiple output change is the transition 3-A $\rightarrow$ 4-A of Table 3.17a), then Procedure 3.1 is clearly still applicable. There are two new situations that generate additional dichotomies that must be covered. An $i \rightarrow j$ transition in the same column with a $j \rightarrow k$ transition must not include k in its transition set or else j may never be entered and a specified output may be skipped. Thus (ij, k) must be covered. It is also necessary to cover (i, jk) in order to prevent i from being reentered during the $j \rightarrow k$ transition. There remains an intersection of $T(i, j)$ and $T(j, k)$; such states are assigned the same output and next-state entries as j. In all other cases there is no problem in filling in the entries for intermediate states of transition sets to correspond to those of the destination states.

The second situation arises if in some column I there are transitions $i \rightarrow j$ and $m \rightarrow j$ where $Z(i, I) \neq Z(m, I) \neq Z(j, I)$. In such a case $T(i, j)$ must not include m or else a false output may occur during the $i \rightarrow j$ transition. Hence (ij, m) must be covered.

The first of the above situations occurs in column A of Table 3.17a in which there is a $6 \rightarrow 2 \rightarrow 1$ transition requiring the row assignment to cover $(1, 26)$ and $(12, 6)$. Column B contains an example of the second situation in that it has $2 \rightarrow 3$ and $4 \rightarrow 3$ transitions where $Z(4, B) \neq Z(2, B) \neq Z(3, B)$. Hence $(2, 34)$ must be covered. The dichotomies corresponding to each

Table 3.17

	A	B	C
1	①, 00	2 , 11	2 , 00
2	1 , 01	3 , 01	②, 00
3	4 , 10	③, 00	5 , 00
4	④, 00	3 , 00	2 , 00
5	⑤, 11	6 , 00	⑤, 00
6	2 , 00	⑥, 00	2 , 00

(a) MOC flow table.

	A	B	C	y_1	y_2	y_3	y_4
1	①, 00	2 , 11	2 , 00	0	0	0	0
2	1 , 01	3 , 01	②, 00	1	0	0	1
3	4 , 10	③, 00	5 , 00	1	0	1	0
4	④, 00	3 , 00	2 , 00	1	0	1	1
5	⑤, 11	6 , 00	⑤, 00	1	1	1	0
6	2 , 00	⑥, 00	2 , 00	1	1	0	1
α	1 , 00	2 , 11	2 , 00	0	0	0	1
β	1 , 00	3 , 01	2 , 00	1	0	0	0
δ	–	6 , 00	–	1	1	0	0
ε	–	6 , 00	–	1	1	1	1

(b) Flow matrix

column in our example are

A: $(12, 34)(12, 5)(12, 6)(1, 26)(26, 34)(26, 5)(34, 5)$
B: $(1, 23)(12, 34)(12, 56)(23, 56)(2, 34)(34, 56)$
C: $(12, 35)(26, 35)(24, 35)$

Eliminating those such as $(12, 6)$ which are covered by others and applying steps 2 to 7 of Procedure 3.1 yields a minimal covering set of dichotomies composed of $(1, 23)$, $(1234, 56)$, $(126, 345)$, and $(135, 246)$. The resulting flow matrix is shown as Table 3.17b, in which $(1, 23)$ has in effect been replaced by $(1, 23456)$. The y-states not shown have only don't care entries.

3.4   The One-hot Code

An interesting special class of unicode row assignments are those termed *one-hot* codes, characterized by the fact that for each row of the flow table, exactly one of the y-variables has the value 1. For example, in Table 3.18, y_i and only y_i is on for each row i. When any MOC flow table is coded in this manner, we shall show that it is always possible to design the circuit logic

Table 3.18   SOC Table with One-hot Assignment

| | $x_1 x_2$ | | | | y_1 | y_2 | y_3 | y_4 | y_5 |
	00	01	11	10					
1	①	2	3	①	1	0	0	0	0
2	–	②	3	–	0	1	0	0	0
3	4	③	③	1	0	0	1	0	0
4	④	–	④	5	0	0	0	1	0
5	1	⑤	4	⑤	0	0	0	0	1

so that each inter-row transition takes place in two steps, with the intermediate state being one in which exactly two y-variables are on. Thus, if the components used are such that it is desirable to keep the state devices in the 0-states as much as possible, perhaps in order to minimize power drain, heat dissipation, or component deterioration, then such an assignment is in this respect optimal. Other advantages become evident as we look into the synthesis process.

Let us consider SOC flow tables in standard form (each unstable state leads directly to a stable state with the same output). If in a column I, there is a transition from row p to row q, then we specify the logic so that *first* y_q goes on (y_p is of course initially on), and *then* y_p goes off. The general form of the excitation function for y_i is $Y_i = F_{i1} + y_i \bar{F}_{i2}$. The F_{i1}-function is a summation of terms representing the unstable total states which lead to row i. Hence F_{q1} includes a term Iy_p. The F_{i2}-function is a sum of terms corresponding to next states reached from row i. The $y_i \bar{F}_{i2}$-term serves to hold y_i on until the y-variable corresponding to the next state goes on. For the $p \to q$ transition, F_{p2} has a term y_q.

The Y-expressions for Table 3.18 are

$$Y_1 = \bar{x}_1 \bar{x}_2 y_5 + x_1 \bar{x}_2 y_3 + y_1 \bar{y}_2 \bar{y}_3,$$
$$Y_2 = \bar{x}_1 x_2 y_1 + y_2 \bar{y}_3,$$
$$Y_3 = x_1 x_2 y_1 + x_1 x_2 y_2 + y_3 \bar{y}_1 \bar{y}_4,$$
$$Y_4 = \bar{x}_1 \bar{x}_2 y_3 + x_1 x_2 y_5 + y_4 \bar{y}_5,$$
$$Y_5 = x_1 \bar{x}_2 y_4 + y_5 \bar{y}_1 \bar{y}_4.$$

Each unstable state produces one component of an F_{i1}-expression and adds one literal to an F_{i2}-product. The logic expressions may be written down by inspection of the flow matrix, and the ease with which they can be obtained is one of the advantages of the one-hot assignment. If m is the number of input variables, r the number of rows, and u the number of unstable states, then an upper bound on the number of gate inputs required for a two-stage implementation of the Y-logic for a one-hot row assignment for a SOC flow table is $2r + u(m + 3)$, an expression arrived at by computing the terms and literals added to the F_{i1}- and F_{i2}-expressions because of each unstable entry. (An upper bound on the logic needed to generate the outputs is $k(m + 2)$, where k is the *total* number of 1's appearing as Z-entries.) Of course, those components associated with the state variables increase in number linearly with r. Particularly when the number of unstable states is relatively small, the amount of logic needed in one-hot circuits is usually not excessive compared with what is needed for row assignments requiring fewer state variables. In any event it is useful to have an easily computed upper bound on the logic necessary to realize a given flow table.

When MOC tables are to be synthesized, modification of the logical design process is necessary; it is indicated below by considering a column-A transition $1 \rightarrow 2 \rightarrow 3 \rightarrow 4$. The sequence of states of $y_1 y_2 y_3 y_4$ (all other y's remain 0) should be $1000 \rightarrow 1100 \rightarrow 0100 \rightarrow 0110 \rightarrow 0010 \rightarrow 0011 \rightarrow 0001$. This can be accomplished by the following expressions, which show only the terms resulting from the transition under discussion:

$$Y_1 = \cdots + y_1 \bar{y}_2 \cdots ,$$
$$Y_2 = \cdots + A y_1 + y_2 \bar{y}_3 \cdots ,$$
$$Y_3 = \cdots + A \bar{y}_1 y_2 + y_3 \bar{y}_4 \cdots ,$$
$$Y_4 = \cdots + A \bar{y}_2 y_3 + y_4 \cdots .$$

The only changes needed are the complement terms added to the F_{i1}-functions to prevent more than two y's from being on at once.

3.5 Coding for Efficient Logic

A major secondary criterion for evaluating row assignments is the complexity of the resulting circuits. In choosing row assignments for pulsed or synchronous systems, it is usually the principal consideration. Hartmanis and Stearns [HART-1] have developed techniques for constructing assignments for synchronous circuits in such a manner that many of the resulting Y-functions depend on only some of the y-variables. Such *reduced-dependence* assignments usually lead to considerably simpler circuits than would be obtain if the row assignments were selected in an unsystematic manner.

A closely related topic that Hartmanis and Stearns have explored fruitfully is that of decomposing synchronous sequential circuits into interconnected subcircuits with all feedback paths internal to the subcircuits. These *loopfree decompositions* are desirable in that they may lead to circuits that are easier to understand, diagnose, maintain, and manufacture (particularly when integrated circuits are involved). The overall component count is also likely to be reduced.

Later in this section, we indicate how the concepts involved have been extended to SOC asynchronous circuits. A sufficient summary of the Hartmanis-Stearns concepts is presented in the following subsection to make the succeeding material understandable to readers unfamiliar with them. However, as becomes evident, the application of the techniques to be presented does entail using some specific procedures that are not given here.

The ideas in this section, being of very recent origin, have not yet been developed into practical design techniques. Nevertheless, the potential importance of the material is felt to justify its inclusion.

3.5.1   Basic Concepts of Machine Structure Theory

A *partition* on a set of states is a grouping of the states into disjoint subsets, called *blocks*, such that every state belongs to exactly one block. For example, we may define a four-block partition of the states $\{1, 2, \ldots, 8\}$ as $\alpha = (156, 2, 38, 47)$. By $a \underset{\beta}{=} b$ (β equates a and b), we mean that states a and b are in the same block of partition β. In the previous example, $1 \underset{\alpha}{=} 5$, $3 \underset{\alpha}{=} 8$, $5 \underset{\alpha}{\neq} 7$. The trivial partition with just one member in each block is called the 0-partition; whereas the partition lumping all states into one block is called the *I*-partition.

Given a flow table with a unicode row assignment, we may associate with each y-variable y_i a unique two-block partition ρ_i having in one block those states for which $y_i = 0$ and in the other block those states for which $y_i = 1$. If α and β are two partitions (unless otherwise noted it is assumed that partitions mentioned together are on the same set of states), we say that $\alpha \geq \beta$ if each block of β is contained in a single block of α. This is equivalent to saying that $a \underset{\beta}{=} b$ implies $a \underset{\alpha}{=} b$; for example, $(1356, 24, 78) \geq (15, 24, 36, 7, 8)$. The *product* $\alpha\beta$ is the partition that equates a and b iff *both* α and β equate a and b. Thus

$$(1356, 24, 78)(1236, 45, 78) = (13, 2, 4, 5, 6, 78).$$

Note that if $\lambda = \alpha\beta$, $\alpha \geq \delta$, and $\beta \geq \delta$, then $\lambda \geq \delta$, so that $\alpha\beta$ is sometimes referred to as the *greatest lower bound* of α and β. If $y_1, y_2, \ldots, y_m$ are the y-variables of a unicode assignment for a given flow table, then $\prod_{i=1}^{m} \rho_i = 0$, which is equivalent to saying that a unique y-state is assigned to each row.

Suppose α and β are partitions on the states of a given flow table. Then (α, β) constitute a *partition pair*, written as $P(\alpha, \beta)$, if for every input I and every pair of states p, q such that $p \underset{\alpha}{=} q$, it follows that $N(p, I) \underset{\beta}{=} N(q, I)$. In the case of Table 3.19, $P(\alpha, \beta)$ where $\alpha = (14, 235)$ and $\beta = (15, 234)$. Observe that 1 and 4 are in the same block of α and that in columns A, B, and

Table 3.19   A Flow Table for a
Synchronous Function

	A	B	C	y_1	y_2
1	4	3	5	0	0
2	5	3	4	1	1
3	5	2	3	1	1
4	2	4	1	0	1
5	1	4	2	1	0

C, respectively, the next-state entries for these rows are 24, 34, and 15, in each case a set contained within a single block of β.

Suppose that $P(\lambda, \phi)$ for some flow table, that S_1 and S_2 are subsets of the y-subscripts, and that a row assignment is made such that $\lambda = \prod_{i \in S_1} \rho_i$ and $\phi = \prod_{j \in S_2} \rho_j$. Then it can be shown that for each $j \in S_2$, Y_j is a function of the input variables and those y_i such that $i \in S_1$. (We assume here that the table is realized with synchronized delay elements.) If S_1 corresponds to a *proper* subset of all the y-variables, then the Y-functions for the variables corresponding to S_2 have as arguments only *some* of the y's. This is what is meant by reduced dependence. For Table 3.19, the reader may verify that, if the y_1 and y_2 columns shown (corresponding to α and β, respectively) are part of any row assignment, then Y_2 is a function of the input state and y_1, and in fact this function can be computed to be

$$A\bar{y}_1 + B + Cy_1$$

even without knowing the rest of the assignment.

The case where $P(\phi, \phi)$ is sufficiently important to warrant special consideration. We say that ϕ has the *substitution property* or SP, and designate it by writing $S(\phi)$. For Table 3.19, $S(12, 3, 45)$.

Instead of considering partitions, it is possible to treat *set systems*, which enable us to cope with multicode state assignments. A *set system* on a given set of states differs from a partition in that its blocks are permitted to overlap. Apart from including every state in at least one block, the only restriction is that no block be a subset of another block. The definitions of SP and partition pairs as well as the reduced-dependence notion carry over in a straightforward manner. If the blocks of ρ_i overlap, it means that y_i is assigned *both* the 0- and 1-values for the states in the intersection; for example, in Table 3.20, $\rho_1 = (123, 345)$ corresponds to the y_1 column. Note that $S(123, 345)$, so that we can compute Y_1 as a function of the input and y_1, *before* any other y columns are specified. In fact

$$Y_1 = A + By_1.$$

Table 3.20 A Flow Table with a Set System Having SP

	A	B	C	y_1
1	4	2	3	0
2	4	1	1	0
3	5	3	2	0, 1
4	3	5	2	1
5	4	5	2	1

As becomes apparent in the succeeding subsections, the reduced-dependence property for the asynchronous case is somewhat less in evidence because of the complications resulting from the possibility of critical races.

3.5.2 Reduced Dependence for Asynchronous Circuits

In the synchronous case, the mere fact that $P(\rho_1\rho_2, \rho_3)$ is sufficient to assure us that in any row assignment Y_3 can be specified without reference to state variables other than y_1 and y_2. An illustration of the difficulty involved in extending the theory to asynchronous circuits is the flow table shown in Table 3.21, with the partial state assignment consisting of y_1 and y_2.

We first compute $\rho_1\rho_2 = (125, 34)(1245, 3) = (125, 3, 4)$ and then observe that $P(\rho_1\rho_2, \rho_1)$, so that a naive extension of the theory developed for synchronous circuits would lead us to expect that Y_1 could be expressed as a function of x_1, x_2, y_1, and y_2. In fact, we can indeed obtain an expression of this form, namely,

$$Y_1 = \bar{x}_1\bar{x}_2y_1 + x_2y_1\bar{y}_2 + \bar{x}_1x_2.$$

However, examining the 3 → 1 transition in the 11 column, we see that *both* y_1 and y_2 change and that, if y_2 changes first, then state 4-11 is entered, and

Table 3.21 SOC Table for Which a Reduced-Dependence Assignment Can Be Found

	x_1x_2 00	01	11	10	y_1	y_2	y_3	Reduced-dependence assignment y_1	y_2	y_3	y_4
1	①, 0	4, 0	①, 0	5, 0	0	0	0	0	0	0	0
2	1, 0	4, 0	②, 1	5, 0	0	0	0	0	0	0	1
3	③, 1	4, 0	1, 0	5, 0	1	1	0	0	1	0	0
4	3, 1	④, 0	④, 0	5, 0	1	0	1	1	1	0	0
5	⑤, 0	4, 0	2, 1	⑤, 0	0	0	0	0	0	1	1

here Y_1 has the *wrong* value. In other words, there is a race between y_1 and y_2 which is critical with respect to Y_1. Thus the values of y_1 and y_2 alone cannot be relied upon to specify Y_1 properly during every transition.

But now consider y_3, also shown in Table 3.21. Since $\rho_1\rho_3 = \rho_1\rho_2$, we have $P(\rho_1\rho_3, \rho_1)$, the *same* partition pair as before. But now we can derive

$$Y_1 = \bar{x}_1\bar{x}_2y_1 + x_2y_3 + \bar{x}_1x_2.$$

No such critical race occurs as was the case before. The key point is that y_1 and y_3 cover all of the dichotomies generated by pairs of transitions in which y_1 has differing values at the destination states. Let us now state formally a theorem that encompasses the above discussion.

THEOREM 3.6 *Given a valid USTT assignment for a SOC flow table where σ is a subset of the state variables, y_0 is a particular state variable, and x is the input vector, $Y_0 = f_0(x, \sigma)$ iff*

(a) $P(\prod_{y_i\in\sigma}\rho_i, \rho_0)$ *and*

(b) *For every pair of transitions $a \to b$ and $c \to d$ in the same column such that $b \underset{\rho_0}{\neq} d$, the dichotomy (ab, cd) is covered by some $y_i \in \sigma$.*

PROOF. Only an outline of the proof is presented.

The necessity for condition (a) is established by paralleling the corresponding proof for synchronous circuits. If condition (b) is not satisfied for some pair of transitions $a \to b$ and $c \to d$, then it can be shown, as in the proof of Theorem 3.2 (establishing the conditions for the validity of a USTT assignment), that in the Boolean subspace defined by the members of σ, $T(a, b)$ overlaps $T(c, d)$. But then there occur states of the σ-variables for which two different Y_0-values are required in the column concerned.

Next, assume that condition (a) is satisfied. That the specified value of Y_0 for every y-state assigned to a flow table row is a function only of the input variables and the members of σ can be shown, as in the synchronous case. If in addition condition (b) is satisfied, then, following the pattern of the proof for Theorem 3.2, it can be shown that no intermediate y-state (considering only the σ-variables) is encountered during transitions to states in the same column with different y_0-values. This means that for *all* total states, Y_0 can be properly generated given only the input and σ-variable values. It has been shown recently that condition (a) of this proof can be omitted since (b) implies (a). The proof, which is not difficult, is left to the reader.

A companion theorem to the one just presented states that, for every partition pair, some reduced-dependence relation can be found.

THEOREM 3.7 *If, for some SOC table T, $P(\alpha, \rho_k)$, then there exists a set of y-variables ρ_k such that $\prod_{y_i\in\sigma_k}\rho_i = \alpha$, and a valid USTT assignment for T such that $Y_k = f_k(\underline{x}, \sigma_k)$.*

PROOF.   The proof, which is only sketched here, depends on our being able to show that, for any transition pair $a \to b$ and $c \to d$ appearing in the same column such that $b \neq d$, we can find a two-block partition $\rho \geq \alpha$ that
$$\underset{\rho_k}{}$$
covers (ab, cd). If this can be demonstrated, then multiplying together these ρ's gives us a partition $\alpha' \geq \alpha$, and we can then add additional ρ's if necessary to refine α' to α. The set of y's corresponding to the resulting set of ρ's then satisfies Theorem 3.6 and hence meets the requirements for the σ_k of the current theorem. The desired ρ can be found by merging the blocks of α containing a and b and merging the blocks containing c and d. The remaining blocks can each be merged with one or the other of the two blocks so formed to obtain a two-block partition covering (ab, cd) and dominating α. However, this result is possible only if neither a nor b is in a common block of α with c or d. We now indicate that this condition does exist, by proving that $a \underset{\alpha}{\neq} d$ ($a \underset{\alpha}{\neq} c$, $b \underset{\alpha}{\neq} c$, and $b \underset{\alpha}{\neq} d$ can be similarly established). Let I be the input in which the $a \to b$ and $c \to d$ transitions occur. Then, since $P(\alpha, \rho_k)$, it follows by definition of partition pairs that $a \underset{\alpha}{=} d$ implies that $N(a, I) \underset{\rho_k}{=} N(d, I)$, which is equivalent to $b \underset{\rho_k}{=} d$. But by hypothesis $b \underset{\rho_k}{\neq} d$ and so $a \underset{\alpha}{\neq} d$.

In Chapter 5 it is shown (Theorem 5.1) that for every nonredundant state variable y_i used in a row assignment for a SOC asynchronous function, Y_i is a function of y_i. Hence when applying the theorem just discussed, we can always expect to find y_k in σ_k.

To illustrate the application of Theorems 3.6 and 3.7, we now develop an efficient USTT assignment for Table 3.21. Using standard techniques developed for synchronous functions, the partition pairs and SP partitions can all be found (here we must refer the reader elsewhere [HART-1]). One pertinent finding is that $S(1235, 4)$. The only transition pairs terminating in states distinguished by $(1235, 4)$ are $3 \to 1$ and $4 \to 4$ in column 11 and $5 \to 2$ and $4 \to 4$ in the same column. Since $(1235, 4)$ covers the corresponding dichotomies $(13, 4)$ and $(25, 4)$, it follows from Theorem 3.6 that, if we set $\rho_1 = (1235, 4)$, then Y_1 is expressible as $f_1(x_1, x_2, y_1)$ in a valid USTT assignment. It can also be shown that $P[(125, 3, 4), (125, 34)]$, which suggests setting $\rho_2 = (125, 34)$. Then, since $P[\rho_1\rho_2, \rho_2]$ and the dichotomies $(12, 34)$, $(34, 5)$, $(13, 4)$, and $(25, 4)$ are all covered by ρ_1 or ρ_2. Theorem 3.6 assures us that we can write $Y_2 = f_2(x_1, x_2, y_1, y_2)$. Similar reasoning starting from the observations that $S(1234, 5)$ and $P[(134, 2, 5), (134, 25)]$ lead to setting $\rho_3 = (1234, 5)$ and $\rho_4 = (134, 25)$ so that $S(\rho_3)$ and $P(\rho_3\rho_4, \rho_4)$. Again the necessary dichotomies are appropriately covered so that Y_3 is dependent only on y_3, and Y_4 only on y_3 and y_4. Since $\rho_1\rho_2\rho_3\rho_4 = 0$, we have the basis for a valid state assignment, which is shown at the extreme right of Table 3.21.

Expressions for the Y-functions are

$$Y_1 = \bar{x}_1 x_2 + x_2 y_1,$$
$$Y_2 = \bar{x}_1 x_2 + x_2 y_1 + \bar{x}_1 y_2,$$
$$Y_3 = x_1 \bar{x}_2 + \bar{x}_2 y_3,$$
$$Y_4 = x_1 \bar{x}_2 + \bar{x}_2 y_3 + x_1 y_4.$$

Several other reduced-dependence assignments requiring comparable amounts of logic exist for this problem. One such solution requires three state variables.

3.5.3 Decomposition of Asynchronous Circuits

The problem to be considered here is that of realizing an asynchronous sequential function in terms of two or more distinct sequential circuits that are interconnected in such a manner that no feedback path incorporates elements from more than one circuit. Two basic types of interconnection are considered. The *parallel decomposition* is illustrated in Fig. 3.2a, where each of the mutually independent sequential circuits C_1 and C_2 receives the external input x and transmits to a combinational circuit its internal state. In the *serial decomposition*, depicted in Fig. 3.2b, the situation differs in that C_2 also receives information from C_1. Our discussion is initially confined to situations in which there is a unique pair of states of C_1 and C_2 for each state of the given flow table. This restricts us to the realm of partition pairs and avoids certain open problems involved with set systems. An example in which set systems are used is presented later.

We begin with parallel decomposition, the simpler case, in which the basic theorem applicable to synchronous functions also applies to asynchronous functions, namely:

THEOREM 3.8 *A SOC flow table can be realized by means of a parallel decomposition into two circuits with a unique state pair corresponding to each flow-table state iff there exists a pair of SP partitions α_1 and α_2 such that $\alpha_1 \alpha_2 = 0$.*

PROOF. The proof is based on the idea that, if we consider the component circuits C_1 and C_2 as *one* sequential circuit, then the combined y-variable sets can be considered as a state assignment for the given table divided into two sets that are mutually independent. This division corresponds to a pair of SP partitions, and if the ordered pair of states taken from C_1 and C_2 is in one-to-one correspondence with the flow-table states, then the product of these partitions must be 0. The argument is reversible, so that the "if" part

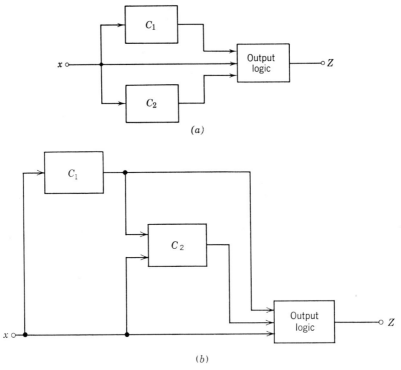

(a)

(b)

Figure 3.2   (a) Parallel decomposition. (b) Serial decomposition.

of the theorem can also be established. It is necessary, of course, that C_1 and C_2 be realized in a manner free of critical races, but this is always possible. If C_1 and C_2 are to be USTT circuits, then the overall equivalent state assignment for the given table will also be USTT, and the satisfying of Theorem 3.6 is equivalent to satisfying the conditions for valid USTT assignments for C_1 and C_2.

As an example note that for Table 3.22a, if $\alpha_1 = (13, 245)$ and $\alpha_2 = (1, 2, 34, 5)$, then $S(\alpha_1)$, $S(\alpha_2)$, and $\alpha_1\alpha_2 = 0$, meeting the conditions of Theorem 3.8. Hence we can form flow tables (Table 3.22 b and c) corresponding to circuits C_1 and C_2 of Fig. 3.2a. The rows of these tables correspond to the blocks of α_1 and α_2, as indicated to the right of each. Circuits can now be found by constructing valid row assignments independently for each table (USTT assignments are shown). The output-logic circuit recognizes the overall internal state as a function of the states of C_1 and C_2. Thus, if C_1 is in state 2 and C_2 in state 3, then the state of the given table is the intersection of the corresponding blocks 245 and 34, namely, 4.

Table 3.22

$$x_1 x_2$$

	00	01	11	10
1	①,0	①,0	4,0	2,0
2	②,0	3,0	②,0	②,0
3	③,1	③,0	4,0	—
4	④,0	—	④,0	5,0
5	⑤,1	1·,0	—	⑤,0

(a) Flow table with SP partitions.

$$x_1 x_2$$

	00	01	11	10	y_1	
1	①	①	2	2	0	(13)
2	②	1	②	②	1	(245)

(b) Table corresponding to α_1.

$$x_1 x_2$$

	00	01	11	10	y_1	y_2	y_3	
1	①	①	3	2	0	0	0	(1)
2	②	3	②	②	1	1	0	(2)
3	③	③	③	4	1	0	1	(34)
4	④	1	—	④	0	1	1	(5)

(c) Table corresponding to α_2.

Turning to the problem of serial decomposition, let α_1 be an SP partition of a flow table T. Then a flow table T_1 can be constructed according to α_1 (its states corresponding to the blocks of α_1). Suppose that a USTT assignment with y-variables σ_1 is found for T_1 and that this assignment is used as a partial assignment for T by assigning to each state of T the code used for the row of T_1 corresponding to the α_1 block containing that state of T. Then it can be shown by applying Theorem 3.6 that the Y-functions for the σ_1-variables depend only on the input $\underline{x}$ and the y's of σ_1. Now assume that a USTT assignment for T is completed by choosing a second set of y-variables σ_2 in such a manner as to cover all dichotomies required by Theorem 3.1 which have not been covered by the initial set. We can now consider a circuit C_1 described by T_1 with the σ_1-variables as the row assignment, and $\underline{x}$ as its input. A second circuit C_2 is defined by the σ_2-variables and has as its inputs $\underline{x}$ and the y's of C_1. Thus we have a serial decomposition in the form of Fig. 3.2b. Note that, if the σ_1-variables do not cover *any* of the required dichotomies, then the decomposition is a trivial one in that the σ_2 circuit *itself* realizes T.

As an example, let T be Table 3.23a, which has the SP partition $\alpha_1 = (123, 45, 67, 89)$. This partition corresponds to Table 3.23b, which has the valid USTT assignment shown with state variables y_1 and y_2. The dichotomies that must be covered by a valid USTT coding for T are: (1, 28), (1, 39), (1, 47), (1, 56), (28, 39), (28, 47), (28, 56), (39, 47), (39, 56), (47, 56), (15, 24), (15, 68), (15, 79), (24, 35), (24, 68), (24, 79), (35, 68), (35, 79), and (68, 79). Any coding of T_1 must distinguish the blocks of α_1; therefore,

Table 3.23a Flow Table T with SP Partition
$\alpha_1 = (123, 45, 67, 89)$

	x		Row assignment for T			
	0	1	y_1	y_2	y_3	y_4
1	①,0	5,0	0	0	0	0
2	②,0	4,0	0	0	1	1
3	③,1	5,0	0	0	1	0
4	7,0	④,0	0	1	0	1
5	6,0	⑤,0	0	1	1	0
6	⑥,0	8,0	1	1	1	1
7	⑦,0	9,0	1	1	0	0
8	2,0	⑧,0	1	0	1	1
9	3,0	⑨,0	1	0	1	0

Table 3.23b Flow Matrix for C_1

	x		y_1	y_2	
	0	1			
1	①	2	0	0	(123)
2	3	②	0	1	(45)
3	③	4	1	1	(67)
4	1	④	1	0	(89)

Table 3.23c Flow Matrix for C_2

	xy_1y_2								y_3	y_4	
	000	001	011	010	110	111	101	100			
1	①	①	①	—	3	3	3	3	0	0	(17)
2	②	②	②	②	②	②	4	4	1	1	(268)
3	③	2	2	③	③	③	③	③	1	0	(359)
4	—	1	1	—	—	—	④	④	0	1	(4)

given any dichotomy composed of two blocks of α_1, there is some y-variable of the coding that covers it. Depending upon the coding used, certain other dichotomies may also be covered. Thus, among the T-dichotomies listed above, (1, 28) can not be covered by any coding of α_1 because $1 \underset{\alpha_1}{=} 2$. The *particular* coding used *does* cover (1, 47) (among others) because of y_2, though one could distinguish the blocks of α_1 without doing so (if, for example, the codes assigned to 67 and 89 were interchanged—which in this case would cause a critical race in C_1). *None* of the dichotomies in the present example are covered by pairs of blocks of α_1 and hence by *all* codings of C_1. All of the T-dichotomies are covered by y_1 and y_2 *except* (1, 28), (1, 39), (28, 39), (47, 56), (15, 24), (24, 35), and (68, 79). Applying steps 3 to 6 of Procedure 3.1 to these dichotomies, we obtain a minimal pair of covering dichotomies (147, 235689) and (13579, 2468), corresponding to y_3 and y_4 in Table 3.23a.

An explicit flow table for C_2 can be found, if desired, from the flow matrix for T by forming a table whose rows correspond to the blocks of $\rho_1\rho_2$, and whose inputs are x, y_1, and y_2. The entries are filled in by noting the required transitions of T and observing that the C_2-entries must (and can) be filled in so that C_2-state changes can occur before or after C_1-state changes. For instance, with T in 2-0, T_1 is in 1-0, and T_2 must be in 2-000. If x now changes, y_2 goes on, corresponding to a C_1-change $1\text{-}0 \to 2\text{-}1$. Thus the C_2 input *first* changes to 100, and *then* to 101. The next-state entries in 2-100, 2-101, 4-100, and 4-101 must all be 4. Summarizing the preceding discussion we have the following theorem.

THEOREM 3.9 *A SOC table can be realized by means of a serial decomposition into two circuits with a unique state pair for each state of T iff there exists an SP partition.*

We have indicated how the decomposition may be trivial if no row assignment corresponding to the partition covers enough of the required dichotomies of T to reduce the number of y-variables needed to cover the remainder.

We now illustrate two more points by means of a final example. There are no SP partitions for Table 3.24a, but the *set system* $\beta = (123, 345)$ has SP. A serial decomposition is now derived based on β. First we construct the flow table B_1 based on β (Table 3.24b) and make the indicated trivial row assignment. At this point we could proceed much as above, noting, for example, that (123, 345) covers (2, 45), one of the necessary dichotomies of B. However, instead we illustrate an alternate approach, which is quite general and which could also have been applied to the previous example. A flow table B_2' (Table 3.24c) is constructed having the same states as B and behaving as B except that it has inputs x_1, x_2, and Y_1. There is at least one stable total state in B_2' for each such state in B, and sometimes several. For example, 3-00 is stable in B, and corresponding to it is 3-000 in B_2'. Both 3-100 and

Table 3.24

x_1x_2

	00	01	11	10
1	①,0	3,0	①,0	3,0
2	②,0	4,0	②,0	②,0
3	③,1	③,0	2,0	③,0
4	2,0	④,0	2,0	5,0
5	2,0	⑤,0	1,0	⑤,0

(a) Flow table B, a table with an SP set system.

x_1x_2

	00	01	11	10	y_1	
1	①	2	①	①	0	(123)
2	1	②	1	②	1	(345)

(b) Flow table B_1 corresponding to (123, 345).

$x_1x_2Y_1$

	000	010	110	100	101	111	011	001
1	①	—	①	3	—	—	3	—
2	②	—	②	2	—	—	4	—
3	③	—	2	③	③	—	③	—
4	2	—	2	—	5	—	④	—
5	2	—	1	—	⑤	—	⑤	—

(c) Flow table B_2'.

$x_1x_2Y_1$

	000	010	110	100	101	111	011	001	y_3	y_4
1	①	—	①	3	—	—	3	—	0	0
2	②	—	②	2	4	—	②	—	1	1
3	③	—	2	③	③	—	③	—	0	1
4	2	—	1	—	④	—	④	—	1	0

(d) Table B_2.

3-101 of B_2' correspond to 3-10 of B because of the fact that there are two stable states of B_1 corresponding to this state. We derive next-state entries of B_2' from B and B_1 in a routine manner, bearing in mind that the input to B_2' involves the next state of B_1, not the current state.

There are many unspecified entries in B_2', and our next step is to reduce B_2' subject to the assumption that those states within any block of β are a priori mutually incompatible. This assumption is necessary in order that the resulting table B_2 be able to distinguish among those states *not* distinguished by B_1. In our example, states 2 and 4 form the only compatible pair and so the reduced table B_2 is as shown in Table 3.24*d*. A valid USTT assignment using variables y_3 and y_4 is shown alongside B_2. The serial combination of circuits realizing B_1 and B_2 realizes B (with, of course, the output logic added on). Note that the B_1 circuit can transmit to the B_2 circuit *either* Y_1 or y_1, since the latter, along with x_1 and x_2 is sufficient to compute the former. The B_2 circuit must be able to accept nearly simultaneous input changes, since both x and the signals from the B_1 circuit may change in rapid sequence (this problem is discussed in Chapter 4.) It is sometimes possible to merge *columns* of B_2' as well as rows (see [GR-3]), and such a merger can sometimes lead to a reduction in the number of necessary B_2-inputs.

In general, the decomposition theorems are valid for multicode assignments if partitions are generalized to set systems, except that requirements such as $\alpha_1 \alpha_2 = 0$ of Theorem 3.8 are not always necessary. This point is illustrated in Problem 3.19, but the matter is not fully understood at the time of this writing.

It is possible to vary our procedures by transmitting information other than y or Y data to B_2 circuits in serial decompositions. For example, the *total states* of B_1 may be transmitted in which case x-inputs are unnecessary.

Finally, just as in the synchronous case, it is possible to decompose the constituent circuits of an initial decomposition. Compound decompositions can often be decided upon in advance by a study of the SP lattice (a structure that reveals all of the SP partitions or set systems of a given table).

3.5.4   Bound on Logic Needed for USTT Assignments

The synthesis procedure presented here is valid for an SOC function. It is fairly easy to carry out, resembling in some respects the synthesis of circuits with one-hot assignments, presented in Section 3.4. A special case of a Liu assignment (subsection 3.3.2) is used, in that a unique y-variable is assigned to each distinct destination set. The complexity of the resulting circuits is easily computed in advance and serves as a useful bound, even though the actual circuits are not in general optimal in any sense. Furthermore, the approach used has been refined to yield synthesis methods that *do* generate circuits relatively efficient in their use of logic elements. The latter work is still in progress at the time of this writing.

We assume that the given SOC function is described in terms of a reduced flow table in standard form (Section 2.6). If D_{iq} is a destination set, then a variable y_{iq} is assigned the value 1 for every row in D_{iq} and 0 for all other rows of the table. In Table 3.24a, for example, the set $\{2, 4, 5\}$ in column 00 gives rise to y_{002}, which is set to 1 in rows 2, 4, and 5 and to 0 in rows 1 and 3. Note that D_{013} and D_{103}, being the same, generate only a single y-variable. Clearly the resulting assignment is a valid Liu assignment, since it dichotomizes each pair of destination sets in every column.

The excitation function Y_{iq} can now be generated easily. For each input column I_j, Y_{iq} should be set equal to 1 in every row k where $N(k, I_j) \in D_{iq}$. But every row of I_j belongs to a *unique* destination set of that column, and if $Y_{iq} = 1$ for $p\text{-}I_j$, then Y_{iq} also must equal 1 for every state $r\text{-}I_j$ where r belongs to the same column-I_j destination set as p. A single y-variable characterizes each such set; hence each product term of the Y_{iq}-expression consists of a product of a single y-term and enough x-terms to specify an input column. In our example, we have $Y_{002} = \bar{x}_1\bar{x}_2 y_{002} + \bar{x}_1 x_2 y_{014} + \bar{x}_1 x_2 y_{015} + x_1 x_2 y_{112} + x_1\bar{x}_2 y_{102} + x_1\bar{x}_2 y_{105}$.

Suppose s is the number of stable states in a flow table (in our example $s = 11$). Then the number of different product terms that must be generated is s, and if we let m be the number of input variables, there are $m + 1$ inputs to each of the AND gates (assuming we do not try to cut this number by exploiting relationships between adjacent columns). Hence the first level of our two-stage AND-OR circuit requires $s(m + 1)$ gate inputs.

Let $p\text{-}I_i$ be a stable state, and let I_j be any input column. Then if all next-state entries in I_j are specified, there is exactly one destination set of I_j, D_{jq} such that $p \in D_{jq}$. Let $I_i y_{ip}$ represent the product term corresponding to I_i and y_{ip}. Then $I y_{ip}$ is a term in the expression for Y_{jq}. If the flow is fully specified, if no two columns have a common destination set, and if we let c be the number of columns, then $I_i y_{ip}$ appears in c Y-expressions, and the total number of OR-gate inputs for the circuit is sc. Hence the circuit complexity as measured by the total number of gate inputs is $s(m + 1) + sc = s(m + c + 1)$.

For each group of k identical destination sets in table, the above bound is reduced by $k - 1$ times the total number of stable states in the rows of these sets. If a table is incompletely specified, then for each different unspecified next-state entry, the bound is reduced by 1 for each distinct destination set whose stable state appears in the same row with that entry.

For Table 3.24a, the formula yields $11(2 + 4 + 1) = 77$, which must be reduced by 5, because the set $\{1, 3\}$ appears twice, yielding a final bound of 72. The bound just presented rises linearly with the number of *stable* states; whereas the bound of Section 3.4, based on the two-step one-hot code, rises linearly with the number of *unstable states.*

SOURCES

The basic concepts of the critical race and the racefree row assignment are due to Huffman [HUF-1], and the notion of intermeshed connected row sets as well as the assignments of Section 3.1 are due to Huffman and Wengert [HUF-2]. The shared-row approach was also introduced by Huffman [HUF-1]. A method for finding shared-row assignments different from that described in Section 3.2 is due to Hazeltine [HAZ-1]. Saucier [SA-1] showed that the $2S_0 - 1$ bound can be broken, at least for SOC functions, and she developed the general assignments of Section 3.2. A concise proof of the validity of the four-variable Saucier assignment (not presented here in detail) was found by TAN [TA-1]. The one-shot assignment based on the Hamming code is the work of Huffman [HUF-2]. C. N. Liu [LIU-1] introduced the USTT assignment referred to here as the Liu assignment. Later, Tracey [TR-1] developed the basic theory of minimal USTT assignments. Procedure 3.1 is a refinement of Tracey's approach, with Theorem 3.3 and the associated part of the procedure due to Unger [UN-6]. Some approaches to reducing the amount of work required to carry out Tracey's procedure are discussed by Friedes [FRD-1]. Gilbert [GILB-1] has made an interesting study of the properties of Gray codes. The linear bound of Subsection 3.3.3 on the number of state variables needed in a universal STT assignment was derived by Friedman and Graham [FRM-5] as were the constructive procedure based on separating systems and the universal multicode STT assignments. Ullman [FRM-5] improved on the Friedman-Graham construction, obtaining the $S_0^{1.59}$ and S_0^2 bounds. The approach outlined in Subsection 3.3.4 for generating tailored multicode STT assignments is the work of Friedes [FRD-1], as is the material dealing with STT assignments for MOC functions. Tan [TA-2] first extended the Hartmanis-Stearns theory to asynchronous circuits, and Subsection 3.5.2 is based on his work. The material on decomposition in Subsection 3.5.3 is due to Friedman, Menon, and Tan [FRM-7]. Work in this area has also been done by Kinney [KI-1, 2]. Tan [TA-3] also developed the material of Subsection 3.5.4 and has come up with further techniques for minimizing logic complexity. Some novel approaches to circuit synthesis rather different from those discussed here are due to Ferrari and Grasselli [FE-1] and to Brzozowski and Singh [BRZ-2].

PROBLEMS

3.1 Starting from Table 3.1*b*, find three ways to complete the state assignment for Table 3.1*a* with connected row sets other than the solution shown in Table 3.1*c*.

3.2   Write the augmented flow matrix for the flow matrix of Table P3.2, using the given flow matrix and employing noncritical races where possible. Write a minimal-sum expression for Y_1.

Table P3.2

	x_1x_2				y_1	y_2	y_3
	00	01	11	10			
1	①, 0	①, 0	3 , –	–,–	$\begin{cases}0\\0\end{cases}$	$\begin{matrix}0\\0\end{matrix}$	$\begin{matrix}0\\1\end{matrix}$
2	②, 1	1 , –	②, 0	–, –	0	1	0
3	2 , –	4 , –	③, 1	–, –	$\begin{cases}0\\1\end{cases}$	$\begin{matrix}1\\1\end{matrix}$	$\begin{matrix}1\\1\end{matrix}$
4	1 , –	④, 1	④, 1	–, –	1	0	1

‡**3.3**   Construct a K-map for a $2S_0 + 1$ universal, intermeshed, connected row-set assignment for eight-row tables, as mentioned in Section 3.1. (See p. 70.)

3.4   Using the row-set concept, find a proper row assignment for Table P3.4 using as few state variables as possible. (Assume here, and in similar situations when outputs are not shown, that the outputs are such as to preclude row reduction.)

Table P3.4

	x_1x_2			
	00	01	11	10
1	①	4	5	①
2	1	5	②	②
3	③	6	③	2
4	④	④	2	7
5	4	⑤	⑤	6
6	3	⑥	⑥	⑥
7	⑦	6	⑦	⑦

3.5   Apply the general $2S_0 - 2$ assignment to Table P3.5. Map Y_3 on a six-variable K-map.

Table P3.5

	x_1x_2			
	00	01	11	10
1	①	2	5	4
2	②	②	3	②
3	1	4	③	4
4	2	④	5	④
5	1	⑤	⑤	6
6	⑥	4	3	⑥

3.6   Consider the $2S_0 - 1$ assignment of Table 3.3. In general how many transition times are necessary in going from state 1001011 in row set 9 to a member of row set 5?

3.7 Find a minimal proper row assignment for Table P3.7.

Table P3.7

x_1x_2

	00	01	11	10
1	①	3	7	①
2	5	②	6	②
3	1	③	7	③
4	④	7	6	④
5	⑤	7	6	1
6	1	2	⑥	3
7	5	⑦	⑦	2

‡3.8 Find a minimal, proper row assignment for Table P3.8 using the shared-row approach.

Table P3.8

x_1x_2

	00	01	11	10
1	①	4	①	3
2	1	②	②	4
3	4	③	2	③
4	④	④	5	④
5	6	3	⑤	3
6	⑥	2	1	⑥

3.9 In an eight-row Hamming row assignment, what variable must change for each of the following transitions? (a) $6 \rightarrow 3$, (b) $2 \rightarrow 4$, (c) $5 \rightarrow 4$.

3.10 For the flow matrix of Table P3.10 (corresponding to a Liu assignment), specify the *complete* Y-matrix, using optional entries whenever possible.

Table P3.10

	A	B	C	y_1	y_2	y_3	y_4
1	①	2	①	0	0	0	0
2	②	②	3	1	0	1	0
3	4	③	③	0	0	1	1
4	④	5	1	0	1	0	1
5	2	⑤	3	1	1	1	–

3.11 Find a Tracey assignment for the flow table of Problem 3.10.

‡3.12 Find a Tracey assignment for the flow table shown as Table P3.12.

Table P3.12

	00	01	x_1x_2 11	10
1	①,0	2,0	3,0	①,0
2	1,0	②,0	3,0	②,1
3	③,1	5,0	③,0	4,0
4	1,0	–,–	④,0	④,0
5	3,1	⑤,0	⑤,1	4,0

3.13 Find a Tracey assignment for the flow table shown as Table P3.13.

Table P3.13

	00	01	x_1x_2 11	10
1	①	2	3	①
2	4	②	②	②
3	4	2	③	③
4	④	5	3	④
5	1	⑤	⑤	⑤

3.14 Find a Liu assignment for Table P3.14.

Table P3.14

	A	B	C
1	①	2	3
2	5	②	②
3	10	③	③
4	7	④	④
5	⑤	6	9
6	5	⑥	2
7	⑦	8	2
8	1	⑧	⑧
9	⑨	4	⑨
10	⑩	⑩	2

3.15 Synthesize Table P3.15 to the point of finding minimal-sum expressions for z and the y's. Use a unicode one-hot assignment.

Table P3.15

	00	x_1x_2 01	10
1	①,0	6,0	2,0
2	1,0	4,0	②,0
3	③,1	4,0	5,0
4	3,0	④,0	2,0
5	3,0	6,0	⑤,0
6	1,0	⑥,0	5,0

3.16 Table P3.16 is to be realized with a relay sequential circuit. In the application involved, it is important to minimize the drain on the power supply. For this reason, the state assignment should be so chosen that, for all stable states, a minimum number of state relays will be energized. This may entail the use of more state variables than would otherwise be necessary. Choose a suitable assignment and complete the design to the point of writing expressions for z and the y's. The circuit should always start in state 1 when the power is first turned on. *Hint:* This problem can be solved in such a manner that at most one state relay is on for any stable state and that during transient states no more than two state relays are ever on.

Table P3.16

	x_1x_2 00	01	10
1	①, 0	2 , 0	3 , 0
2	3 , 0	②, 0	4 , 0
3	③, 0	4 , –	③, 0
4	1 , 0	④, 1	④, 0

3.17 Find a USTT state assignment for Table P3.17, and construct the complete flow matrix that results.

Table P3.17

	A	B	C
1	①, 0	2 , 1	4 , 0
2	②, 0	3 , 0	②, 0
3	1 , 0	③, 1	③, 1
4	④, 0	5 , 0	④, 0
5	2 , 1	⑤, 0	4 , 1

3.18 Realize the flow table of Problem 3.10 with a one-hot state assignment.

‡**3.19** Find a parallel decomposition of Table P3.19. (There is a solution consisting of a pair of circuits realizable with one- and two-variable USTT assignments, respectively, but it is *not* easy to find. A pair of set systems is involved.)

Table P3.19

	A	B	C	D
1	①, 00	2 , 00	6 , 00	①, 00
2	3 , 11	②, 00	5 , 00	1 , 00
3	③, 11	3 , 10	5 , 00	1 , 00
4	1 , 00	3 , 10	6 , 00	④, 11
5	3 , 11	⑤, 01	⑤, 00	1 , 00
6	1 , 00	2 , 00	⑥, 00	4 , 11

CHAPTER 4

Delays, Hazards, and Analysis

This chapter is principally concerned with the effects on sequential-circuit behavior of delays in logic elements and wiring under various assumptions regarding the distribution of the delays. The problem of deriving from a sequential circuit a flow table describing its behavior is also treated. We consider only Huffman circuits and begin with a discussion of the relevant properties of delays.

4.1 Types of Delays

It is important to distinguish between *delay elements*, which are delays that have been deliberately introduced by the designer, and *stray delays* that are unavoidably present because of the physical properties of components introduced for other purposes [for example, propagation delays in wiring, stray capacitances in conjunction with unavoidable resistances, and in relay circuits, the added effects due to contact stagger (see Section 4.6).] We generally assume that delay elements can be specified to have some minimum value and that, in a given situation, this minimum determines some maximum value that they may have (a function of the tolerance and hence cost of the devices used). It is also assumed that the stray delays may have values ranging from 0 to some known upper bound. The locations and relative values of stray delays in our model are not restricted, except as noted in Section 4.4. In particular, it is assumed that there may be a stray delay in *any* wire. Circuits designed without any delay *elements* being specified are said to be *delayfree*. This of course does *not* mean that we expect such a circuit to be free of stray delays.

A *pure* delay is defined as one that acts only to transform an input signal $f(t)$ into a signal $f(t - D)$. The pure delay is what is ordinarily considered as a delay, and such behavior may be approximated by a transmission line, although it represents an ideal that cannot be fully realized by any physical device.

118

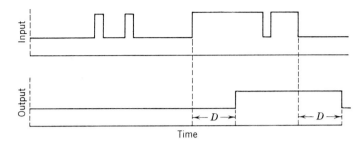

Figure 4.1 Input-output behavior of an inertial delay of magnitude D.

An *inertial* delay, defined only in terms of binary signals, responds to an input change only after it has persisted for time D (see Fig. 4.1.) Thus, if the input Y and the output y of an inertial delay of magnitude D are both 1 at some time, then y will remain at 1 until Y changes to 0 and remains at that value without interruption, for time D. Note that, under this definition, if $y = 1$ and Y alternates between 0 and 1 with the 0-intervals of duration $D - \epsilon$, for $D > \epsilon > 0$, and the 1-intervals of duration $\delta > 0$, then y will *remain* at 1. (Of course the same statement holds if we interchange the 0- and 1-signal values.) It is not possible to construct an actual device that behaves exactly

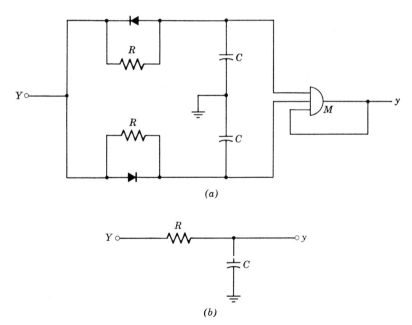

Figure 4.2 (*a*) A nearly ideal inertial-delay element. (*b*) A simpler approximation of an inertial delay.

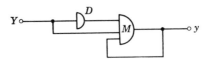

Figure 4.3   A feedback circuit realizing
an inertial delay with a pure delay.

as described above, but the circuit of Fig. 4.2a serves as a good approximation. (Readers not interested in physical implementations need not concern
themselves with the discussion of Fig. 4.2.) It is assumed that positive and
negative voltages represent 1- and 0-signals respectively, and that the majority
gate (labeled M) incorporates a threshold device. The deviation from the ideal
behavior described by the definition is in the fact that δ and ϵ cannot be made
arbitrarily small. If r_f is the forward resistance of the diodes of Fig. 4.2a,
then δ and ϵ must be bounded below by a value proportional to r_f/R.

Fortunately inertial-delay elements significantly less powerful than that of
Fig. 4.2a are adequate for most purposes. What is usually required is a
device for filtering out occasional, isolated pulses of short duration. A simple
RC circuit as shown in Fig. 4.2b is often quite adequate. In cases where the
waveform degradation occurring in this circuit is unacceptable, a threshold
device such as Schmitt trigger circuit can be incorporated at the output end.
Note that a conventional electromagnetic relay behaves very much like the
last-mentioned combination.

There are several ways of constructing a device with inertial-delay properties from pure-delay elements and logic elements. One such circuit is shown in
Fig. 4.3, based on a majority gate in a feedback loop. Input pulses (0-pulses
if $y = 1$ and 1-pulses if $y = 0$) of duration less than D do not reach y,
provided that the period between consecutive pulses is never less than D,
Thus this circuit behaves like an ideal inertial delay except that δ must
exceed D.

As becomes evident in Chapter 5, it is sometimes desirable to achieve a
similar effect with a circuit having no feedback. The circuit of Fig. 4.4 accomplishes this, although the constraints on its proper use are somewhat more
complex. Input changes of duration exceeding $\max(D_1, D_2)$ are transmitted
with delay D_1; whereas input pulses of duration less than $\min(D_1, D_2)$ are
filtered out, provided that consecutive pulses are separated by intervals

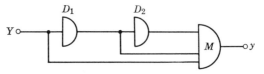

Figure 4.4   A circuit realizing an inertial delay with
pure delays and no feedback.

exceeding $D_1 + D_2$. Pulses of intermediate widths produce outputs with delay and width dependent on the relative values of D_1 and D_2 (see Problem 4.2).

Both of the circuits using majority gates can serve as satisfactory inertial-delay elements, provided that spurious input pulses are separated by sufficient time intervals. The problem of neatly classifying various types of inertial delays with respect to their behavior, requirements for realization, and application remains substantially open.

We generally assume that stray delays can be approximated as inertial delays or as inertial delays cascaded with pure delays (see Problem 4.1).

4.2 Combinational Hazards

In this section we discuss the effect of stray delays on the transient behavior of combinational switching circuits. As pointed out in Section 1.4, stray delays in such a circuit may cause spurious pulses to appear on the output leads after certain input changes. A circuit in which such pulses may occur for some distribution of stray delays is said to have one or more *combinational hazards*.

Note that hazards are associated with circuit configurations, not with physical circuits. A particular physical circuit corresponding to a configuration with a hazard may or may not malfunction, depending upon the magnitudes and locations of its stray delays at a particular time. A hazardfree (HF) circuit is one that does not display the type of malfunction under discussion regardless of the distribution of stray delays.

In a strictly combinational circuit, spurious output pulses may or may not be harmful, depending on how the output is used. For example, if the circuit controls a relatively slow acting relay that turns a motor on and off, the effects of the hazard pulses may be absorbed by the relay and have no effect on the system. On the other hand, if the pulses were to cause a traffic light to blink occasionally, this effect would probably be considered objectionable. In cases where a combinational circuit is controlling the state devices of a sequential circuit, false output pulses may take the system to the wrong stable state, thus converting a transient error into a steady–state error.

We begin with a discussion of two-stage AND-to-OR logic with only one input variable at a time permitted to change. The results are then generalized to cover a broader class of circuits, and the case of multiple input changes.

It is assumed throughout this section that, for any particular physical circuit, there are known bounds on the stray-delay values and that these bounds are used to space the input changes sufficiently apart so that all the effects of one change reach all the outputs before any of the effects of the next change reach any of the outputs. This assumption has essentially the same effect as the stronger assumption that the circuit is a steady-state condition before any input signal is changed.

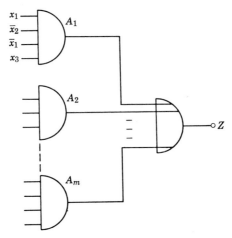

Figure 4.5   An AND-to-OR circuit.

Corresponding to each AND gate A_i of a given two-stage AND-to-OR circuit (see Fig. 4.5), let p_i be a product term containing all of the literals that are inputs to A_i. In Fig. 4.5 gate A_1, for example, would produce the term $p_i = x_1 \bar{x}_2 \bar{x}_1 x_3$. (For the purpose of later generalization, it is useful to permit both a variable and its complement to appear among the inputs to one AND gate, even though it appears to make very little sense at present.) The combinational function corresponding to the circuit can then be expressed as $\sum_{i=1}^{m} p_i$, where the p_i terms are product terms of the function, or null (as in the case of p_1 in the example).

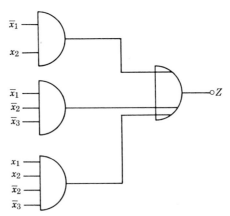

Figure 4.6   A circuit with a 0-hazard for transitions between 110 and 100 with $x_j = x_2$, and a 1-hazard between 000 and 010 with $x_j = x_2$.

Let I_1 and I_2 be two input states differing only in the values of x_j. Then we say that a combinational circuit realizing a function $f(I_k)$ has a 0-*hazard for transitions between* I_1 *and* I_2 iff

1. $f(I_1) = f(I_2) = 0$, and
2. A 1-pulse may appear (depending on stray-delay values) after a change in x_j when the initial input is I_1 or I_2.

(See Fig. 4.6, for an example of a circuit with such a hazard.)

For the two-stage circuits under discussion we can state simply when 0-hazards exist.

LEMMA 4.1 *A circuit has a 0-hazard between the adjacent input states I_1 and I_2 that differ only in x_j iff $f(I_1) = f(I_2) = 0$, there is a p-term p_h of the circuit that includes x_j and $\bar{x}_j$, and all other literals of p_h have 1-values in I_1 and I_2.*

PROOF. First assume that such a p_h exists and that $f(I_1) = f(I_2) = 0$. For states I_1 and I_2, all p-terms clearly have 0-values. Assume now, without loss of generality, that $x_j = 0$ in I_1. With the input initially in I_1, if x_j is turned on, a stray delay at the $\bar{x}_j$-input to A_h that is sufficiently large can have the effect of making both x_j and $\bar{x}_j$ appear to have 1-values simultaneously as far as A_h is concerned. Since all other inputs to A_h are fixed at 1 throughout the transition, this effect causes A_h to emit a 1-output, which in turn causes Z, the circuit output, to go to 1. This output persists until the 0-value of $\bar{x}_j$ makes its effect felt by returning the A_h-output to 0. Thus the "if" part of the lemma is proved.

Now assume that a 0-hazard exists in that a momentary 1-output appears after a change in the input state I_1 to I_2. It follows then that at least one AND gate must emit a 1 during the transition. (Certainly there is no way that a 1 can appear at the output of an OR gate if all of its inputs remain fixed at 0.) Let us call such a gate A_h. Suppose some literal x_q (or $\bar{x}_q$) where $q \neq j$ had the value 0 in I_1 (it would also be 0 in I_2 since these states differ only in x_j) and that this literal were an input to A_h. Then, since only x_j changes during the transition under discussion, the A_h gate would have at least one input constant at 0 throughout the transition. Since we are tacitly assuming that the basic logic elements in our circuits do not by themselves generate false outputs, it follows that the A_h-output would remain 0 throughout the transition. But this contradicts the assumption that A_h emits a 1-pulse after the input change, hence no such x_q (or $\bar{x}_q$) literal can exist. Thus all inputs x_i or $\bar{x}_i$ to A_h such that $i \neq j$ must have 1-values in I_1 and I_2 as specified in the statement of the lemma. But p_h must be 0 for both I_1 and I_2 [since $f(I_1) = f(I_2) = 0$], and this is possible only if both x_j and $\bar{x}_j$ are components of p_h, which completes the proof of the "only if" part of the lemma.

One simple conclusion that can be drawn from Lemma 4.1 is that an AND-to-OR realization of any combinational function is free of 0-hazards provided that we are not so foolish as to incorporate an AND gate with a pair of complementary inputs.

Let us now define a circuit as having a 1-*hazard for transitions between I_1 and I_2* (again I_1 and I_2 are adjacent—differing only in x_j) if $f(I_1) = f(I_2) = 1$ and a transient 0-output may occur during a transition between I_1 and I_2. (The circuit of Fig. 4.6 has such a hazard also.) With respect to AND-to-OR circuits the situation is *not* the dual of the previous case (it would be only if we turned to a discussion of OR-to-AND circuits), and the following lemma is necessary to relate 1-hazards to circuits of the form of Fig. 4.5.

LEMMA 4.2 *A circuit has a 1-hazard between I_1 and I_2 where $f(I_1) = f(I_2) = 1$ iff there is no p-term that has the value 1 in both I_1 and I_2.*

PROOF. Suppose there is a p_f for the circuit such that $p_f = 1$ for both the I_1- and I_2-inputs. Then neither x_j nor $\bar{x}_j$ can be a component of p_f; hence all p_f-inputs must be fixed throughout transitions between I_1 and I_2. But this means that p_f feeds a constant 1-signal to the OR gate, which in turn must therefore have a constant 1-output, so that there is no 1-hazard for such transitions. Thus the "only if" part of the lemma is established.

Assume now that there is no p-term with a 1-value in both I_1 and I_2. Then P_1, the set of all p-terms with 1-values in I_1, must be nonempty and disjoint with P_2, the necessarily nonempty set of p-terms that have 1-values for input I_2. Assume now the input is I_1, so that the AND gates corresponding to members of P_1 all have 1-outputs, and the AND gates corresponding to P_2-terms all have 0-outputs. If x_j is changed, then the P_1-AND gates switch to 0-outputs, and the P_2-AND gates switch to 1-outputs. Suppose that the stray delays at the outputs of the P_2 gates are all long relative to those at the outputs of all the P_1 gates. Then there will be an interval during which the OR gate inputs coming from the P_1 gates will all have switched to 0; whereas the inputs from the P_2 gates will not yet have switched to 1. During this period *all* of the OR-gate inputs are 0, and so its output will be 0, thus producing the 1-hazard predicted by the "if" part of the lemma.

Given any combinational function, if we derive a sum-of-products expression such that not only is every 1-point covered by some product term (the usual requirement) but also each *adjacent pair* of 1-points is also covered by a single product term, then Lemma 4.2 assures us that an AND-to-OR circuit corresponding to such an expression is free of 1-hazards, and according to Lemma 4.1 there are no 0-hazards either. For the same reasons that apply in the case in which only steady-state outputs are of interest, the most economical two-stage logic results if only prime implicants are used as product terms. *K*-maps can be used in the synthesis process, or prime-implicant tables can be used. In the latter case, for each adjacent pair of 1-points of the function, a column is added to the table having a 1 in each row corresponding to a prime implicant covering that pair.

Thus far our discussion has concerned *static* hazards, those that occur in the course of input transitions during which the output is supposed to remain constant. It is also possible to have hazards involving input changes that cause the output to change. These manifest themselves in the form of superfluous pairs of output changes that occur before the output settles down at its final value. Suppose now that I_1 and I_2 are once again adjacent input states differing only in the value of x_j. Then a circuit is said to have a *dynamic hazard with respect to transitions between I_1 and I_2* if $f(I_2) \neq f(I_1)$, and the possibility exists that, because of stray delays, Z will change three times after an input change from I_1 to I_2. The circuit of Fig. 4.7 has such a hazard, which manifests itself if there is a relatively large stray delay in the x_2-input to A_2 (or the A_2-output lead), a smaller delay in the $\bar{x}_2$-input to A_3, and a negligible delay in the x_2-input to A_3. In this case, if x_2 is switched on with the input initially 100, Z, initially equal to 0, will change to 1 as A_3 goes on because of a fast response at its x_2-terminal, then Z will return to 0 as A_3 goes off in response to the signal on its $\bar{x}_2$-terminal, and finally Z attains a steady-state 1-value as the 1-signal from x_2 turns on the A_2 gate. For AND-to-OR circuits the conditions for the existence of dynamic hazards are given by the following lemma:

LEMMA 4.3   *An* AND-*to-*OR-*circuit has a dynamic hazard between the adjacent input states I_1 and I_2 that differ only in x_j, iff $f(I_1) \neq f(I_2)$, the circuit has a p-term p_f that contains x_j and $\bar{x}_j$, and all other literals of p_f have 1-values in I_1 and I_2.*

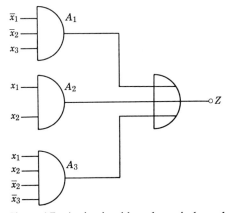

Figure 4.7   A circuit with a dynamic hazard between 100 and 110.

PROOF. Suppose there is such a p_f-term as described above. Then, as described in the proof of Lemma 4.1, the output of A_f, the gate associated with p_f, may change from 0 to 1 to 0 in the course of the transition from I_1 to I_2. Assume first that $f(I_1) = 0$ and $f(I_2) = 1$. Let P_2 be the set of all p-terms with 1-values in I_2. These must, of course, all have 0-values in I_1. If there are relatively long delays in the outputs of all the AND gates associated with P_2, then the 010 sequence at the output of A_f will reach Z while all other gate outputs are 0; hence the Z-signal will also change in this manner. When the 1-signal from one of the P_2 gates reaches Z, the third and final Z-change occurs, as specified by the "if" part of the lemma. To complete the proof of the "if" part, we note that, if $f(I_1) = 1$ and $f(I_2) = 0$, then if the delays in the x_j- and $\bar{x}_j$-inputs to A_f are relatively long, the gates keeping Z on in the I_1-state will have gone off, turning Z off, prior to the 010 sequence emerging from A_f. Thus the output from Z will be 1010.

Now assume there is a dynamic hazard between I_1 and I_2. If $f(I_1) = 0$ and $f(I_2) = 1$, then the hazard corresponds to the possibility that the sequence 0101 will appear at the Z-terminal during the $I_1 \rightarrow I_2$ transition. On the other hand, if $f(I_1) = 1$ and $f(I_2) = 0$, then the "hazard sequence" is 1010. In either case, 010 is a subsequence, which means that some A gate must go on and then off during the transition. But the argument in the second part of the proof of Lemma 4.1 establishes that such a gate must correspond to the p_f-term in the hypothesis of the present lemma, which is all we need to complete the proof of the "only if" part.

An immediate consequence of this lemma is that the procedure described above for synthesizing two-stage logic free of static hazards also produces circuits free of dynamic hazards, since none of the gates in such a design has both x_i- and $\bar{x}_i$-inputs for any i. Note though that, as illustrated by the circuit of Fig. 4.7, a circuit may have a dynamic hazard even though it has no static hazards.

The presence of more than one p_f-term covering a particular transition can result in as many spurious pairs of output changes occurring during the transition as there are p_f-terms. This is true both for 0-hazards and for dynamic hazards. Thus output sequences such as 01010 or 010101 are possible after $I_1 \rightarrow I_2$ input changes. In the case of a transition with a 1-hazard, only a single spurious 0-pulse is possible *unless* there are p_f-terms covering the two input states involved.

As shown above it is always possible to synthesize AND-to-OR circuits that are free of combinational hazards involving changes in single input variables. The price paid is in the form of added logic gates, but the resulting circuits are immune to the type of trouble discussed, regardless of the distribution of stray delays, and no slowing of circuit operation is entailed. In certain cases, however, it may be feasible to eliminate the effects of hazards by inserting delay elements to ensure that certain signal changes do not occur in the wrong order. For example, such an element inserted in the output lead to one of the P_1-AND gates referred to in the proof of Lemma 4.2 would prevent malfunctioning due to the 1-hazard involved in that argument. This solution is not always possible since a delay placed to *prevent* the manifestation of one hazard may *ensure* malfunctioning because of a different hazard. In addition, the circuit may be slowed down because of the added delay.

Another approach is to accept the possibility of spurious output pulses occurring and to provide inertial delays in the output leads to filter out these pulses. This solution has the drawback of slowing down the circuit and will result in output waveforms with long rise and fall times unless inertial delays with threshold devices are used. These devices may be costly and may also further slow the operation of the circuit. Thus there are often good reasons for designing hazardfree circuits.

We now consider the effect of permitting simultaneous changes of two or more input variables. In particular, assume that the function displayed on a K-map in Table 4.1 is realized by an AND-to-OR circuit. Observe that no single product term of the function, and hence no single AND gate, can cover both of the 1-points labeled a and c. If the stray delays in the outputs of the AND gates covering c are longer than those covering a, then a transient 0-signal will occur in the course of an input change from state a to state c (which involves switching A and D simultaneously). Thus a 1-hazard is *unavoidable* for this function. It is useful to think of this situation in terms of the order in which the individual input variable changes affect the output, taking into account the effects of the stray delays. The situation may be discussed with respect to the *apparent* sequence of input states that are sensed by the output. In the above case, it is possible for the output to "see" the input as changing from $a \rightarrow h \rightarrow c$, which would result in the false output signal occurring

Table 4.1 Hazards Involved During Multiple Input Changes

f		g	1
	e	1_b	
1_k	1_a	h	1_i
1_d	1_j	1_c	

in response to the apparent input state h. No such false signal would have resulted for this input change if the stray delays had been so distributed as to cause the apparent input sequence to have $a \rightarrow j \rightarrow c$. This suggests the possibility of *fixing* the race between the A and D variables by inserting delay elements in such a manner that, for this transition, the D-change would reach the output first, thus making j the apparent intermediate state. In some situations, this technique may be useful, although the same comments apply that were made in connection with the analogous approach for combatting hazards in the single-input-change case. For some transitions, such as $a \rightarrow b$, the method is entirely unworkable, since regardless of *which* variable appears to change first, an intermediate state (e or h) with a 0-output is passed through. In other words, there is no path through mutually adjacent 1-points of the function that links a and b. Since it is not generally feasible to arrange the delays in the circuit so that all of the changes affect the output simultaneously, the only remedy is to use an inertial delay in the output to filter out spurious transients. The cases typified by both of the above case ($a \rightarrow c$ and $a \rightarrow b$ transitions) are characterized as *function hazards* to denote the fact that these hazards are inherent in the function itself rather than in any particular logic circuit that realizes it.

A third case is illustrated by the pair of 1-points (a, d). Here every minimal-length path linking these points consists exclusively of 1-points of the function. This case may alternately be stated as "the subcube spanned by the two points (the set of points lying between them) corresponds to a product term of the function." It is *possible* therefore to cover this region with a single AND gate which remains on during any transition between a and d, thereby precluding the possibility of a spurious signal occurring. In fact, there is obviously a prime implicant covering such a subcube; hence, if a function is realized by summing the outputs of a set of AND gates corresponding to its prime implicants, then no *avoidable* 1-hazard exists. When a particular circuit has such an avoidable 1-hazard (which can occur in our example if the circuit has no $\bar{A}C$ gate but covers the same points with gates corresponding to $\bar{A}\bar{B}C$ and $\bar{A}BC$), then a *logic* 1-*hazard* is said to exist, denoting the fact that the fault lies in the particular logic used rather than in the function. It is not difficult to see that the presence of a logic 1-hazard implies the absence of an AND gate corresponding to some prime implicant.

A parallel situation exists with respect to 0-hazards. Transitions $e \rightarrow h$, $e \rightarrow g$, and $e \rightarrow f$ illustrate cases in which, respectively, none, some but not all, and all of the paths are free of transients. The first two cases illustrate *function* 0-*hazards*; whereas the possibility of a $0 \rightarrow 1 \rightarrow 0$ output from a circuit during an $e \rightarrow f$ transition means the presence of a *logic* 0-*hazard*. Note that the latter implies the existence of an AND gate with complementary appearances of literals corresponding to one or more of the variables involved in the transition (A and D in our example). Our results with respect to multiple input changes may be summarized in the following two theorems, whose proofs are embedded in what has already been said.

THEOREM 4.1 *A function hazard exists for a transition $p \to q$ iff there is a minimal-length path from p to q along which the function value changes more than once.*

THEOREM 4.2 *An* AND-*to-*OR *circuit has no static logic hazards if its p-terms are in one-to-one correspondence with the prime implicants of the function being realized. It has a logic 1-hazard iff there is some prime implicant not represented by a p-term. It has a logic 0-hazard iff for some pair of input states I_1 and I_2 such that $f(I_1) = f(I_2) = 0$ there is a p-term with no literal equal to 0 in both I_1 and I_2 and with complementary literals of some variable that changes between I_1 and I_2 (see Problem 4.20).*

With regard to dynamic hazards, the situation is greatly complicated when multiple input changes are permitted. Fortunately they do not appear to be important, and so we confine ourselves to indicating some of the possibilities. In Table 4.1 all minimal paths linking g and i involve three changes in the function value, and three such paths link a and g. Hence transitions between these pairs involve dynamic-function hazards. *No* such path links d and e, and so we might conclude that there is no dynamic-function hazard involving transitions between d and e. This conclusion is true in the sense that the function *can* be realized without such a hazard. However, as we now show, this can be accomplished only by introducing otherwise avoidable static hazards for different transitions! Consider the 1-point i which can be covered by the essential prime implicant $\bar{B}CD$. We *must* use this prime implicant in order to avoid a 1-hazard between i and k. But then, during a $d \to e$ transition, the $\bar{B}CD$ gate may be turned on, and if there is a relatively long delay at its output, its effect may be felt at the output only *after* the $\bar{A}C$ gate goes off. Thus Z may go off as $\bar{A}C$ goes off, on as $\bar{B}CD$ goes on, and finally off again with $\bar{B}CD$. A similar situation involves $BC\bar{D}$ which is needed to cover c. In addition to the types of dynamic hazards just discussed, there is a more conventional type due to *p-terms* with complementary inputs.

In summary then, any function is realizable with a circuit free of all combinational hazards involving single input changes. Such a circuit is termed *hazardfree* (HF). However, when multiple input changes are concerned, every function with more than one prime implicant contains function hazards that cannot be circumvented though logical design alone. In such cases, *static* hazards can be minimized by using all prime implicants, but the situation regarding multiple-input-change dynamic hazards is more complex (more is said later on this topic).

Having restricted our attention thus far to AND-to-OR circuits, we now proceed to generalize our results to apply to arbitrary circuits. The approach is to examine various circuit transformations to determine how they affect various types of hazards. A sufficient set is developed so that any circuit can be reduced to an equivalent AND-to-OR circuit with the *same* set of static hazards. A special technique for detecting dynamic hazards is developed, and a set of transformations that converts two-stage logic to multistage logic without adding hazards is also presented. We begin with two lemmas that permit us to operate on portions of a circuit.

LEMMA 4.4   *The transformations of a circuit* (see Fig. 4.8) *corresponding to the interchange of subexpressions $A + (B + C)$ and $A + B + C$ are hazard-preserving, as are the corresponding transformations for AND gates.*

PROOF.   It is evident from an inspection of Fig. 4.8 that the only difference between the two subcircuits is in the lengths of some of the signal paths, and the lengths have no effect on the presence or absence of hazards.

Let us define a *subcircuit* of a given circuit C as a circuit embedded in C, having a single output that may be an output of C or may feed other gates in C, and having inputs that are inputs to C or come from other gates of C.

LEMMA 4.5   *A transformation of a circuit C that consists of applying a hazard-preserving transformation to a subcircuit of C is itself hazard-preserving.*

PROOF.   Let S be the original subcircuit and S^* the transformed subcircuit. Since S^*, under all circumstances has the same possible set of outputs as S, interchanging them can have no effect on the output of C.

LEMMA 4.6   *The dual of a circuit* (AND *and* OR *gates are interchanged*) *realizes the dual function with dual hazards.*

PROOF.   In every discussion in this section we can interchange the operations AND and OR and the values 0 and 1 to obtain a dual statement that is also true. This fact stems from the duality of the postulates of switching algebra. Thus, if a given AND-to-OR circuit has a static 1-hazard for an $I_1 \rightarrow I_2$ transition, then the dual circuit (an OR-to-AND circuit) has a 0-hazard for

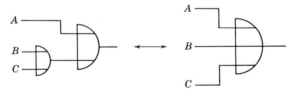

Figure 4.8 Circuit transformations corresponding to $A + (B + C) = A + B + C$.

the transition between the states dual to I_1 and I_2 (obtained by complementing the components of the vectors denoting I_1 and I_2).

LEMMA 4.7 *The insertion or deletion of inverters at the output of a circuit does not introduce or remove hazards, but only interchanges 0- and 1-hazards. The insertion or deletion of inverters at the inputs to a circuit does not introduce or remove hazards, but relocates them to the duals of the original transitions involved.*

PROOF. Obvious.

LEMMA 4.8 *The circuit transformation corresponding to the application of the generalized DeMorgan theorem (complement inputs and outputs and interchange AND and OR gates) is hazard-preserving.*

PROOF. Given a circuit C, if we complement the inputs, the hazards are moved to dual locations as indicated in Lemma 4.7. Taking the dual of C now restores the hazards to the same transitions, but complements them, as shown by Lemma 4.6. Finally, complementing the output restores the hazards to their original forms as shown by Lemma 4.7. The original function is of course realized by the resulting circuit.

LEMMA 4.9 *Transformations of circuits corresponding to the application of the distributive law preserve static hazards.*

PROOF. We must show that, if we assume that each of the variables A, B, and C changes at most once, then the circuits mirrored by $A(B + C)$ and $AB + AC$ have the same transient behavior if the steady-state value of $A(B + C)$ is unchanged by the input change. (We know of course that in the *steady state*, the circuits behave the same way.)

1. First we consider 0-hazards. For transitions in which A is fixed at 0, neither circuit can have a hazard. If A is fixed at 1, both circuits correspond to $B + C$ which can have no 0-hazard. If A changes from $0 \rightarrow 1$, then $A(B + C)$ has a 0-hazard when $B + C$ simultaneously changes from $1 \rightarrow 0$. An examination of $AB + AC$ reveals that the same is true; furthermore, for both circuits, when A changes from $1 \rightarrow 0$, 0-hazards exist when $B + C$ changes from $0 \rightarrow 1$. Hence, in all cases the expressions $A(B + C)$ and $AB + AC$ correspond to circuits with the same 0-hazards.
2. With regard to 1-hazards, it is immediately evident that, in both cases, they exist only when A is constant at 1 and B and C change in opposite directions. Hence transformations between circuits describable by $A(B + C)$ and $AB + AC$ neither eliminate nor introduce 1-hazards, and the lemma is thereby established. We note that this lemma must be restricted to *static* hazards since the circuit corresponding to $A\bar{A} + AB$

has a dynamic hazard when $B = 1$ and A changes; whereas the circuit corresponding to the $A(\bar{A} + B)$, the factored form, does not have a dynamic hazard.

The above lemma is however partly true with respect to dynamic hazards.

LEMMA 4.10 *If a circuit corresponding to $A(B + C)$ has a dynamic hazard for some transition, then any circuit corresponding to $AB + AC$ has a dynamic hazard for the same transition.* (We have already seen that the converse is not true.)

PROOF. As we have just seen, for any transition in which A is fixed, $A(B + C)$ reduces to either a constant 0 or to $B + C$. In either case a dynamic hazard cannot exist. Hence A must change. If A is initially 0, then a dynamic-hazard condition requires that $B + C = 1$ *after* the input change and that $B + C$ *change* from $1 \to 0 \to 1$ during the transition. These requirements imply that B and C change in opposite directions, which means that, in effect we can set $B = A$ and $C = \bar{A}$. But then the circuit corresponding to $AB + AC$ behaves as $AA + A\bar{A}$, which also has a dynamic hazard. Since essentially the same argument holds if A changes the other way, the lemma is established.

Both of the preceding lemmas as well as Lemma 4.4 are valid if we replace $B + C$ with a sum of more than two elements, as the essential arguments of the proofs would not be changed.

Along similar lines we also have the following:

LEMMA 4.11 *If circuits corresponding to A or to $A + B$ have hazards for any transitions, then for the same input transitions, circuits corresponding to $A + AB$ or $A + \bar{A}B$, respectively, also have the same hazards.*

PROOF. The part involving the $A + AB \to A$ transformation is trivial since clearly a circuit corresponding to the "expression" A can have no hazard. The reverse transformation *can* add a hazard as shown in Problem 4.10. An $A + B$ circuit has a hazard only when $B = \bar{A}$, in which case $A + \bar{A}B$ becomes $A + \bar{A}\bar{A}$, so that the corresponding circuit has the same 1-hazard. Hence the fact that $A + \bar{A}B \to A + B$ transformations add no new hazard is immediately evident.

We can now state two important theorems concerning the analysis of arbitrary circuits for static hazards, and the synthesis of multistage logic with no logic hazards. The proofs of these theorems follow at once from Lemmas 4.4 to 4.10.

THEOREM 4.3 *Given any algebraic expression $\mathcal{E}$, if we transform it into a sum-form expression $\mathcal{S}$ through the use of the associative, distributive, and*

DeMorgan laws (this is, of course, always possible), then circuits corresponding to $\mathscr{E}$ and $\mathscr{S}$, respectively, have precisely the same static hazards.

Hence a multistage logic circuit can be analyzed for static hazards by reducing the corresponding algebraic expression to a sum form and then applying Lemmas 4.1 and 4.2 to the result. Series-parallel contact networks can be similarly analyzed after obtaining the corresponding algebraic expressions. Non-series-parallel contact networks can be analyzed by generating a *p*-term for *every* path through the network and again applying Lemmas 4.1 and 4.2. Analysis for dynamic hazards is discussed after we present the synthesis theorem.

THEOREM 4.4   *Given any expression $\mathscr{E}_1$ if we generate from it an expression $\mathscr{E}_2$ by using only the generalized DeMorgan law, the associate law, factoring (but not multiplying out), and transformations of the form $A + AB \rightarrow A$ and $A + \bar{A}B \rightarrow A + B$, then a circuit corresponding to $\mathscr{E}_2$ will have no combinational hazard not present in circuits corresponding to $\mathscr{E}_1$.*

Thus, if we use the procedure described earlier to synthesize AND-OR logic free of logic hazards (including dynamic hazards), we can apply the indicated transformations to obtain multistage logic with the same desirable feature.

Although the above discussion is conducted in terms of circuits constructed with AND gates, OR gates, and inverters, the results are applicable to gate circuits using other building blocks, such as NAND gates. For analysis purposes circuits of this type can be transformed by simply replacing each building block by an equivalent circuit without hazards constructed with AND-OR-INVERTER logic. Synthesis can be carried out by finding a satisfactory circuit using AND-OR-INVERTER logic and then applying Theorem 4.3 to transform it into a circuit with the desired basic elements. Optimal synthesis of hazardfree circuits with arbitrary building blocks is, in general, a difficult problem, but the difficulty is of the same kind as that encountered if we are *not* concerned with hazards.

Series-parallel contact networks can be designed in a completely analogous manner, but the synthesis of non-series-parallel contact networks does not seem to lend itself to efficient systematic treatment, whether or not we are concerned about hazards.

In order to be able to detect dynamic hazards, it is necessary to distinguish among the various signal paths through a network, identifying relationships among those sets of signal paths that can activate the output. It is not enough to know, for example, that, when signals reach the z-terminal from the A, $\bar{B}$, and C inputs, z goes on. We must know *which* path from A is used, *which* $\bar{B}$ path, and *which* C path. We achieve this discrimination by attaching numerical superscripts in increasing order from left to right to each appearance of each literal in the expression that corresponds to the circuit; for example, the expression

$$AB + \bar{B}C(\bar{A} + D) + [(\bar{A} + D)E + B](\overline{CD})$$

becomes

$$A^1B^2 + \bar{B}^3C^4(\bar{A}^5 + D^6) + [(\bar{A}^7 + D^8)E^9 + B^{10}](\overline{C^{11}D^{12}}).$$

Having done this, we can now apply DeMorgan's law and the distributive law to obtain a sum form:

$$A^1B^2 + \bar{B}^3C^4\bar{A}^5 + \bar{B}^3C^4D^6 + \bar{A}^7E^9\bar{C}^{11} + \bar{A}^7E^9\bar{D}^{12} + D^8E^9\bar{C}^{11}$$

$$+ D^8E^9\bar{D}^{12} + B^{10}\bar{C}^{11} + B^{10}\bar{D}^{12}.$$

Two elements with different superscripts denote different signal paths through the circuit. In the above example, $\bar{A}^5$ refers to a path from the $\bar{A}$-input terminal through an OR gate (with a D-signal as the other input), then through an AND gate (with $\bar{B}$ and C signals merging), and finally through an OR gate (that receives signals from two other subcircuits). The $\bar{A}^7$-signal represents a distinctly different path between the same two terminals. It may start through the same OR gate, if $\bar{A} + D$ is generated as a subfunction and then fed to two different places, but in any event the path then is through an AND gate (having E as the other input) then through an OR gate (shared with B), then through an AND gate (fed also by a $\overline{CD}$-signal, and finally through the last three-input OR gate to z.

In discussing a transition between two input states I_1 and I_2 (not necessarily adjacent), let us partition the literals into four categories: f_0- and f_1-literals that remain *fixed* at 0 and 1, respectively, during the transition and c_0- and c_1-literals that *change to* 0 and 1, respectively, during the $I_1 \rightarrow I_2$ transition. Now the key theorem on identifying dynamic hazards can be stated.

THEOREM 4.5   *Given a circuit corresponding to an expression $\mathscr{E}$ realizing a function f, such that $f(I_1) = 0$ and $f(I_2) = 1$, let $\mathscr{S}$ be the sum form obtained by attaching superscripts to the elements of $\mathscr{E}$ and multiplying out, using DeMorgan's theorem when necessary. Then a dynamic hazard exists for the $I_1 \rightarrow I_2$ transition iff there is a p-term p_j containing no f_0-elements, at least one c_0-element, and at least one c_1-element and such that every p-term stable at 1 in I_2 (contains no c_0- or f_0-elements) has at least one c_1-element not in p_j.*

(Note that this theorem applies to *all* dynamic hazards, both logic and function hazards, and for multiple, as well as single input changes.)

PROOF.

1. Suppose first that the conditions are satisfied. Then, if the delays in the circuit path corresponding to one of the c_0-elements of p_j are sufficiently long compared with those in each path associated with the c_1-elements

of p_j, a 1-signal will reach the output Z because of the effects of the p_j-signals. Hence Z changes from $0 \rightarrow 1$. Now for each term p_k that is stable at 1 in I_2, let c_{1k} be one of the c_1-elements of p_k that is not shared by p_j (our hypothesis assumes that there is always such an element), and let the delay in the c_{1k}-path be long compared with the c_0-delays of p_j. Then none of the p_k's will send 1-signals to Z until *after* the c_0-signals of p_j have reached Z and turned it off. Finally, if any other term p_t can also generate a transient 1-pulse, the timing of this pulse can be made such as to keep it off for an interval after p_t goes off by making either one of its c_1-delays long or one of its c_0-delays short, assuming that it has at least one c-element not in p_j; or else it has exactly the same set of c_0- and c_1-elements as p_j, its pulse will exactly coincide with the p_j-pulse. Hence the Z-signal is turned on by p_j, then it goes off with p_j, and finally it goes on with some p_k. Hence a dynamic hazard exists and the "if" part of the theorem is established.

2. Now assume that a dynamic hazard exists for the $I_1 \rightarrow I_2$ transition. Then some p-term must go on and then off. This is possible only for a term whose elements correspond to p_j of the hypothesis. In order that the p_j-action not be blanketed by a 1-signal produced by another p-term, it must be possible for stray delays to prevent any p-term stable at 1 in I_2 from going on before p_j goes off. This can occur only if each such term has a c_1-element not in p_j, since the c_1-elements of p_j correspond to paths that must have relatively short delays. This justifies the "only if" part of the theorem.

For contact networks the superscripts denote distinct contacts, and the p-terms transmission paths through the network. It is a simple matter to transpose the above arguments to show that they apply equally well to contact networks.

In the example discussed just before the theorem, in which the sum form found was

$$A^1 B^2 + \bar{B}^3 C^4 \bar{A}^5 + \bar{B}^3 C^4 D^6 + \bar{A}^7 E^9 \bar{C}^{11} + \bar{A}^7 E^9 \bar{D}^{12} + D^8 E^9 \bar{C}^{11}$$
$$+ D^8 E^9 \bar{D}^{12} + B^{10} \bar{C}^{11} + B^{10} \bar{D}^{12},$$

we note that $D^8 E^9 \bar{D}^{12}$ is the only possible p_j-term for a single input transition. In this case E would have to be an f_1-literal and D and $\bar{D}$ the c-literals. Assuming D is the c_1-literal and $\bar{D}$ the c_0-literal, then $\bar{D}$ is 1 at I_1. Since $f(I_1) = 0$, the $B^{10} \bar{D}^{12}$-term must be 0 at I_1; hence B must be an f_0-literal. Similarly, since $\bar{A}^7 E^9 \bar{D}^{12}$ must 0 in I_1, A must be an f_1-literal. After getting rid of the literals thus far fixed, the residual expression is

$$C_4 D^6 + D^8 \bar{C}^{11} + D^8 \bar{D}^{12}.$$

Fixing C as an f_0-literal would leave

$$D^8 + D^8 \bar{D}^{12}.$$

There is *no* dynamic hazard here, since the D^8 p-term has no D-element not in the p_j-term $D^8 \bar{D}^{12}$. Hence D^8 (or rather $D^8 E^9 \bar{C}^{11}$, the original p-term) would go on when $D^8 E^9 \bar{D}^{12}$ went on and would not go off again. But if we make C an f_1-literal, we have

$$D^6 + D^8 \bar{D}^{12}$$

which *does* meet the conditions of Theorem 4.5, and so we see that there is a dynamic hazard when D changes and $ABCE$ is fixed at 1011. Dynamic hazards for changes only in X can often be found more directly from the *original* unsuperscripted expression by determining whether the variables other than X can be fixed in such a manner that, after the effects of adding and multiplying by the various 1's and 0's so introduced are computed, after DeMorgan's theorem is used, and finally after the transformations $X + X \rightarrow X$ and $XX \rightarrow X$ are applied, the resulting expression includes either $X + X\bar{X}$ or $X(X + \bar{X})$. In the above example we would have fixed $ABCE$ at 1011 to obtain

$$1 \cdot 0 + 1 \cdot 1(0 + D) + ((0 + D)1 + 0)(\overline{1 \cdot D}),$$

which reduces to $D + D\bar{D}$.

For $ABCE = 1001$ we would have

$$1 \cdot 0 + 1 \cdot 0(0 + D) + ((0 + D)1 + 0)(\overline{0 \cdot D}),$$

which reduces to D. We shall not state and prove this formally.

Returning again to our basic procedure and our example, consider the transition $00000 \rightarrow 00101$. Here after disposing of the fixed literals, we have

$$C^4 + E^9 \bar{C}^{11} + E^9.$$

The p-term $E^9 \bar{C}^{11}$ can serve as the p_j-term of the theorem, but E^9 violates the restriction on the p_k-terms since it contains no C- or E-element not also in $E^9 \bar{C}^{11}$; hence there is no dynamic hazard here. What about the transition $00000 \rightarrow 11001$? Here, after fixing C and D at 0, we obtain

$$A^1 B^2 + \bar{A}^7 E^9 + B^{10}.$$

Since $\bar{A}^7$ is a c_0-element, and E^9 a c_1-element, $\bar{A}^7 E^9$ meets the condition for the p_j-term. Both B^{10} and $A^1 B^2$ have c_1-elements not in $\bar{A}^7 E^9$, and so there is a dynamic hazard for this transition.

We close this section with two examples. First we synthesize the function of Table 4.1 with a multistage circuit having no logic hazards. The first step is to write a sum-form expression whose terms are all of the prime implicants of the function. The expression is

$$\bar{A}C + BC\bar{D} + \bar{B}CD + AB\bar{C}D + A\bar{B}\bar{C}\bar{D},$$

and it corresponds to a two-stage circuit free of logic hazards. Next we factor out a C and an $A\bar{C}$ to obtain

$$C(\bar{A} + B\bar{D} + \bar{B}D) + A\bar{C}(BD + \bar{B}\bar{D}).$$

Finally, applying DeMorgan's theorem to a subexpression, we obtain an equivalent expression in which $BD + \bar{B}\bar{D}$ appears twice

$$C(\bar{A} + (\overline{BD + \bar{B}\bar{D}})) + A\bar{C}(BD + \bar{B}\bar{D}).$$

The circuit corresponding to this expression has no logic hazards and is shown in Fig. 4.9.

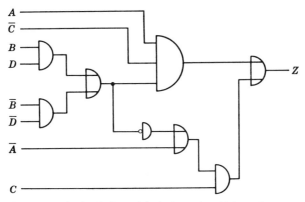

Figure 4.9 A circuit free of logic hazards which realizes the function of Table 4.1.

Next we analyze the circuit of Fig. 4.10 for static hazards. First we write the expression corresponding directly to the circuit:

$$\bar{A}(\bar{B} + \bar{C}) + (A + \bar{B})(B + C)D.$$

Multiplying out yields the sum-of-products expression that corresponds to a two-stage circuit with the same hazards (note that we do not use the theorem $B\bar{B} = 0$, since it does not correspond to a hazard-preserving transformation):

$$\bar{A}\bar{B} + \bar{A}\bar{C} + ABD + ACD + \bar{B}CD + \bar{B}BD.$$

It is immediately evident from Table 4.2, on which the above terms (except $\bar{B}BD$) are shown, that there is a 1-hazard for the transition between 0101 and 1101 because of the missing prime implicant $B\bar{C}D$. There are numerous function hazards and we list only a few:

0-hazards: $1001 \leftrightarrow 1010$, $0111 \leftrightarrow 1010$.

1-hazards: $1101 \leftrightarrow 1011$, $0011 \leftrightarrow 0100$.

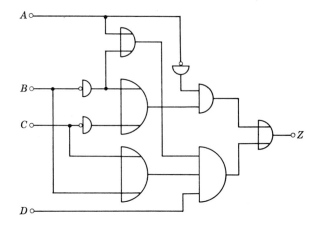

Figure 4.10   Circuit to be analyzed for combinational hazards.

Table 4.2   Product Terms for it Circuit of Fig. 4.10

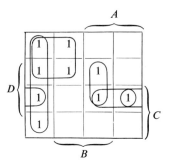

In Subsection 4.5.3 we discuss a procedure that is useful in detecting hazards in complex circuits for specific transitions.

4.3   Sequential Hazards in Circuits with Arbitrarily Placed Stray Delays

In this section (in which only SOC functions are discussed unless otherwise noted) we consider sequential-circuit malfunctions that result from stray delays and that inherently involve the feedback that is usually present in sequential circuits (a topic that is thoroughly treated in Chapter 5). It is assumed here that stray inertial delays may be present in any branch of the circuit, even if that branch consists only of a wire connecting two logic elements. This assumption is sometimes necessary, even when wiring delays are negligible, in cases in which a signal with a nonzero rise time is fed to two gate inputs with different thresholds. Even if they arrive simultaneously, they will exceed the thresholds at different times so that they take effect at different times just as if the stray delays were different in the input leads (see Robertson [RO-1]). The relative magnitudes of these delays is unconstrained, and it is assumed only that, for any particular physical circuit, upper bounds on the stray delays are known. This assumption is necessary in order that consecutive input changes can be spaced far enough apart to permit the circuits to resolve them into distinct actions. In Section 4.4 we consider circuits in which the relative magnitudes of the stray delays are restricted to correspond to the frequently valid assumption that delays in logic elements are substantially greater than those in connecting wires. It is seen there that significantly different results stem from this assumption.

Let us now describe what we mean by a *properly* designed Huffman sequential switching circuit. First of all, if upper bounds on the stray-delay and delay-element magnitudes are known, it must be possible to specify a *lower* bound on the spacing of consecutive input changes such that, if this bound is respected, then the circuit will behave as specified regardless of how far apart consecutive input changes occur. A relationship between internal reaction times and allowable input rate is fundamental in any real system that does not control by means of feedback signals the rate at which data is presented to it. (Systems with such signals are considered in Chapter 6.)

The second basic requirement concerns delay elements. As is demonstrated in this section, delay elements, when necessary, are needed to overcome certain effects of stray delays. Thus there is an inevitable relationship between the stray-delay values and the delay-element values. It is desirable that this relationship be minimal in order that delay-element values be constrained to a minimal extent, thus minimizing cost and maximizing reliability. This minimal relation consists of imposing a *lower* bound on delay-element values (the *same* bound for all elements in a circuit) as a function of the *upper* bounds on the stray-delay values. As long as every delay element meets this bound and input changes are sufficiently separated in time as indicated above, the circuit should work as specified.

The design of a proper circuit in the sense just indicated may be described in terms of a game played by the designer and some possibly diabolical opponent. The opponent $\mathscr{O}$ makes the opening move by presenting the designer $\mathscr{D}$ with a flow table. The response by $\mathscr{D}$ is to design a circuit that realizes the flow table and that may or may not contain delay elements. After studying this circuit, $\mathscr{O}$ then makes his second move by stating an upper bound on each stray delay (in a minor variation of the game, he may instead specify a single figure bounding every stray delay). Now $\mathscr{D}$ replies by computing a value to serve as the lower bound on the delay-element magnitudes. The third move of $\mathscr{O}$ consists of stating a tolerance figure for the delay-element values, which is equivalent to specifying an *upper* bound on them. Replying to this, $\mathscr{D}$ states a minimum time to be maintained between consecutive input changes. The game-ending move is now made by $\mathcal{O}$, who chooses specific values for each stray-delay element, ranging between 0 and the upper bound, and for each delay element within the allowed range. He also selects an initial total state of the circuit and a finite sequence of input changes, indicating precisely when each change is to occur within the minimum spacing constraint. At this point, the referee $\mathscr{R}$ steps in, verifies that the rules have been adhered to, constructs the circuit with delay values chosen by $\mathcal{O}$, initializes the system, and applied the inputs according to $\mathcal{O}$'s no doubt diabolical plan. If the circuit operates according to the flow table, then $\mathscr{D}$ wins. Otherwise .... A circuit produced by $\mathscr{D}$ in his opening move is *proper* if it leads to a victory by $\mathscr{D}$ regardless of $\mathcal{O}$'s strategy. If the circuit fails *only* in that, immediately after certain input changes, pairs of false output changes occasionally occur on some output leads, then *transient* hazards are said to exist. If $\mathcal{O}$ can cause the system to enter the wrong stable state, then *steady-state hazards* exist. The penalties imposed on $\mathscr{D}$ might under certain conditions be assessed according to which of these two forms his defeat assumes. We refer to a circuit having no steady-state hazards as being *S-proper*—regardless of whether there are transient hazards.

The game is often played with the precondition imposed on $\mathcal{O}$ that each input change must consist of a change in exactly *one* input variable (*single-input-change operation*). When multiple input changes are permitted, a common variation is to have $\mathcal{O}$ state as part of his second move some interval t_s such that, if several input variables change within time t_s, they are to be considered as having changed simultaneously. In this case $\mathcal{O}$ may then include such quasi-simultaneous input changes as part of his final move. Until Subsection 4.3.4, we confine ourselves to the single-input-change game.

A principal goal of this book is to enable the conscientious reader to become a master of any version of this game regardless of whether he chooses the role of $\mathscr{D}$ or $\mathcal{O}$. In this section the role of delay elements is made clear. It is shown that, for a special class of sequential functions, proper circuits can always be designed without delay elements (delayfree circuits) provided that only one input signal at a time may change. For a larger class of functions, delayfree circuits can be designed that are free of steady state, but not necessarily of transient hazards, again with the single-input-change restriction. Every other sequential function requires at least one delay element in any proper realization, and it is shown that realizations using exactly one delay element always can be found (even when multiple input changes are permitted.)

It should be understood that, although in general it is very desirable to design proper circuits, improper circuits are sometimes quite satisfactory.

It may sometimes be reasonable, for example, to specify one delay element as being larger than another delay element in order to "fix" a critical race and perhaps thereby save a considerable amount of circuitry. Or it may be seen that a particular hazard might never lead to a malfunction in a particular circuit because the stray delays are clearly not going to assume the values that $\mathcal{O}$ would have selected. An understanding of the underlying theory greatly facilitates the ability to recognize and exploit such situations.

4.3.1   Functions Properly Realizable with Delayfree Circuits

Consider a unicode-single-transition-time (USTT) flow matrix $\mathcal{M}$ for an SOC function, in which only one input variable at a time may change. We now derive a condition that, if satisfied by $\mathcal{M}$, allows us to realize it S-properly by a delayfree circuit. The class of flow tables that can be so realized will become evident, as will the complete synthesis procedure.

Let 1-B be a stable total state of $\mathcal{M}$, and let E be an input state differing from B only in the value of input variable x. We now enumerate the kinds of regions that may be encountered in B and E as a result of changing x three times with $\mathcal{M}$ initially in 1-B. (The input at the *beginning* of the first transition is B, that at the *end* is E.)

If 1-E is a stable state as shown in Table 4.3a, then repeated changes of x do not involve any portion of the matrix other than 1-B and 1-E. When 1-E is unstable, leading to a state 2-E, there are three basic cases to be considered, depending upon the 2-B entry. If $N(2, B) = 2$, we have the segment shown in

Table 4.3   Kinds of Regions Involved in a Sequence of Three Changes of One Input Variable

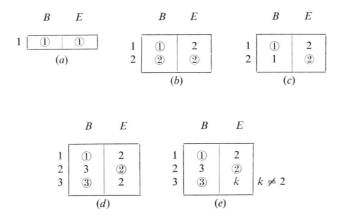

Table 4.3*b*. The second case is depicted in Table 4.3*c*, where $N(2, B) = 1$. In both of these situations, further x-changes do not lead to internal states other than 1 or 2. The third case involves a transition from 2-*B* to some other state 3. This case can be subdivided into two categories, depending on $N(E, 3)$. If $N(E, 3) = 2$, we have the flow-matrix segment shown in Table 4.3*d*. If $N(E, 3) = k$, where k is different from 1 and 2, then we have the pattern shown in Table 4.3*e*. Given any flow matrix of the type under discussion, or any SOC flow table, the region incorporating any stable state and any neighboring input column is one of the five types shown in Table 4.3 (assuming, of course, an appropriate renaming of the internal states.)

Assume now that $\mathcal{M}$ is realized by a delayfree circuit with no logic hazards in the combinational part. For each segment of Table 4.3, let us investigate the consequences of changing x *once* when $\mathcal{M}$ is initially in 1-*B*

(*a*) Since no internal state change is specified, no state-variable excitation (that is, no Y) is supposed to change its value. Only one input to the hazardfree (HF) logic circuit, namely x, changes; hence, since there are no static hazards, it is indeed the case that no Y changes value. Any output changes occur as specified since there are also no dynamic hazards for single input changes. Hence this transition involves no difficulty.

(b) Here the transition $1 \rightarrow 2$ is specified (see Subsection 3.3.2 for basic concepts and notation); hence the circuit may pass through any y-state in $T(1, 2)$. As shown earlier in the discussion of STT assignments, if there are any $p \rightarrow q$ transitions in E, where $q \neq 2$, it is necessary that the assignment be such that $T(1, 2)$ and $T(p, q)$ are disjoint. In this case, since there are no delay elements, it is possible that, in certain parts of the circuit, the x-change that precipitated the internal-state transition may, because of stray delays, not be perceived until *after* one or more of the y-changes have been detected. Thus, at some Y- or Z-terminals, the system may be seen as being temporarily in column B with some y-state in $T(1, 2)$. Two consequences result from this. First, if any output variable Z_t is constant at 1-*B* and 2-*E* and has a different value at 2-*B*, there will be an unavoidable transient hazard for this transition, since Z_t may see the sequence of total states as 1-*B*, 2-*B*, 2-*E*. In addition, if any y-state in $T(1, 2)$ has a next-state entry in column B corresponding to a y-state not in $T(1, 2)$, then some Y-signals may change in an unspecified manner and the final stable state may not be in 2-*E*.

(*c*) As in the preceding case, the apparent state of the system at various points may be in B or E, with the internal state being any member of $T(1, 2)$. However, since for an SOC function $Z(2, B)$ can be made equal to $Z(1, B)$, and $Z(1, E)$ made equal to $Z(2, E)$, there need be no transient hazard. Furthermore, since there is a $2 \rightarrow 1$ transition in B to match the $1 \rightarrow 2$ transition in E, the constraints on the state assignment imposed in Subsection

3.3.2 suffice to prevent any Y-terminal from receiving a false signal as described for (b).

(d) This case is more complex. Since the variables distinguishing $\underline{y}^2$ from $\underline{y}^3$ (the y-states assigned to rows 2 and 3, respectively) may see the system in 2-B as pointed out in the two preceding cases, these variables may change. There is no way to avoid this possibility (short of using delay elements, which are excluded here). Hence, after the x-change, the internal state may become (or be perceived at some points in the circuit as being) any member of $T(1, 2, 3)$. Thus, by a parallel argument to the one given for case (b), the B-column next-state entries of $\mathscr{M}$ for every member of $T(1, 2, 3)$ must correspond to members of $T(1, 2, 3)$ in order to avoid further spurious y-changes. If, in addition, the E-column next-state entry for every member of $T(1, 2, 3)$ is set equal to 2, then as soon as the x-change penetrates to all of the Y-terminals, all of the y-signals assume values corresponding to $\underline{y}^2$ and the system arrives safely at the specified stable state. However, there will be a transient hazard as in case (b) unless every Z-signal has the same value in 3-B (and 2-B) that it has in either 1-B or 2-E.

(e) As in case (d) the system may be seen in B or E and in any state of $T(1, 2, 3)$. In particular it may be seen in 3-E by some or all of the variables distinguishing $\underline{y}^3$ from $\underline{y}^k$. Should these variables change, the system might enter k-E, a stable state that is *not* the specified destination of this transition. There is now way to prevent this possibility in the framework of a USTT assignment (bearing in mind that we are not using delay elements) and, in fact, it is shown in the next subsection that, if a flow table includes a segment such as that in case (e), there is *no* way to realize it without delay elements in such a manner as to avoid the steady-state hazard just discussed. Such a configuration is an *essential hazard*, an inherent property of a sequential function (or flow table) that is defined as follows: For some initial total state and input variable x, three consecutive changes in x take the system to a state that is different from (and not equivalent to) the state reached after a single x-change. In Table 4.3e, the initial total state is 1-B, the state reached after one x-change is 2-E, and the state reached after the third x-change is k-E.

The configuration shown in Table 4.3d is referred to as a *d-trio* (sometimes also called a nonessential hazard), and the 1-$B \to$ 2-E transition is referred to as a *d transition*. The *d-trio* in the table consists of the three rows 1, 2, and 3, and the d transition starts in B and ends in E. Formally, we define this configuration as follows: There is an initial state, and an input variable x, such that after three x-changes, the internal state reached is the *same* as that reached after the first change, but the *internal* state reached after the *second* change differs from both the initial state and the state reached after the first change.

Table 4.4   Flow Table with no Essential
Hazards, but with Four d-Trios

$$x_1 x_2$$

	00	01	11	10
1	①, 0	2 , 0	7 , 0	①, 0
2	3 , 0	②, 0	②, 0	3 , 0
3	③, 0	2, 0	4 , 0	③, 0
4	5 , 0	④, 0	④, 0	3 , 0
5	⑤, 0	6 , 1	⑤, 0	⑤, 0
6	5 , 0	⑥, 1	7 , 0	⑥, 0
7	1 , 0	6 , 1	⑦, 0	⑦, 0

Our preceding discussion has shown that, when delay elements are not used, we cannot simply consider interactions among transitions in the same column as is the case in Subsection 3.32. The fact that the input change that precipitated an internal state change may be perceived *after* the y-changes means that intersections among the T-sets corresponding to transitions in adjacent columns must be considered. This means that conditions more complex than those of Theorem 3.2 must be satisfied, particularly when d-trios are involved. We now present a synthesis procedure that produces the necessary generalized Tracey conditions, and then prove that it leads to circuits free of steady-state hazards.

Let $i, j, \ldots \neq p, q, \ldots$ represent the statement that every term on the left side of the inequality is different from every term on the right side. Type b, c, and d transitions refer to the corresponding parts of Table 4.3. Table 4.4 is used to illustrate the procedure.

PROCEDURE 4.1   *Finding A USTT Assignment for A Delayfree S-proper Realization of A Flow Table without Essential Hazards*

1. For each transition of the flow table, form the dichotomies indicated below, deleting any dichotomy covered by any that was previously formed.

    1.1 If $i\text{-}B \rightarrow j\text{-}E$ is a d transition, with k as the third row of the trio, then form the following dichotomies:

    1.1.1 (ijk, pqr) if $p, q, r \neq i, j, k$ and pqr is a d-trio that begins or ends in B or E. In our example, letting $B = 00$, $E = 01$, $ijk = 123$, $pqr = 567$, (corresponding to a d-trio in 11 and 01), we obtain (123, 567).

    1.1.2 (ijk, pq) if $p, q \neq i, j, k$ and if $p \rightarrow q$ is a b or c transition (but *not* a d transition) in B or E. For example, in Table 4.4 if $B = 11$, $E = 10$, $ijk = 234$, then the $6 \rightarrow 7$ transition in 11 gives us (234, 67).

1.1.3 (ijk, p) if $p \neq i,\ j,\ k$, p-E is stable, and no transition in E terminates in p-E. [That is, for no $q \neq p$ is $N(q, E) = p$.] For example, the 234 d-trio from 11 to 10, and the stable 1-10 entry yield (1, 234).

1.2 If i-$B \rightarrow j$-E is a b or c (but not a d) transition, then add the following dichotomies:

    1.2.1 (ij, pq) if $p, q \neq i, j$ and $p \neq q$ is a b or c transition (but *not* a d transition) in B or E. For example, 7-10 $\rightarrow$ 1-00 and 4-11 $\rightarrow$ 3-10 generate (17, 34).

    1.2.2 (ij, p) if $p \neq i, j$, p-E is stable, and no transition in E terminates in p-E.

2. Find a minimal covering set of dichotomies by executing steps 3 to 6 of Procedure 3.1 (on page 85), operating on the dichotomies found above in step 1.

3. Form a flow matrix by associating a state variable with each member of the set found in step 2. For each transition, i-$B \rightarrow j$-E, the next-state and output entries in column E for each y-state in $T(i, j)$, or $T(i, j, k)$ if the transition is of type d, should be the same as that for j-E. The column-B entries for these sets may correspond to any member of $T(i, j)$, or $T(i, j, k)$.

We now establish the validity of the above procedure.

THEOREM 4.6 *Given any SOC function without essential hazards, Procedure 4.1 yields a flow matrix that can be S-properly realized by a delayfree circuit, assuming single-input-change operation. Transient hazards may be present in some cases.*

PROOF. In the discussion preceding the presentation of Procedure 4.1 it is shown that for a transitions (no change in internal state) any row assignment is satisfactory. For b, c, and d transitions, it is shown that a USTT assignment is valid if certain sets of y-states, defined as functions of the y-states assigned to the rows involved in the transitions, are assigned appropriate next-state values for the input columns in which the transitions begin and end. We prove that our procedure is valid by showing that, if the dichotomies produced in step 1 are all covered, then there are no intersections among y-sets that must have different entries in a particular column, and hence there are no contradictions involved in the process of filling in flow matrix entries.

1. Consider first a d transition i-$B \rightarrow j$-E, with k the third state of the d-trio. It has been shown that the y-states of $T(i, j, k)$ must be assigned next-state values corresponding to j in column E and to any member of $T(i, j, k)$

in column B. The dichotomies generated in step 1.1.1 (we refer here always to Procedure 4.1) ensure that, if there are any other d-trios that involve column B or column E and a disjoint set of rows, then $T(i, j, k)$ will be disjoint from the corresponding y-sets that that they constrain.

Any other d transition whose d-trio includes 1 or more of the rows of ijk (we say it *overlaps ijk*) and which also terminates in E must have j-E as its final state and hence must also have j as the next-state entry in its column-E y-set, so that there is no conflict in this column.

If some other d transition terminates in column B and overlaps ijk, then its final state must be i-B or k-B; hence the next-state entries in its column-B y-set must be i or k, respectively. Either is satisfactory for the column-B entries of $T(i, j, k)$ as constrained by the ijk-trio; hence again there is no conflict.

Now suppose some other d-trio pqr begins in column B and overlaps ijk. Then $T(i, j, k)$ has a nonempty intersection with $T(p, q, r)$, and for the y-states in this intersection, the constraints imposed by both d-trios are satisfied if the next-state entries are made to correspond to any member of the intersection.

Finally, assume that some d-trio pqr begins in column E and overlaps ijk. Then j-E must be in this d-trio; hence either p or r must equal j. Thus j would satisfy the pqr constraints on the $T(p, q, r)$ entries in column E that overlap $T(i, j, k)$, since j is in $T(p, q, r)$.

Thus Procedure 4.1 ensures that no pair of d-trios impose conflicting requirements on the next-state entries in the flow matrix.

Next we consider conflicts between ijk and type b or c transitions. Step 1.1.2 ensures that for any b or c transition that does not overlap ijk, the constrained y-set is disjoint from $T(i, j, k)$. The arguments for b or c transitions ending in B or E exactly parallel those just given for the corresponding cases of overlapping d-trios, establishing that our procedure also avoids conflicts between constraints imposed by d transitions and b or c transitions.

No harm is done if, during a d transition, some Y-terminal sees the system in a stable state of column B, since no y-variable that was supposed to remain stable during the transition would thereby be switched. Step 1.1.3 guarantees that $T(i, j, k)$ does not include a y-state assigned to an isolated stable state in column E. Thus the constraints imposed by any d transition can always be satisfied without conflicting with any other constraints.

2. A similar, but simpler argument can be made to show that step 1.2 of Procedure 4.1 makes it possible to satisfy the constraints imposed by b and c transitions without conflict. This concludes the proof of the theorem.

The question of where unavoidable transient hazards may appear (limited to b or d transition) is discussed prior to the statement of Procedure 4.1.

It should be noted that, unlike the somewhat analogous Theorem 3.2, the theorem just proved involves sufficiency, but not necessity. In some instances some of the dichotomies produced in step 1 of Procedure 4.1 can be replaced by other dichotomies without introducing steady-state hazards (see Problem 4.12). It seems to be difficult to utilize such cases in a systematic matter to gain any advantage.

We now illustrate Procedure 4.1 by finding an appropriate flow matrix for Table 4.4. In step 1.1.1 the d-trios 123, 456, 234, and 567 yield dichotomies (123, 456), (123, 567), and (234, 567). Step 1.1.2 adds (17, 456) and (17, 234). No dichotomies not already covered are added by steps 1.1.3. and 1.2.1. For example, (123, 4), generated by the former, is covered by (123, 456), and (17, 23), generated by the latter, is covered by (17, 234). Step 1.2.2 yields (2, 34) and (5, 67) to complete this part of the process. It may be convenient when carrying out step 1 to first list all of the transitions by category, along with the columns involved.

Following step 2, we construct the pair chart of Table 4.5, from which we obtain a minimal set of compatible dichotomies $\{ad, bc, e, fg\}$ (many other minimal sets exist) yielding the set of covering dichotomies: (1237, 456), (1234, 567), (17, 234), and (25, 3467). To avoid the extraneous complications that are involved in not completely specifying some y-columns in order to leave opportunities for minimizing logic later (see comment on page 86), we replace the last two dichotomies with (17, 23456) and (125, 3467), respectively, to obtain the assignment shown in Table 4.6.

Table 4.5   Pair Chart for Step 2

	a (123, 456)	b (123, 567)	c (234, 567)	d (17, 456)	d̄ (456, 17)	e (234, 17)	f (5, 67)	f̄ (67, 5)
b (123, 567)								
c (234, 567)	×							
d (17, 456)		×	×					
d̄ (456, 17)	×	×	×	×				
e (234, 17)	×	×		×				
f (5, 67)	×	×	×	×	×			
f̄ (67, 5)	×	×	×	×	×	×	×	
g (2, 34)	×	×	×		×	×		

Table 4.6   Flow Matrix for Table 4.4

	00	01	11	10	y_1	y_2	y_3	y_4
			x_1x_2					
1	①, 0	2 , 0	7 , 0	①, 0	0	0	0	0
2	3 , 0	②, 0	②, 0	3 , 0	0	0	1	0
3	③, 0	2 , 0	4 , 0	③, 0	0	0	1	1
4	5 , 0	④, 0	④, 0	3 , 0	1	0	1	1
5	⑤, 0	6 , 1	⑤, 0	⑤, 0	1	1	1	0
6	5 , 0	⑥, 1	7 , 0	⑥, 0	1	1	1	1
7	1 , 0	6 , 1	⑦, 0	⑦, 0	0	1	0	1
8	1 , 0	2 , 0	7 , 0	1/7/8/9, 0	0	0	0	1
9	1 , 0	6 , 1	7 , 0	1/7/8/9, 0	0	1	0	0
10	–	6 , 1	5/6/7/9/10/11/ 15/16, 0	–	0	1	1	0
11	–	6 , 1	7 , 0	6/7/11/16, 0	0	1	1	1
12	–	–	–	–	1	0	0	0
13	–	–	–	–	1	0	0	1
14	5 , 0	4/5/6/14, 0	2/3/4/14, 0	3 , 0	1	0	1	0
15	–	6 , 1	5/6/7/9/10/11/ 15/16, 0	–	1	1	0	0
16	–	6 , 1	7 , 0	6/7/11/16, 0	1	1	0	1

Examining in turn each transition in Table 4.6, we fill in the entries in rows 8 to 16 according to step 3. For example, 8-00 might be seen during the *d* transition 1-00 → 2-01 *or* during the *b* transition 7-10 → 1-00. In the former case, successful operation requires the next-state entry for 8-00 to correspond to a row whose *y*-state is in 00—. In the latter case, the entry *must* be 1. Since 1 satisfies both conditions, it is the entry used (the 0-output entry is also satisfactory for both transitions). All other similar cases of states involved in several transitions also have satisfactory solutions, as guaranteed by Theorem 4.6. These states include 11-11, 16-11, 8-10, and 9-10. There is a transient hazard associated with the transition 4-01 → 5-00, but it is a property of the flow table and cannot be eliminated without using delay elements. Other flow matrices can be found by choosing row assignments based on different sets of covering dichotomies for Table 4.5.

4.3.2 Functions Requiring Delay Elements for Proper Realizations

In this subsection, it is proved that flow tables with essential hazards cannot be *S*-properly realized without delay elements. This is accomplished by means of a "destructive proof" in which, given a delayfree circuit that is supposed to realize a function with an essential hazard, we show how to assign stray-delay values in such a manner that the system will reach state *k-E* instead of 2-*E* when a transition such as the one in Table 4.3e is attempted.

The proof is valid *regardless* of the kind of row assignment used, even if cyclic sets of y-states represent some of the stable flowtable states. A preliminary lemma is pertinent to this question of cyclic states, but the reader may wish to pass over it lightly for the present until its place in the overall proof becomes clear.

LEMMA 4.12 *Suppose that in some S-proper delayfree realization of a flow table, the set S_i of y-states is assigned to row i and that in input column I, C_{ij} is a cyclic subset of S_i with no exit. Then in every column-I state of $T(C_{ij})$, those y-variables constant in C_{ij} have the same excitations as in C_{ij}, and the output entries must be $Z(i, I)$.*

PROOF. If $\underline{y}^p$ is a state in $T(C_{ij})$, then it may be perceived at any Y- or Z-terminal to be the current y-state at *any* time during the C_{ij} cycle, since there are no delay elements to fix the order in which y-changes are seen. Hence the Z-value at $\underline{y}^p$ must be $Z(i, I)$ in order to avoid a possibly indefinitely repeated output error, and any Y_j that is constant in every state of C_{ij} must have the same value at $\underline{y}^p\text{-}I$, or else y_j may change, causing an exit from the cycle, which is excluded by hypothesis.

The next lemma simplifies considerably the problem of analyzing the behavior of delayfree circuits, by showing that we can always select a set of y-variables such that there is a distinct logic circuit associated with each Y_i. That is, we can always put a given circuit in the form of Fig. 4.11, referred to as a *separate excitation circuit*, merely by an appropriate choice of state variables. Outputs are not shown since they are unaffected by the transformation under discussion.

LEMMA 4.13 *Given any S-proper delayfree sequential circuit, y-variables can be so chosen that the circuit can be represented in separate excitation form.*

PROOF. The y-variables can be selected as follows:

1. Choose a set of nodes sufficient to break every closed signal path in the circuit, and label these points with an initial set of y-symbols. It is now possible to derive a combinational function for the signal at any point in the circuit as a function of the input variables and the y's just chosen.
2. If there are two y-nodes y_i and y_j and a node n in the circuit not directly connected to an input terminal or a y-terminal such that there are signal paths from n to y_i and y_j which do not pass through any other y-nodes, then label n as another y-node.
3. Repeat step 2 until it is no longer applicable. Since the circuit is, of course, finite and our procedure adds no new nodes, it must terminate with no

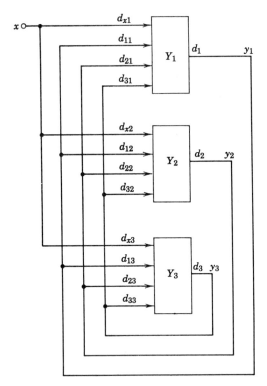

Figure 4.11 Separate excitation form.

non-y gate output feeding more than one y-node. Flow matrices can be constructed on the basis of the variables chosen after step 1 or after any number of iterations of step 2. The corresponding reduced flow tables must clearly be equivalent, since they all describe the terminal behavior of the same circuit and this behavior is unique, except possibly for transients, because the circuit is S-proper.

We now proceed to the principal result:

THEOREM 4.7 *No flow table with an essential hazard can be realized with a delayfree S-proper circuit.*

PROOF. Assume that such a circuit exists and that we represent it in separate excitation form according to Lemma 4.13. Suppose that Table 4.7 (in which columns B and E differ only in the value of x) represents a portion of the table with an essential hazard. Then if the input state and initial y-state (y^{1i}) correspond to 1-B and if x changes, at least one y-variable must become

**Table 4.7   Essential
Hazard Transition**

	B	E
1	①	2
2	3	②
3	③	4
4	④	④

unstable. If more than one become unstable simultaneously, let y_1 be one of them and assume it is the first to change. Some other set of y-variables may next become unstable, and we label one of them y_2 and assume it changes next. Continuing this process, we find that there must be a sequence of y-changes after the x-change (possibly some of the y's appear more than once in the sequence) such that ultimately the y-state corresponds to one assigned to row 2. There may be many such sequences leading to various y-states of row 2, with the one actually followed in any particular case depending upon the stray-delay distribution. We have simply selected one, labeling the y-variables so that $i < j$ implies that the initial appearance of y_i in the sequence precedes the initial appearance of y_j. The key point is that the logic must be such that, if Y_1 see x change, it changes value; then when Y_2 sees the x- and y_1-changes, it changes; etc. In general, if a prefix of the sequence is $xy_{i_1}y_{i_2} \cdots y_{i_{k-1}}y_{i_k}$ and if Y_{i_k} sees all of the changes in $xy_{i_1}, y_{i_2}, \ldots, y_{i_{k-1}}$ indicated by the sequence, then Y_{i_k} will change. Such a sequence, describing a transition from 1-B to 2-E, is termed a C_{12}-sequence, and for *any* circuit realizing the table, at least one C_{12}-sequence must exist.

In a similar manner there must exist a C_{23}-sequence, starting with an x-change, that takes the system from 2-E to 3-B, and a C_{34}-sequence, also starting with an x-change, that takes the system from 3-B to 4-E.

Suppose that for initial state $\underline{y}^{1i}$-B we have a C_{12}-sequence terminating in some y-state $\underline{y}^{2j}$, a C_{23}-sequence that starts in $\underline{y}^{2j}$ and ends in $\underline{y}^{3k}$, and a C_{34}-sequence starting in $\underline{y}^{3k}$ and ending in $\underline{y}^{4m}$, where $\underline{y}^{4m}$-E is either stable or a member of a cycle with no exit in column E. (We can always choose $\underline{y}^{4m}$ in this manner, since 4-E is stable.) Then the sequence obtained by concatenating these three sequences, namely, $C = C_{12}C_{23}C_{34}$, will take the system from $\underline{y}^{1i}$-B to $\underline{y}^{4m}$-E.

Assume that the y-variables involved in some C-sequence range from y_1 through y_n. If a variable y_i undergoes a *net* change in the C-sequence (appears an *odd* number of times), then we write $\mathrm{Ch}(y_i)$, otherwise $\overline{\mathrm{Ch}}(y_i)$. Clearly, if the system is initially in $\underline{y}^{1i}$-B and if x and each y_i, such that $\mathrm{Ch}(y_i)$, change exactly once, with no other y's changing, then the final state will be $\underline{y}^{4m}$-E. We now show how the stray delays may be so distributed as to cause the following events to occur when, at time $t = 0$, x changes with the system initially in $\underline{y}^{11}\text{-}B$ (assuming some arbitrary unit of time):

    (a) At $t = i$ (for $i = 1, 2, \ldots, n$), y_i changes.

    (b) At $t = n + i$ (for $i = 1, 2, \ldots, n$), y_i changes iff $Ch(y_i)$.

If this sequence of events occurs, then the final state will be $\underline{y}^{4m}\text{-}E$ corresponding to 4-E, which is *not* the state specified by the flow table. Hence incorrect steady-state behavior would be possible because of the effects of stray delays, as was to be shown.

First we define another predicate $Prec(a, b)$ to mean that, in the C-sequence under discussion, an *odd* number of a-appearances (that is, a net change in a) precedes the first b-appearance. Let d_{xj} be the stray delay between the x-terminal and the input to the Y_j circuit, and let d_{ij} be the stray delay between y_j and the input to the Y_j-logic (see Fig. 4.11). Suppose that all stray-delay values are negligible except those specified below:

1. If $Prec(x, y_i)$, $d_{xi} = i$.
2. If $\overline{Prec}(x, y_i)$, $d_{xi} = n + i$.
3. If $Prec(y_j, y_i)$, $d_{ji} = i - j$.
4. If $\overline{Prec}(y_j, y_i)$ and $Ch(y_j)$,   then $d_{ji} = n + i - j$.
5. If $\overline{Prec}(y_j, y_i)$ and $\overline{Ch}(y_j)$,   then $d_{ji} = 2n$.

Then if, with the system initially in $\underline{y}^{1i}\text{-}B$, x is changed at $t = 0$, the x-change is seen by Y_1 at $t = 1$ (because of item 1 above) and y_1 will then change. Assume now that for $i = 1, 2, \ldots, j - 1$, y_i changes at $t = i$. Then at $t = j$, items 1 and 2 ensure that Y_j sees the x-change *if* $Prec(x, y_j)$, and, because of items 3, 4, and 5, Y_j sees just those y_j-changes for which $Prec(y_i, y_j)$. Thus Y_j sees the system in the state preceding the initial y_j-change and hence changes. This completes the inductive argument that y_i changes at $t = i$ $(1 \le i \le n)$.

Consider now what happens at $t = n + 1$. If Y_1 has not already seen the x-change, it will see it now because of item 2. Furthermore, for every j, if y_j undergoes a net change during the C-sequence, then Y_1 sees the y_j-change at this time because of item 4. Hence, Y_1 sees the system in $\underline{y}^{4m}\text{-}E$. If this state is stable, then y_1 remains unchanged if $Ch(y_1)$, or changes for the second time if $\overline{Ch}(y_1)$. The same alternatives apply if $\underline{y}^{4m}$ is a state in a cyclic set with no exit and y_1 is one of the fixed variables, because of Lemma 4.12. If y_1 is one of the changing variables in such a set, then it may or may not change at the time under discussion.

Assume now that, for $i = 1, 2, \ldots, j - 1$ at $t = n + i$, Y_i sees the system in $\underline{y}^{4m}\text{-}E$, *or* in some other state in the set spanned by the cycle containing $\underline{y}^{4m}\text{-}E$ if this state is cyclic, and that y_i then changes appropriately as described above for the y_1-case. Then, at $t = n + j$, Y_j will see the x-change, if it did not see it at $t = j$, and also will see the second changes (if any) of those y-variables whose initial changes Y_j saw at $t = j$ (because of item 3). In addition, item 4 results in Y_j seeing the initial changes in those y-variables that undergo net changes during the C-sequence but that Y_j did *not* see change at $t = j$. Because of item 5, Y_j does not at this time see any changes in variables y_i for which $\overline{\text{Ch}}(y_i)$ *and* $\overline{\text{Prec}}(y_i, y_j)$. If the stray delays are inertial, then Y_j will *never* see *any* change in such y_i's. Hence at $t = n + j$, Y_j sees every variable in its $\underline{y^{4m}}$-E-state unless $\underline{y^{4m}}$-E is cyclic, in which case Y_j may see some of the *oscillating* variables in other states. Nevertheless, in the latter case, Y_j sees the system in some state spanned by the cyclic set containing $\underline{y^{4m}}$-E, and so in either event y_j behaves according to the induction hypothesis. This establishes the fact that, given the specified distribution of stray delays, the sequence of y-changes that was to be imposed does indeed occur, leaving the system at $t = 2n - 1$ in a state corresponding to 4-E, in which all significant y-variables are stable. This completes our proof.

Note that, if some stray delays are *pure*, then some further changes may occur starting at $t = 2n$, because of item 5. Although one feels intuitively that pure stray delays are more likely to cause trouble than inertial delays are, the proof given here requires that the stray delays have an inertial component so that we can be sure that the system will come to rest in the wrong state. It should be possible to find a proof that does not require this assumption.

Of course the particular distribution of stray delays postulated in the above proof is not the only one that can cause malfunction. Also, small variations about the given delay values do not affect the end result, so that the probability of an unfortunate delay distribution occurring is not zero. However, it should be clearly understood that it is often possible to determine, in particular cases, that the stray delays are *not* unfavorably distributed, so that a circuit that is not S-proper may nevertheless be perfectly satisfactory.

Although explicitly discussed in terms of gate circuits, Theorem 4.7 applies equally to relay circuits, in which contact stagger plays a role along with effects due to stray reactances in producing stray delays.

4.3.3   Circuits with Delay Elements

We have just seen that sequential functions with essential hazards can be realized properly only with the aid of delay elements. In some cases we may also wish to use delay elements even when there are no essential hazards, perhaps in order to be able to exploit row assignments that are more efficient with regard to logic, number of state variables needed, or in some other respect. Although we continue to assume single input changes and SOC functions unless otherwise noted, in this subsection we note several instances in which the use of delay elements permits the relaxation of some of these constraints. (Subsection 4.3.4 deals specifically with the multiple-input-change case.)

First let us assume that an inertial-delay element is used in every state branch and in every output lead. If d_M is the maximum value of response time of the combinational logic to any change at any input terminal (that is, the maximum sum of the stray delays in any path through the logic), and d_m the minimum such time, then let us conservatively specify a minimum delay-element value of $D = d_M - d_m$. Assume further that any valid (free of critical races) row assignment is used (see Chapter 3).

Now suppose that an input change occurs. It may cause some transient pulses to occur at some Z-terminals (because of combinational hazards) followed perhaps by a steady-state change at some of them. The inertial delays in the Z-leads filter out the pulses. In a similar manner, some Y-signals may change spuriously a few times, and some may take on new steady-state values. The inertial state-branch delays permit only the steady-state changes to get through to the y-inputs and then only after a delay sufficient to ensure that *every* terminal has first seen the input change. The y-changes, if more than one result, in general occur at different times, but since there are no critical races, the order does not affect the next set of Y- and Z-values. Once again, transients are filtered out by the inertial-delay elements, and the process continues, with new sets of y-signals appearing at the input to the logic block, only after the previous values have influenced all of the Y's and Z's. Eventually a stable state is reached, and a new input change may be presented D-units of time after the last y-change. Neither combinational hazards nor essential hazards can cause malfunction.

Next, let us eliminate the Z-delays and replace the y-delays with pure-delay elements of the same value. Assume further that the logic circuits have no logic hazards. Now the initial input change causes only specified changes at certain Y- and Z-terminals. If a noncritical race occurs, then the Z-values and the excitation for each y-variable will be constant within the subcube spanned by the initial and final y-states, so that no transient errors will occur. A sequence of y-states may be traversed as in the preceding case, without error.

Both MOC and UOC functions can be realized under the same assumptions of the preceding paragraph, since the Z-values can be assigned so as to change independently of the particular paths taken through the transition subcubes. The USTT assignments of Subsection 3.3.5 can be used if time-dependent operation is desired. In general, hazardfree logic is necessary when realizing MOC or UOC functions, because we cannot place inertial delays in the output leads without eliminating specified, as well as spurious, output pulses.

Suppose now that it is desirable to realize a given function with a minimum number of delay elements, perhaps because delay elements are costly in the technology being used. We describe here a number of techniques for meeting this objective, including several in which only *one* delay element is needed.

First consider the state assignment shown in Table 4.8, which is a universal, intermeshed, connected row-set assignment of the type discussed in Section 3.1. The particular assignment shown here is of the $2S_0 + 1$ class in which the y-space is divided into two sectors, distinguished by y_1. All transitions can take place in two steps: a noncritical race within a row (or column) belonging to the initial row set, followed by a change in y_1 to switch the y-state into the column (or row) in the opposite sector that corresponds to the next state.

Assume now that a delay element is placed in the y_1 state branch, but in no other state branch, and that an input change occurs that is to take the system from row i to row j. Then, in general, there will occur the noncritical race in R_i (the row set assigned to row i) referred to above. Regardless of the order in which the resulting y-changes *and* the input change are perceived, no y-variable other than those that designate the y-state *within* the initial row (column) of R_i can change (we assume no logic hazards). Only when all of these y's have assumed values corresponding to the R_i-state s_{ij} adjacent to R_j, can Y_1 change. The next significant event occurs after time D, when y_1 changes. On the assumption that D is suitably chosen, this change can occur only after *all* Y's and Z's have perceived *all* previous input changes and y-changes. Thus the system will surely reach state j, and there are no transient hazards.

Table 4.8   A $2S_0 + 1$ Assignment

1	1	1	1	1	1	1	1	1	2	3	4	5	6	7	8
2	2	2	2	2	2	2	2	1	2	3	4	5	6	7	8
3	3	3	3	3	3	3	3	1	2	3	4	5	6	7	8
4	4	4	4	4	4	4	4	1	2	3	4	5	6	7	8
5	5	5	5	5	5	5	5	1	2	3	4	5	6	7	8
6	6	6	6	6	6	6	6	1	2	3	4	5	6	7	8
7	7	7	7	7	7	7	7	1	2	3	4	5	6	7	8
8	8	8	8	8	8	8	8	1	2	3	4	5	6	7	8

(Bracket labels: y_1, y_3, y_6, y_4, y_2, y_5, y_7)

If state j is unstable in the new input column, with k as the specified next state, then the Y-excitations in all of the R_j-states of this column, *except* for s_{jk}, the R_j-state in this sector adjacent to R_k, correspond to s_{jk}. Only y_1 is unstable in s_{jk}, so that once again there is a noncritical race followed by a delayed change in y_1. Thus, since the single delay element is involved in all internal state transitions, there is no problem about the order in which pertinent variables change, even if a sequence of transitions occurs. This means that the $2S_0 + 1$ assignment can be used as indicated here with a single delay element and hazardfree logic to realize MOC and UOC as well as SOC functions.

Another approach to synthesis with one delay element is to construct a delay box, a circuit of the form of Fig. 4.12 having n input-output pairs, and having the property that under certain conditions it appears as though, for $i = 1$, $2, \ldots, n$, Y_i feeds y_i through a delay element. We present two realizations of delay boxes that require just one delay element, regardless of the value of n. They differ somewhat in the restrictions under which they must be used.

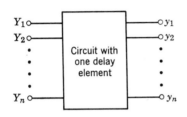

Figure 4.12 A delay box.

The first circuit, drawn for $n = 3$ (the generalization will become obvious), is shown in Fig. 4.13, in which the logic elements used are majority gates and modulo 2 adders. (It can, of course, be implemented with other types of basic components.) There is a majority gate M_i and an adder A_i associated with each y_i. Note that A_i receives inputs from each y_j such that $j \neq i$ and from a delay element fed by A_0. The A_0 gate receives inputs from every Y_i. Suppose now that we assume for the moment that $Y_i = y_i$ for all i and that the Y's have been constant for a long time. Then the output of A_0 is equal to the modulo 2 sum of all the y's. Hence the output of each A_i is

$$\sum_{j=1}^{n} y_j \oplus \sum_{j \neq i} y_j = \sum_{j \neq i} (y_j \oplus y_j) \oplus y_i = 0 \oplus y_i = y_i.$$

Then all three inputs to M_i are equal to $y_i = Y_i$ and so the system is in a state of equilibrium. If Y_j is changed, then the immediate effect is felt only at A_0 and at M_j, the only gates fed directly by Y_j. After some interval determined by stray delays, the A_0-output changes, but this changes does not propagate further for a period D equal to the magnitude of the delay element. The M_j gate does not respond at all to the Y_j-change, since two of its inputs, from y_j and from A_j, remain fixed. Thus all the y's remain constant for a period at least equal to D. Finally, when the A_0-change emerges from D, each A_i receives an input change, to which it responds after another stray-delay

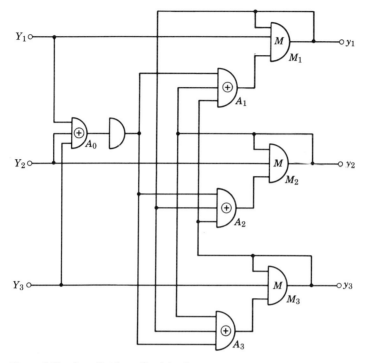

Figure 4.13   A realization of a delay box.

interval. This response in turn causes *one* input to each M_i to change. But
this is the *second* M_j-input to change, and so M_j switches and the value of y_j
changes to agree again with Y_j. None of the other M_i change, since for each
of them their Y_i- and y_i-inputs are still at their original values. When the
y_j-change takes effect at the A_i gates (for all $i \neq j$), the outputs of these gates
switch back to their original values, and once more the system is in equilibrium with $Y_i = y_i$ for all i. Thus, the sole effect of the Y_j-change is to change
y_j after a delay equal to D plus some stray-delay values. Hence the system
does indeed behave as though the box contained a delay element between Y_j
and y_j.

   Let us now consider the conditions under which this box operates correctly.
First let us assume that the gates are free of combinational hazards. Next
observe that, if an *even* number of Y's change, then the output of A_0 remains
fixed so that none of the y's ever change. If three or more Y's change, the
circuit may behave correctly, but there will be hazards due to the fact that
some of the y-changes may race with changes in the A's associated with other
y's. Reliable operation can be attained only if just one Y at a time is permitted
to switch. If d is the maximum stray delay between y_i and the output of any

A_j ($j \neq i$), then we must wait until d-units of time after y_i has responded to a Y_i-change before permitting another input change.

Even if the delay element is pure, the box simulates inertial delays, to a certain extent, since if Y_i should change an even number of times in an interval less than D, there will be no response from y_i. The reason for this is that if $Y_i = y_i$ at the time A_i changes, M_i will not respond because two of its inputs are at their old values.

The delay box just described can be used in conjunction with any one-shot row assignment (Subsection 3.3.1) and hazardfree logic to realize any SOC function properly. All the y-variables are delayed via the delay box, and the one-shot feature of the row assignment ensures that only one delay-box input will change at a time and that the changes will not occur too close together. Hazardfree logic is necessary to ensure that a y_i-change is not followed by a spurious Y_j-pulse that might occur before A_j has seen the y_i-change.

A second one-delay realization of a delay box is shown in Fig. 4.14a. Apart from the modulo 2 adders, the OR gate, and the delay element, this circuit contains a switch box. This box, shown at the left in Fig. 4.14b, operates as follows: When the control signal C is on (equals 1), the output E is connected to input B (lower dotted line connected), and when $C = 0$, E takes on the value of A. Thus the box acts as a single-pole, double throw switch under the control of C. A hazardfree combinational circuit realizing this switch is shown on the right of Fig. 4.14b.

Now let us see how the delay box works. First of all, if $Y_i = y_i$ for every i, then the output of each A_i gate will be 0, and if this situation persists, C will be 0. Then all of the switch "arms" will be in the upper positions "locking up" each y_i in a feedback loop, so that the delay-box outputs will remain fixed, and the system will be in a stable state. If some Y_j changes, then A_j will soon thereafter go on and turn on the OR gate. Note that the OR gate goes on if *any* $Y_i \neq y_i$. No further changes occur, and in particular all y-outputs remain fixed, until the 1-signal gets through the delay to switch on C. This swings all the switch "arms" to the lower positions, connecting each y_i to Y_i. Shortly after y_j changes value to agree with Y_j, A_j changes to 0, and the OR-gate output then follows suit. When the 0-signal emerges from the delay, changing C back to 0, the switches change position locking up the y's again until further input changes occur.

One important feature of this circuit is that multiple input changes are allowed. If a number of Y's change during an interval of duration D, then all of the corresponding y's will change D units of time after the first Y-change. Thus any number of simultaneous input changes will be appropriately delayed. Furthermore, if the input changes are spread out in time to some extent, the output changes will nevertheless occur almost simultaneously, so that the circuit has a resynchronizing effect that may be useful in some cases.

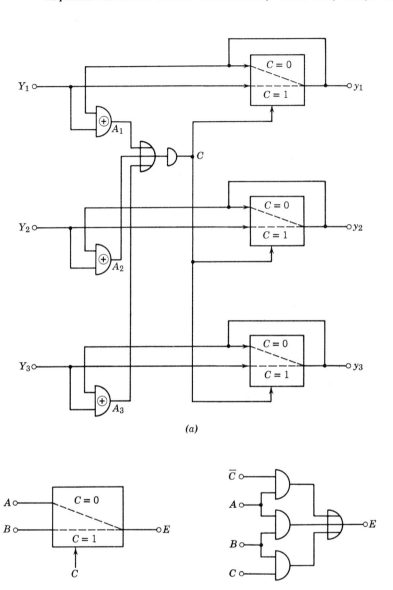

(a)

(b)

Figure 4.14 (a) Another type of delay box. (b) A hazard-free realization of the switch.

After an output change however, the system presents only stray delays for subsequent input changes until C has switched back to 0, which takes somewhat more than D units of time (depending on stray delays). Thus, input changes must be spaced apart by an amount $2D + d$, as opposed to the $D + d$ time required for the other delay box. As in the previous circuit, the delays presented by this box also have some inertial properties.

The box in Fig. 4.14 can be used to realize SOC functions as in the case of the box in Fig. 4.13 and under the same conditions except that the state assignment only need be STT and not necessarily one-shot. The exceptions are because multiple Y-changes are allowed. It is necessary to space consecutive x-changes somewhat further apart because of the slower recovery time.

Finally, we note that a two-input version of either delay box can be used in conjunction with the $2S_0$ state assignment of Chapter 3 (see Table 3.2) to realize any SOC function. The box would be used to delay only the two quadrant variables y_1 and y_2. This scheme is similar to that discussed in conjunction with the $2S_0 + 1$ assignment of Table 4.8. It is workable because, when the $2S_0$ assignment is used, each internal-state transition entails a change in exactly *one* of the two quadrant variables—never both. We cannot extend this scheme to three-input boxes with the $2S_0 - 1$ assignment (Table 3.3) because in that case several octant variables may change in the course of one state transition and the delay boxes do not function properly under this condition (after the first octant variable has switched, the boxes may not delay subsequent changes since there is no way to ensure that they recover in time.)

We now present a method for designing proper circuits in which no delay elements are included in any feedback loops. A single delay element is associated with each input signal. Consider, as an example, the function of Table 4.9a, which has several essential hazards. Suppose that we introduce for each input signal x_i an additional signal x_{iD} obtained by delaying x_i with a delay element. An expanded flow table can then be constructed in which the x_{iD}'s are considered as independent input variables in addition to the x_i's. (The number of columns is thus squared.) In each column in which $x_j \neq x_{jD}$ for some j, the entries are all made stable. Those columns for which $x_i = x_{iD}$ for all i, are constructed as duplicates of the columns of the original table that have corresponding x_i-values. Table 4.9b consists of six of the sixteen columns of the expanded version of Table 4.9a. Note that columns 0000, 0101, and 1111 of the former correspond to columns 00, 01, and 11, respectively, of the latter.

Suppose now that part (a) of Table 4.9 is in 1-00. Then, if the inputs have been constant for a period of at least D (the nominal delay element value), then (b) will be in state 1-0000. If x_2 is switched on, the state of (b) changes

Table 4.9a   Flow Table with Essential Hazards

	$x_1 x_2$			
	00	01	11	10
1	①, 0	2 , 0	4 , 0	①, 0
2	3 , 1	②, 0	3 , 0	②, 0
3	③, 1	4 , 0	③, 0	2 , 0
4	④, 0	④, 0	④, 0	1 , 0

at once to 1-0100 and remains there until x_{2D} goes on, about D units of time later. By this time all Y- and Z-terminals will have seen the system in column 0100, so that the system will behave as though two separate input changes have occurred: $0000 \rightarrow 0100$, and then $0100 \rightarrow 0101$. Each involves a change in just one input variable, and there are no essential hazards or d-trios involved in either transition since the *buffer* column 0100, which is involved in both transitions, is stable in every row. Thus, if any valid STT assignment is used (for example, see Section 3.3), along with circuit free of logic hazards, proper operation is assured. The same pattern is followed for all transitions initiated by a change in one x_i-variable. Note that each of the buffer columns is uniquely associated with a particular ordered pair of adjacent input states. The output entries in the buffer columns are made equal to the outputs of the next stable states to be reached in the corresponding destination columns. This eliminates inherent transient hazards (Subsection 4.3.1).

The synthesis of circuits with input delays can be carried out without actually constructing the rather unwieldy expanded tables. Let $C = \sum_{i=1}^{m} (x_i \oplus x_{iD})$, where the summation is Boolean, so that $C = 1$ for just those input states that correspond to the buffer columns, and let $\underline{Y}_i$ be the Y_i-excitation, in terms of the y's and the undelayed x's which would have been generated directly from the original flow table (assuming some valid STT assignment). Then, since each y_i is stable in every buffer column and behaves in the other columns as does the corresponding variable in the original matrix, we can write each Y_i as

$$Y_i = Cy_i + \bar{C}\underline{Y}_i.$$

Table 4.9b   A Portion of the Expanded Version of (a) with Delayed Inputs

	$x_2 x_2 x_{1D} x_{2D}$					
	0000	0100	0101	0001	1101	1111
1	①, 0	①, 0	2 , 0	①, 0	①, 0	4 , 0
2	3 , 1	②, 0	②, 0	②, 1	②, 0	3 , 0
3	③, 1	③, 0	4 , 0	③, 1	③, 0	③, 0
4	④, 0	④, 0	④, 0	④, 0	④, 0	④, 0

This expression describes the appropriate *function*, which must then be realized by a hazardfree circuit with the x's x_D's, and y's as fundamental inputs. The Z-functions are simply those computed from the original matrix (they are independent of the delayed inputs.)

By recognizing that, in particular cases, not all of the entries in the buffer columns need be stable, economies can sometimes be achieved.

It is sometimes worthwhile to assign delay elements to one or more of the y-variables on the basis of a detailed examination of the flow matrix. We illustrate this technique here in connection with Table 4.7, a portion of a flow table containing an essential hazard. Suppose that a row assignment has been found such that, for the transition $1\text{-}E \rightarrow 2\text{-}E$, only the variable y_{12} changes and, for the $2\text{-}B \rightarrow 3\text{-}B$ transition, only y_{23} changes. We have seen earlier that the essential hazard involved in the transition $1\text{-}B \rightarrow 1\text{-}E \rightarrow 2\text{-}E$ manifests itself in the possibility that Y_{23} may see the y_{12}-change before it sees the input change, in which case a false y_{23}-change may occur. There are two basic ways of dealing with this situation through the use of delay elements:

1. Insert a pure- or inertial-delay element in the y_{12}-branch so that the y_{12}-change does not actually occur until the input change has been seen throughout the circuit.

2. Insert an inertial delay in the y_{23}-branch so that even if Y_{23} changes for a brief interval, y_{23} will not respond.

In some cases the state assignment may happen to be (or be chosen) such that some small subset of y-variables are involved in all hazardous transitions. This circumstance may make possible a proper design that is economical in terms of the number of state variables and the amount of logic, as well as in terms of the number of delay elements needed. A supreme example of such a situation is represented by Table 4.10, which is a flow matrix for a four-state counter, with a reflected Gray-code row assignment (Subsection 3.3.1). Note that *every* transition involves an essential hazard.

Table 4.10   A Four-State Counter with a Gray-Code Row Assignment

	x 0	1	y_1	y_2	y_3
1	①, 00	2 , 00	0	0	0
2	3 , 01	②, 00	0	0	1
3	③, 01	4 , 01	0	1	1
4	5 , 10	④, 01	0	1	0
5	⑤, 10	6 , 10	1	1	0
6	7 , 11	⑥, 10	1	1	1
7	⑦, 11	8 , 11	1	0	1
8	1 , 00	⑧, 11	1	0	0

The row assignment is one-shot, and the variable y_3 changes for half of the transitions and is the variable that may *falsely* change for the other transitions. Therefore, a single *inertial*-delay element, inserted in the y_3-branch ensures proper operation. The same is true for any 2^n-state counter for any $n > 0$ if realized in terms of a matrix with the same pattern as Table 4.10, with a reflected Gray-code assignment.

A variety of minimal-delay element designs has been presented in order to illustrate the range of possibilities. The $2S_0 + 1$ approach, for example, shows that a single delay element is sufficient and that the number of state variables, at least for "worst cases," need not increase at a rate exceeding the logarithm of the number of rows. Note though that internal-state transitions may take as much time as a signal requires to pass through the delay element once and the logic box *twice*. The delay-box approach requires *one* passage through the logic. Other variations in the characteristics of the various techniques presented may be noticed by the reader and perhaps exploited in specific situations. Possibly other methods and variations may prove to be even more useful.

4.3.4 Realizations Permitting Multiple Input Changes

Suppose that starting in state 1-00 of Table 4.11a, both x_1 and x_2 are changed simultaneously. This situation should lead the system to stable state 1-11. However, if x_1 and x_2 do not change at *exactly* the same instant, or if, because of stray delays, it *appears* at certain key points in a circuit realizing the function that the changes are not simultaneous, then the system may behave as though the state immediately following 1-00 was 1-01 or 1-10. Since these states are unstable, false signals would appear at the Y_2- or Y_1-terminals, respectively. If the false signal persists for a period exceeding that of the delay in the corresponding Y-y loop, then the system never reaches 1-11, but instead terminates in state 2-11 or 4-11.

If there is a pure-delay element of magnitude D in the state branch involved and if the error interval d_e is less than D, the system will go to 1-11, then jump to 2-11 (or 4-11) when the error signal emerges from the delay. An oscillation between 1-11 and 2-11 (or 4-11) will then occur until the input state is changed.

The situation outlined above cannot be remedied by manipulating the row assignment or the circuit logic. It is inherent in the structure of the flow table. The solution is to use inertial-delay elements in the state branches. If this is done, then as long as $d_e < D$, the false signals will be filtered out by the inertial delays and never cause an unspecified change in the y-state.

Any of the inertial-delay elements described in Section 4.1 will do. Furthermore, if an STT assignment is used, then the delay box shown in Fig. 4.14

Table 4.11a A SOC Flow Table

	x_1x_2				y_1	y_2
	00	01	11	10		
1	①, 0	2 , 1	①, 0	4 , 1	0	0
2	3 , 1	②, 1	②, 0	②, 0	0	1
3	③, 1	③, 0	4 , 0	③, 0	1	1
4	1 , 0	3 , 0	④, 0	④, 1	1	0

can be used, since it has the desired inertial characteristic. If a one-shot assignment is used, then the box in Fig. 4.13a can be used, and finally, the $2S_0 + 1$
row assignment (Table 4.8) can be used with an inertial-delay element in the
y_1-branch. Thus S-proper realizations exist for SOC functions requiring only
one delay element (possibly pure if a delay box is used) even when multiple
input changes are allowed. Note that the magnitudes of the delays required
depend both on variations in the values of stray delays in the paths from
x-terminals to Y-terminals and on the maximum time allowed between
x-changes that are to be considered as having occurred simultaneously.

Assuming now that Table 4.11a is realized with the row assignment shown
and that inertial-delay elements are used in both state branches, there remains
the problem of transient hazards. During the error interval that may occur in
the course of the 1-00 → 1-11 transition discussed earlier, the Z-signal may
go to 1, which is the output value in the intermediate states 1-01 and 1-10.

An obvious remedy, discussed in Section 4.2 in connection with combinational hazards, is to insert an inertial delay in each output lead. The drawbacks of this solution are as pointed out earlier. An alternative solution
without these drawbacks, but generally requiring more logic is to convert
the flow table to an equivalent "Moore-form" table in which the output
is constant in each internal state. If this conversion is made, then after any
multiple input change the output during the input transition does not change,
and in fact no output change occurs until the internal state changes.

Table 4.11b is a Moore-form equivalent of Table 4.11a. Such a transformation is made as follows: If row i has k different outputs associated with its

Table 4.11b Moore Equivalent of Table 4.11a

	x_1x_2			
	00	01	11	10
1	① , 0	2B , 0	① , 0	4B , 0
2A	3B , 0	2B , 0	②A, 0	②A, 0
2B	3B , 1	②B, 1	2A , 1	2A , 1
3A	3B , 0	③A, 0	4A , 0	③A, 0
3B	③B, 1	3A , 1	4A , 1	3A , 1
4A	1 , 0	3A , 0	④A, 0	4B , 0
4B	1 , 1	3A , 1	4A , 1	④B, 1

stable states, then spit i into k rows $iA, iB, \ldots$, each of which contains the stable states of i with one of the k output states. Within each row, all output entries are the same, and the pattern of next-state entries is exactly the same for all the rows derived from row i. An examination of Table 4.11 should suffice to make the process clear.

Since in a Moore-form table is it not generally true that $Z(N(s, I), I) = Z(s, I)$, the procedure for finding USTT assignments must be modified slightly. In particular, if in some column I there are transitions $i \to j$ and $k \to j$ where where $Z(i, I) = Z(j, I) \neq Z(k, I)$, the dichotomy (ij, k) must be covered. (The situation is essentially the same as that encountered when developing a USTT assignment for MOC tables. See Subsection 3.3.5.) In Table 4.11b, for example, $(2B\ 3B, 3A)$ must be covered because of transitions $2B \to 3B$ and $3A \to 3B$ in column 00.

With the above techniques, any SOC function can be properly realized even if multiple input changes are permitted. An interesting alternative approach involves the use of a "source box," a circuit which preprocesses the input signals to a realization of a somewhat modified version of the given flow table.

The general idea is as follows: We add *one* stable buffer column to our flow table (see Table 4.12, the modified version of Table 4.11a), and recode the inputs in one-hot form, with the 0-state assigned to the buffer column. The x-inputs are fed to the source box, which in the steady state produces an output on exactly *one* of its output leads, corresponding to the code for the associated flow-table column. In our example, if the x-input is 11, the source box output would be 0010. This output serves as the input to a circuit realizing the modified flow table; hence in the steady state the effect is the same as if the x-inputs were connected directly to a circuit realizing the original table. However, immediately after the x-signal changes (regardless of how many of the x_i's change) the solitary 1-signal at the source-box output goes off, and all source-box outputs remain at 0 for a period D, corresponding to the value of a delay element in the box. After this "spacer" interval, the source-box output corresponding to the new input state goes on. During the spacer interval, the internal state of the sequential circuit remains unchanged, as does its output (the S symbol in the stable column of Table 4.11 means

Table 4.12 Modified Version of Table 4.11a

	$v_1 v_2 v_3 v_4$				
	0000	1000	0100	0010	0001
1	①, S	①, 0	2 , 1	①, 0	4 , 1
2	②, S	3 , 1	②, 1	②, 0	②, 0
3	③, S	③, 1	③, 0	4 , 0	③, 0
4	④, S	1 , 0	3 , 0	④, 0	④, 1

that the output in each state of this column remains the same as the output state that existed prior to the last input change.)

Thus, corresponding to a typical transition 1-11 → 1-10 → 4-10 in Table 4.11a is the transition 1-0010 → 1-0000 → 1-0001 → 4-0001 in Table 4.12, with the system remaining in the spacer state 1-0000 for about D units of time. The situation is essentially the same as that discussed in Subsection 4.3.3 with respect to the use of input delays (see Table 4.9b). In the present case there is a single buffer column that is used to bridge transitions between *any* two columns; whereas in the earlier case there is a buffer column for every ordered pair of input states. Ordinary STT assignments based on the methods of Section 3.3 lead to proper operation even if no delay elements are used, since every transition is effectively converted into a sequence of two transitions—one ending and the other beginning in the stable column—so that there are no essential hazards or d transitions. Output signals are taken from FF's that are set or reset only in the states *not* in the buffer column. The FF's may be omitted if the flow table is in Moore form (or is converted to this form). We note that the input-delay method referred to above may be used directly (without the source box) with output FF's or with Moore-form tables to properly realize functions when multiple input changes are permitted.

Now we consider how a source box can be realized. One possibility, depicted in Fig. 4.15, utilizes one of the delay boxes (Fig. 4.14) described in Subsection 4.3.3 which, it may be recalled, simulates with one delay element the behavior of a set of independent delay elements, even when several of its inputs change simultaneously. The logic box of Fig. 4.15 contains an AND gate for each output terminal; there is one terminal for each state of x. The AND gate is activated if and only if both x and x_D correspond to the state associated with it. For example, if $m = 3$, there is a gate for state 101 which has as its inputs $x_1, \bar{x}_2, x_3, x_{1D}, \bar{x}_{2D}$, and x_{3D}. In the steady state

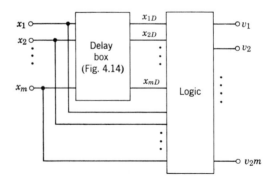

Figure 4.15 Realization of a source box.

with $x_1 x_2 x_3 = 101$, the values of x_{1D}, x_{2D}, and x_{3D} are 1, 0, and 1, respectively, so that this gate is energized. No other v-signal will be on. Should the input state change, say to 110, the 101 gate goes off, since x_1, x_2, and x_3 change at once. But the 110 gate does not go on, since $x_{1D} x_{2D} x_{3D}$ remains at 101. Thus all v's are off, as required, for the spacer interval of duration D, the nominal value associated with the delay box. At the end of this period $x_{1D} x_{2D} x_{3D}$ changes to 110 (by this time the state of $x_1 x_2 x_3$ is seen *everywhere* to be 110), and when the 110 gate sees this change occur, it goes on, as specified. After a further delay somewhat in excess of D, the box is ready for another input change. Other source-box realizations are possible.

The source-box approach may be advantageous for flow tables with many rows and relatively few columns; whereas the method discussed earlier, using a delay box for the state variables, may be more economical in the reverse situation.

By combining a $2S_0 + 1$ row assignment, with an inertial-delay element for the sector variable, hazardfree logic, and a Moore conversion, MOC functions can be properly realized by proper circuits using no other delay elements, even when multiple input changes are allowed.

4.4   Circuits with Stray Delays Largely Concentrated in Logic Gates

Instead of assuming that the stray-delay values are only bounded, we now make the more stringent assumption that stray delays appear only in logic gates—not in connecting wires. In other words, suppose that there is a single stray inertial delay appearing at the output terminal of each gate, but nowhere else in the circuit. This means that, if the signal from a given terminal, which may be an input terminal or the output of a gate, is fed to several gate inputs, changes in that signal will be sensed simultaneously at all of these destination points. Later on we show that the results obtained are valid if we permit delays in the connecting wires, provided that in any such wire the delay does not exceed the minimum delay in any path through the logic network.

If this restriction on the stray delays can be satisfied, then *any* SOC function can be properly realized with delayfree circuits. It should be noted that one of the assumptions made in the theory of speed-independent circuits (see references to papers by Muller) is that stray delays are confined to the logic elements. The validity of such assumptions must, of course, be judged in the context of the particular technology being used. The remarks at the beginning of Section 4.3 are relevant here.

Let us now consider a specific example to illustrate the principles involved. Table 4.13*a* is a flow matrix with an STT assignment for a SOC function with an essential hazard for an x_2-change starting in state 3-11. Karnaugh maps

Table 4.13

| | x_1x_2 | | | | | |
	00	01	11	10	y_1	y_2
1	2 , 0	4 , 1	① , 0	① , 0	0	0
2	② , 0	② , 0	1 , 0	② , 0	0	1
3	③ , 1	③ , 1	③ , 1	4 , 1	1	1
4	3 , 1	④ , 1	1 , 0	④ , 1	1	0

(a) Flow matrix.

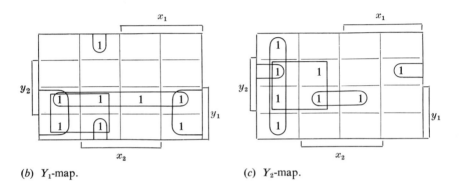

(b) Y_1-map.   (c) Y_2-map.

for the Y_1- and Y_2-functions are shown in parts b and c of the same table. We need not consider the Z-function (in this case $Z = Y_1$) since it does not affect the problem. A two-stage logic realization of Y_1 and Y_2 with single-rail inputs is shown in Fig. 4.16a.

Suppose that, with the system initially in 3-11, x_2 is turned off. Then the $x_2y_1y_2$ gate (labeled A_3 in Fig. 4.16a), which is the one AND gate holding Y_2 on, goes off (see also Table 4.13c). If there is a sufficiently large delay in the inverter that produces $\bar{x}_2$ from x_2, then the y_2-change may reach gate A_1 (the only gate holding Y_1 on) before the $\bar{x}_2$-signal at the input to A_2 goes on (see Table 4.13b). In effect as discussed in Section 1.4 in connection with Fig. 1.2, and in Subsection 4.3.2, the Y_1-signal behaves as though the system state moved from 3-11 to 4-11. That is, the effect is the same as if Y_1 saw the y_2-change *before* the x_2-change. This results in Y_1 going off. If the y_1-input to A_2 goes off while $\bar{x}_2$ is still 0, then A_2 will never go on, and the system will end up in 1-10 instead of in 4-10 as specified. We see then that, even under the restriction imposed in this section, the essential hazard *may* cause the same type of malfunction encountered when the demon setting the stray delays is less hampered.

Our first step in remedying the situation is to make sure that the sequence of total states for any transition is perceived in the correct order at all

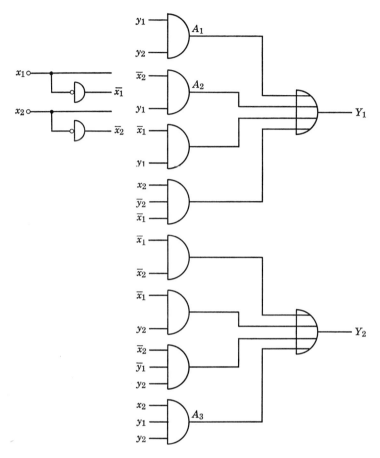

Figure 4.16a First unsuccessful attempt to realize Table 4.13a without delay elements.

circuit terminals. Observe that the AND-gate outputs in Fig. 4.16a indicate the current total state. Our approach is to replace each of the AND gates with a logic circuit that realizes the same function, but with all x-inputs uncomplemented. Furthermore, the y-inputs will appear at a level at which y-changes cannot affect any logic decisions before x-changes that occur first.

The general form of such a circuit is shown in Fig. 4.16b, which realizes the product term $\bar{x}_1 \cdots \bar{x}_m \bar{y}_1 \cdots y_k x_p \cdots x_q$. The complemented x-signals and all of the y-signals are fed to the NOR gate, while the uncomplemented x-signals are fed directly to the AND gate. In cases in which all three types of variables are not in a product, only a part of the circuit is needed. Under the assumption that wiring delays are negligible, any x-change is now bound to make its effect felt on the output of this *compound* AND gate before a subsequent y-change can do so. Suppose, for instance, that in Fig. 4.16b, $x_p = \cdots = x_q = 1$, $x_1 = \cdots = x_m = 0$ and all the other inputs (y's or their complements) are 0 except for y_1. Then the output $P = 0$. If x_1 goes to 1 and thus causes y_1 to change to 0, then the immediate effect of the x_1-change is to hold the NOR-gate output (and hence P) at 0, since the later y_1-change (which tends to turn the NOR gate on) occurs later at the input to the same gate. We are assuming that the x_1-change at *this* gate occurs simultaneously with the x_1-change at the gate that caused y_1 to go off. No special stray delay can appear at the *input* to any gate.

In Fig. 4.16c, the AND gates of part a have all been replaced by compound AND gates. Now in the course of the 3-11 → 3-10 → 4-10 transition, the A_3' gate goes off (turning off y_2), while the A_2' gate goes on. Then, when the y_2-change is sensed, the A_1' gate goes off. This corresponds to a correct sensing of the order of the x_2- and y_2-changes. No longer is there a possibility of the gate corresponding to A_2 of part a seeing the x_2-change only *after* y_2 and y_1 have changed, and thus remaining off.

Unfortunately averting this type of malfunction is not sufficient to assure correct overall circuit behavior. Although the A_1' does not go off until A_2' goes on (it may be helpful here to examine the Y_2-map), the delay at the *output* of the A_2' gate may be sufficiently long to keep the corresponding input to the Y_1-OR gate at 0 until *after* the input from A_1' has gone off. Thus Y_1 may still erroneously go to 0. Having averted trouble in the first level of the logic, we may still be defeated at the last stage.

In order to see how to solve the latter problem, it is necessary to consider the transient behavior of an OR gate when its inputs are changing. Assume that each input changes at most once during some interval. If the initial output is 0, then regardless of whether the final output is 0 or 1, *no* spurious output transients can occur. This is clear on the basis of the sort of reasoning followed in Section 4.2 in connection with 0-hazards. It is also true that, if the output changes from 1 to 0, then the change occurs as soon as the last 1-input goes to 0, and again no transients can occur since none of the inputs goes on. But if the initial and final outputs are 1, then it is possible for a 0-pulse to occur

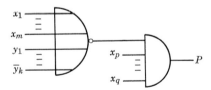

Figure 4.16b   General form of circuits replacing AND-gates.

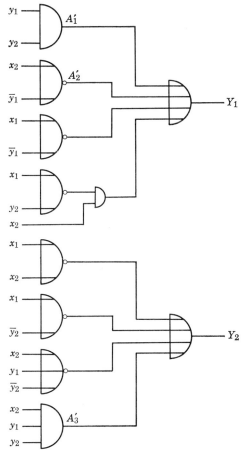

Figure 4.16c   Second unsuccessful attempt to realize Table 4.13a without delay elements.

during the transient interval. This occurs if all the signals that were initially
1 go off before any of the signals changing from 0 to 1 go on. Thus the only
false signals generated are 0-pulses.

This fact can be exploited if we can devise a system in which no state
changes can be precipitated by 0-signals. Consider the set-reset flip-flop
(SR-FF) of Fig. 4.17a. Assume that there are never 1-signals simultaneously
present on both the S- and R-terminals. Then there will be a 1-output on the
y-terminal and a 0 on the $\bar{y}$-terminal (characterizing the *set* state) if the last 1-
input occurred on the S-terminal. When in the set state, a 1 on the R-terminal
will reset the FF, that is, switch y to 0 and $\bar{y}$ to 1. When both S and R are 0,

the FF state remains unaltered. We note in passing that if there are no wiring delays, then during state transitions, y and $\bar{y}$ are never simultaneously equal to 1. For our present purposes, the key point is that a transient 0-pulse at an input terminal of a SR-FF never causes a state change.

It is well known that SR-FF's can be used as memory devices in asynchronous as well as synchronous sequential circuits (see, for example,

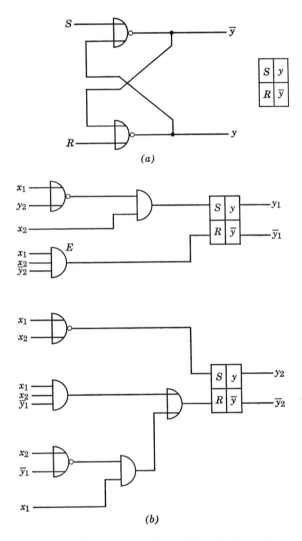

Figure 4.17   (a) A set-reset flip-flop. (b) Delay-free realization of Table 4.13a.

[McC-4]). Precisely the same criteria apply for valid row assignments, and once the row assignment has been made, it is necessary to specify appropriate S- and R-functions for each FF (one per y-signal). For example if the next-state entry in some total state in which $y_i = 1$ corresponds to a state in which $y_i = 0$, then we specify $R_i = 1$ and $S_i = 0$. If in both the current and next state $y_i = 1$, then we specify $R_i = 0$ and leave S_i unspecified. Note that a set signal applied when the FF is in the set state has no effect, and similarly if $\bar{y} = 1$ and R is set equal to 1, the FF remains in the reset state. Table 4.14a depicts the maps for the control signals required to realize the flow matrix of Table 4.13a. The resulting logic expressions are

$$S_1 = \bar{x}_1 x_2 \bar{y}_2, \qquad R_1 = x_1 x_2 \bar{y}_2,$$
$$S_2 = \bar{x}_1 \bar{x}_2, \qquad R_2 = x_1 x_2 \bar{y}_1 + x_1 \bar{x}_2 y_1.$$

They are realized in the special form discussed earlier in Fig. 4.17b.

Since, as has already been shown, under our current assumption regarding stray delays there can be no false 1-signals emanating from the logic and since the FF's do not react to false 0-signals, it follows that the delayfree

Table 4.14

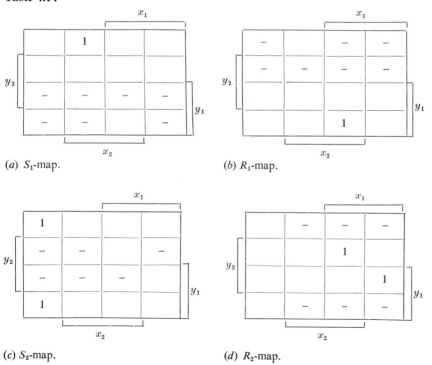

(a) S_1-map.

(b) R_1-map.

(c) S_2-map.

(d) R_2-map.

circuit of Fig. 4.17*b* properly realizes Table 4.13*a*. The same procedure can be used to implement any SOC function assuming single input changes and negligible wiring delays. Note that, since there is no need to guard against static 1-hazards, it is not necessary to cover every adjacent pair of 1-points in the *Y*-maps with prime implicants. Although we have assumed the use of STT state assignments, there exist other synthesis techniques that are valid with any state assignment free of critical races.

Let us now see how far the stray-delay restriction may be eased before malfunctioning of the Fig. 4.17*b* circuit becomes possible. Consider again the essential-hazard transition 3-11 → 3-10 → 4-10, this time assuming that a stray delay of magnitude d is in the x_2-input lead to the AND gate E feeding R_1. Under this assumption (other wiring delays are still negligible), the $1 \to 0$ change of x_2 will switch on the lowest NOR gate, then the following AND gate, then the OR gate, and finally the y_2-FF will be reset, switching on $\bar{y}_2$. If d is sufficiently long so that the x_2-change fails to affect E before the $\bar{y}_2$-change switches on E, then the y_1-FF receives an erroneous reset signal and the final state will be 1-10. In order for this to occur, d must exceed the *total* delay in the path between x_2 and $\bar{y}_2$ which includes both the delay through the logic and the time it takes the FF to switch. We may say, in general, that, if the delay in every wire is less than the minimum delay through the logic and a FF, then the type of circuit developed in this section will operate properly. (Actually in order for malfunctioning to occur, d would have to exceed the value specified above by a magnitude exceeding that of the largest inertial delay between gate E and R_2, as well as the time required to switch a FF. Thus some safety margin is implicit in the bound we have indicated.)

4.5 Analysis of Asynchronous Sequential Circuits

Given an arbitrary sequential circuit, with some input terminals and some output terminals (such as Fig. 4.18), how do we go about finding a flow table relating the output to the input, and how do we determine the relationships that must prevail among the stray delays, delay elements, and spacing of input signals in order for the circuit to behave properly? These questions are treated in this section.

4.5.1 Selecting State Variables and Forming a Flow Table

The basic problem encountered in analyzing a circuit such as that shown in Fig. 4.18 (in which NAND gates are used as the logic elements—for variety) is to determine an appropriate set of *state branches* that generate signals that can be used as state variables. When delay elements are present, the problem is somewhat reduced, since each delay element must be designated as a state branch. Otherwise, contrary to our basic assumptions, there would be delay elements interior to the logic block when the circuit is put into standard form.

In our present example there is one delay, and so we may label its output (the point marked a in the figure) as y_1 (and its input, of course, becomes Y_1). Is it possible now to express the output Z as a function of x_1, x_2, and y_1? The output comes from an inverter fed by the signal at c. This signal in turn comes from a gate whose inputs are x_1 and the signal at the point labeled b, and so we may write $Z = \overline{\overline{x_1 b}} = x_1 b$. But b is itself a function of c; hence we cannot obtain a combinational function describing Z in terms of the inputs and y_1. The same problem would occur if we tried to specify Y_1.

The difficulty stems from the fact that there are feedback paths in the circuit that do not contain the y_1 state branch. It is necessary that our set of state branches have at least one member in every closed path of the circuit. Hence, in our example, we must select at least one more state branch, and a careful study of the circuit reveals that the branch containing b will complete the set. In other words, if we cut the circuit at points a and b, *all* closed circuits are interrupted, we therefore designate y_2 as the signal leaving b, and Y_2 as the signal entering b. (Since there is no delay element in this branch, $y_2 = Y_2$.)

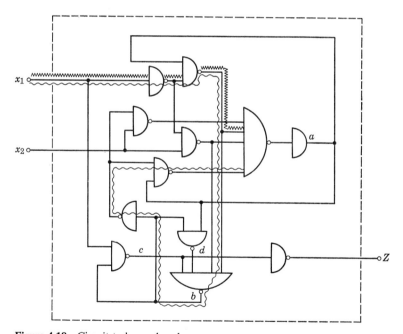

Figure 4.18 Circuit to be analyzed.

It is now possible to compute Y_1, Y_2, and Z as

$$Y_1 = \overline{(y_1\bar{y}_2)(\bar{x}_1 x_2)(\bar{x}_1 y_1)(x_2\bar{y}_2)} = y_1\bar{y}_2 + \bar{x}_1 x_2 + \bar{x}_1 y_1 + x_2\bar{y}_2,$$

$$Y_2 = \overline{(x_1 y_2)(y_1 y_2)(\bar{x}_1 x_2)(\bar{x}_1 y_1)} = x_1 y_2 + y_1 y_2 + \bar{x}_1 x_2 + \bar{x}_1 y_1,$$

$$Z = \overline{\overline{x_1 y_2}} = x_1 y_2.$$

From these expressions, the K-maps of Table 4.15 a, b, and c can easily be obtained. Combining the Y_1- and Y_2-maps yields the excitation matrix of part d, and this leads at once to the flow matrix of part e. The extent to which

Table 4.15

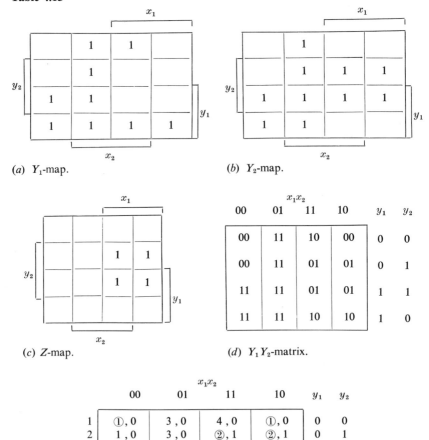

(a) Y_1-map.

(b) Y_2-map.

(c) Z-map.

(d) $Y_1 Y_2$-matrix.

(e) Flow matrix.

this table actually describes the behavior of any physical circuit corresponding to Fig. 4.18 must be determined by a further analysis pertaining to races, hazards, and delays. But first some concluding words on the selection of state branches are in order.

Every branch containing delay elements is selected as a state branch. Additional branches are added to the set of state branches until every closed path of the circuit includes at least one state branch. There are, in general, many solutions, with varying numbers of state branches. If the circuit is free of hazards, then the flow tables obtained are all similar, differing only with respect to purely transient states (rows that contain no stable states and that cannot be reached from any row that has stable states), sets of rows that can be merged, and outputs in transient total states. One may, for example, find that, as a result of some other choice of state branches, a flow table with a 1-output in the total state corresponding to 2-00 of Table 4.15e may be derived.

There is some advantage in finding a *minimal* feedback cut set, since, otherwise, the derived flow table will not be minimal. This problem has received some attention from graph theorists (see, for example, [YOU-1]).

When analyzing sequential circuits composed of relays, the problem of choosing state branches essentially disappears (see Section 4.6).

4.5.2 Analysis for Hazard Conditions

Having obtained a flow table from an analysis of the circuit logic, we now proceed to determine the conditions under which the circuit behavior conforms to the flow matrix. First we should check the row assignment for critical races, bearing in mind that some of the rows of the derived matrix may be equivalent, which indicates a multicode state assignment. In our example, there are no critical races.

Next we apply the methods of Section 4.2 to detect single-input-change combinational hazards. In the present case we see that there is a 1-hazard for Y_2 because of the absence of an $x_2 y_2$-term. The hazard appears in the course of the transition 2-11 → 2-01. Although there may be a temporary false transition to 1-01, the final state is always correct, since there is only one stable state in the 01 column. One should be alert to the possibility that such features of sequential circuits may sometimes prevent the possibility of a significant malfunction resulting from a combinational hazard.

Now we must check for d-trios and essential hazards. There are two d-trios, but the destination column is in both cases 01, in which there is only one stable state, and so in this case no steady-state malfunction is possible. However there may be a transient output hazard in the course of the 4-11 → 4-01 → 3-01 transition, because of the 1-output in 3-11 and the fact that y_2

is not delayed. In general, when the flow matrix is not so favorably arranged as to preclude trouble in the manner just illustrated, we must examine the path delays in the manner to be described below in connection with essential hazards.

There is an essential hazard in Table 4.15e for the transition starting with 3-00 → 3-10 with y_1 as the state variable that is supposed to change. The delay element in the y_2-branch can avert malfunction during this transition if its magnitude is sufficient. Instead of computing the required lower bound for this delay, let us use another example, which arises in connection with the other essential hazard in this table, involving the transition beginning with 4-10 → 4-00. Here, the undelayed variable y_2 is the one that is to change. Examining the Y-maps and Y-expressions, we see that after the x_1-change, the $\bar{x}_1 y_1$-term goes on, which in turn switches on Y_2. Once y_2 goes on, the $y_1 \bar{y}_2$-term that was holding Y_1 on goes off, and the $\bar{x}_1 y_1$-term must keep Y_1 on. The danger is that the effect of the change in $\bar{x}_1 y_1$ on Y_1 will fail to act on the Y_1 gate before the effect of the $y_1 \bar{y}_2$-change turns it off. (Assume that the y_1-delay is not inertial so that a false Y_1-signal will ultimately affect y_1.) We must thus compare the delays in the path (marked with a wavy line in Fig. 4.18) from x_1 through the $\bar{x}_1 y_1$ gate, the Y_2 gate, and the $y_1 \bar{y}_2$ gate to the Y_1-gate input with the path (marked with a saw-toothed line) from x_1 through the $\bar{x}_1 y_1$ gate to the Y_1-gate input. Since these paths start out together, we need compare the delays only in the portions after the point of divergence (after the $\bar{x}_1 y_1$ gate). If the stray delays in the former path exceed those in the latter path, then all is well. But, if the delay in what appears in the diagram to be a short piece of wire (beware of such illusions—circuit diagrams display topological, *not* geometric features!) is greater, then a false Y_1-signal will appear for an interval equal to the excess. The result will be an oscillation among various states of column 00. As indicated in Section 4.3, the trouble can be averted by a delay element in the y_2-branch sufficient to redress the balance. (Actually this delay can be located at *any* point in the wavy path not common to the toothy path, but, in general, locations other than the y_2-branch may lead to difficulties in other transitions, hence requiring greater caution.) If the y_1-delay had an inertial effect of the same magnitude, this would also solve the problem.

A similar analysis can be carried out for each d transition and essential hazard in the flow matrix. In general, we must identify two signal paths, both starting at the input terminal corresponding to the x-variable that initiates the transition. One path (the *error-producing path*) is that of the signal that changes the y-variable that is supposed to respond, cascaded with the path of the signal from that y-terminal to the Y-terminal that may *falsely* respond. The second path (the *error-correcting path*) is that of the signal that tends to *prevent* the false response by conveying the new x-value to the second Y-terminal. Trouble may occur if the delays in the error-correcting path exceed those in the error-producing path.

The situation is more complex, but not essentially different when there are noncritical races present. It is necessary to analyze a larger set of paths. In cases in which a series of y-changes occurs in succession, corresponding to a multistep row assignment or a MOC function, the analysis must be carried out for each step. For example, if a change in y_i is to be followed by a change in y_j, then the y_i-variable (and all of the other y-variables that changed before y_i in this sequence) must be considered as the initiating variables for this part of the transition.

It is often useful to determine if a less discriminating, but easier to check, *sufficient* condition for proper operation is satisfied, particularly when the situation is complicated by the kind of factors discussed in the preceding paragraph. Let d_{Lm} and d_{LM} be, respectively, the minimum and maximum delays through the logic from any x- or y-terminal, and let d_{fm} be the smallest delay in any state branch (feedback path). Then, since the error-producing paths under discussion entail two traversals through the logic, whereas the error-correcting paths involve only a single traversal, it follows that the malfunctions under discussion will always be avoided if the inequality

$$2d_{Lm} + d_{fm} > d_{LM}$$

is satisfied. This is a useful criterion to apply in synthesizing sequential circuits.

4.5.3 A Ternary Logic Test for Hazards

Particularly when analyzing large circuits, it is useful to be able to determine whether timing problems exist for specific transitions. The approach to be discussed here is particularly suitable for use in conjunction with computer simulations of digital systems. It can be applied to both combinational and sequential circuits.

The basic idea is to postulate a third value that can be assumed by what have hitherto been treated as *binary* variables, thus converting two-valued logic to three-valued, or *ternary*, logic. The new value, $\frac{1}{2}$, will be considered as intermediate between 0 and 1 in the sense that during transient intervals when x is changing between 0 and 1 (in either direction), it is assumed that $x = \frac{1}{2}$. Variables are also assumed to have the value $\frac{1}{2}$ when it is not known whether they equal 0 or 1. Transitions are studied by computing circuit outputs for the initial and final input states, *and* for the transient input state, specified by setting the changing variables to $\frac{1}{2}$.

We begin with a discussion of combinational circuits, which can be examined for static hazards resulting from single or multiple input changes. Note first that, if any input to an OR gate is a 1, then the output is 1 regardless of the values of the other inputs. Then, assuming no hazards are inherent in any of the gates, *changing* any of the other inputs does not affect the output. Hence the output of this gate is 1 even if some of the other inputs have the value $\frac{1}{2}$. On the other hand, if all but one input has the value 0, then the gate output will be equal to 0 or 1 if the remaining input is 0 or 1, respectively. Therefore, if the remaining input is $\frac{1}{2}$, it follows that the output is $\frac{1}{2}$. A dual argument applies to AND gates. In general, if a gate realizes the function $f(x_1, x_2, \ldots, x_n)$ and if $f(x_1, x_2, \ldots, x_p, a_{p+1}, a_{p+2}, \ldots, a_n)$ (where x_i is fixed at a_i for $i = p + 1, p + 2, \ldots, n$ with each $a_i = 0$ or 1) is equal to 0 (or 1) *regardless* of the values of the x_i for $i = 1, 2, \ldots, p$, then we assume $f(\frac{1}{2}, \frac{1}{2}, \ldots, \frac{1}{2}, a_{p+1}, a_{p+2}, \ldots, a_n) = 0$ (or 1). Otherwise $f(\frac{1}{2}, \frac{1}{2}, \ldots, \frac{1}{2}, a_{p+1}, a_{p+2}, \ldots, a_n) = \frac{1}{2}$. Using this assumption, it is easy to determine the output of any gate for any set of inputs. Note, for example, that the output of an exclusive-OR gate is always $\frac{1}{2}$ if *any* of its inputs equal $\frac{1}{2}$, since changing any input value *always* changes the output value. It is not difficult to show that, if any input to any gate changes *to* $\frac{1}{2}$, then the output either remains unchanged or changes *to* $\frac{1}{2}$. Conversely, if any gate input changes *from* $\frac{1}{2}$ (to 0 or 1), then the gate output remains unchanged or changes *from* $\frac{1}{2}$ (to 0 or 1—not necessarily respectively).

Consider now a gate network. Suppose some input signal changes *to* $\frac{1}{2}$. Then the outputs of the gates it feeds can change to only $\frac{1}{2}$, and by iterating this argument as we progress through the network, we see that the network output signals must remain at 0 or 1 or change to $\frac{1}{2}$. Similarly if an input changes *from* $\frac{1}{2}$ to 0 or 1, then the network outputs also must change *from* $\frac{1}{2}$ to 0 or 1 (or vice versa), or remain constant.

A given output signal may change while a subset of the input signals are changing iff the output at that terminal is $\frac{1}{2}$ when the changing inputs are set to $\frac{1}{2}$ and the fixed inputs held at their initial 0- or 1-values. This is clearly true for one-stage logic and by induction can be shown to hold in general. We are now in a position to specify the following:

PROCEDURE 4.2   *Detecting Static Hazards in Combinational Circuits for Specific Transitions*

1. Determine if the specified output is the same for the initial and final states.
2. If so, then a hazard exists if the output is $\frac{1}{2}$ when the changing inputs are set to $\frac{1}{2}$.

This procedure is justified by the preceding discussion. As an example, consider Fig. 4.19 (a reproduction of Fig. 4.10, analyzed for hazards in

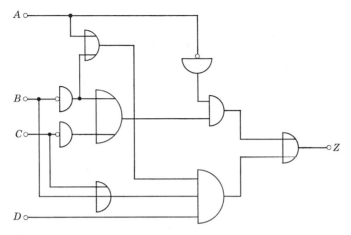

Figure 4.19 Circuit to be analyzed for combinational hazards.

Section 4.2) with respect to $ABCD$ transition $0011 \rightarrow 1111$. The initial and final steady-state outputs are both 1, and the output for $\frac{1}{2}\frac{1}{2}11$ is $\frac{1}{2}$. Hence our test indicates that there is a static 1-hazard for this transition a conclusion verified by our earlier examination of this circuit, which indicated the presence of a function 1-hazard. An examination of the transition $0101 \rightarrow 1101$ indicates that $Z = 1$ for the initial and final states and that $Z = \frac{1}{2}$ for $ABCD = \frac{1}{2}101$. Thus another static 1-hazard is indicated, and our earlier analysis shows that it is a *logic* hazard.

We now turn to sequential circuits, where the procedure to be discussed indicates whether or not, after a given input change (*not* limited to changes in one variable), the y-variables assume a specific stable state not dependent on specific delay values. Assume at first that the circuits involved are delay-free. (The method is not valid if oscillatory y-states are incorporated in the design.) There are two basic parts to the procedure:

PROCEDURE 4.3A *Determining Which y-variables May Change During The Transition*

1. Set the y-variables and the fixed x-variables to their initial 0- or 1-values, and set the changing x-variables to $\frac{1}{2}$.
2. Evaluate the Y-functions to determine those Y's that switch to $\frac{1}{2}$.
3. Change to $\frac{1}{2}$ the values of the y's corresponding to the Y's found in step 2.
4. Repeat steps 2 and 3 in sequence until no additional Y's are added to the list of those with value $\frac{1}{2}$. Then the final set of those y's equal to $\frac{1}{2}$ is precisely the set that may undergo some type of change during the transition.

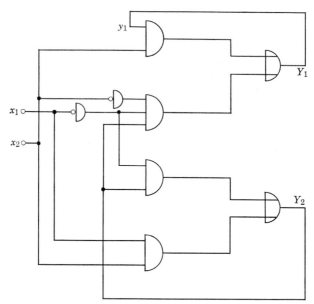

Figure 4.20   Sequential circuit to be analyzed.

This procedure can be justified in terms of the ideas discussed earlier. Before going on to the second part of the process, we illustrate Procedure 4.3A by analyzing the circuit shown in Fig. 4.20 to determine the set of y-variables that may change after simultaneous changes in x_1 and x_2 when the initial state is $x_1x_2y_1y_2 = 0000$. First we note that the initial state is indeed stable. Next we see that setting $x_1x_2y_1y_2$ to $\frac{1}{2}\frac{1}{2}00$ changes Y_2 to $\frac{1}{2}$ (because of the bottom AND gate). Iterating the procedure, we set $x_1x_2y_1y_2$ to $\frac{1}{2}\frac{1}{2}0\frac{1}{2}$ and compute Y_1 to be $\frac{1}{2}$. (We need not recheck Y_2, since it has previously been shown that changing an input from 0 *to* $\frac{1}{2}$, namely y_2, in the above calculation cannot change any output *from* $\frac{1}{2}$ to 0 or 1.) Hence *both* y-variables are subject to change.

Now, in order to determine which y-signals can be relied upon to assume specific values (0 or 1) after the transition, we introduce the following:

PROCEDURE 4.3B   *Determining The* y-*variables That Attain Definite Values*

1. Set the y's to correspond to their final values in part A, and set the x's to the values corresponding to the *new* input state.
2. Evaluate the Y's (only those previously equal to $\frac{1}{2}$ need be checked).
3. If any Y changes to 0 or 1, change the corresponding y, and repeat step 2. Continue until no further changes occur. At this time the y's with values

0 or 1 are at their final values for the transition, and any y's still equal to $\frac{1}{2}$ either are oscillating or may assume values of 0 *or* 1 depending on the distribution of stray delays.

Again the justification rests on the preceding theory. In our example, with $x_1x_2y_1y_2 = 11\frac{1}{2}\frac{1}{2}$, we find that $Y_2 = 1$. Repeating step 2 with $x_1x_2y_1y_2 = 11\frac{1}{2}1$ yields no further change, indicating that y_1 can*not* be relied upon to assume any particular 0- or 1-value.

When there are delay elements in the circuit, a modification is necessary as follows: After an input change all of the undelayed y's that become unstable assume their new values before any of the delayed y's that become unstable change. Hence we apply parts A and B of the procedure holding the delayed y's fixed at their initial values. If the input signal (Y-value) to a *pure*-delay element becomes $\frac{1}{2}$ during part A, we hold its value at $\frac{1}{2}$ throughout part B without bothering to check it again, since once the input to a pure delay changes, the output eventually follows suit regardless of the duration of the change. Inputs to *inertial* delay elements are not checked until the end of part B, since transient changes will be absorbed. If any Y-signals feeding delay elements change values (to $\frac{1}{2}$, 0, or 1) during the above process, we change the corresponding y's to these new values and repeat the operations. This is done until no further Y-changes occur *or* until a y-state occurs that was encountered earlier. The latter situation reveals an oscillatory condition, and in this case all y's that changed during the course of the cycle are set to $\frac{1}{2}$ and the process resumed.

With the aid of computer programs embodying the techniques of this subsection, large systems have been analyzed for hazards or critical races during the course of specific input sequences. Once such a condition has been detected, the specific nature and cure of the trouble must be found via a more detailed analysis. Tracing the paths of $\frac{1}{2}$-signals through a circuit may be a useful approach, given an understanding of the concepts discussed in the other sections of this chapter.

4.6 Special Problems Associated with Relay Sequential Circuits

Although all of the circuit examples presented thus far have been gate circuits, the theory developed is also applicable to circuits employing relays as elementary components. There are, however, a few aspects of relay circuit design that merit special attention. They are discussed after a brief introduction in which we show how the notation and techniques developed earlier may be related to relay circuits.

A typical relay sequential circuit is shown in Fig. 4.21, where the following points are significant:

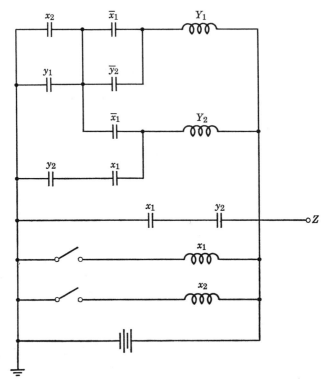

Figure 4.21   A relay sequential circuit realizing the flow matrix of Table 4.15*e*.

1. One end of each relay coil is connected to a voltage source, and the other end is connected to a contact network which provides a path to ground (the other terminal of the voltage source) under appropriate conditions.

2. When the coil of a relay R is energized, the *excitation* variable R is equal to 1.

3. The normally open (*front*) contacts r close ($r \rightarrow 1$) some time after R becomes 1. There is an inertial-delay-element relation between R and r. The normally closed (*back*) contacts $\bar{r}$ open ($\bar{r} \rightarrow 0$) some time after $R \rightarrow 1$.

4. Different contacts on the same relay may respond to an excitation change at slightly different times. This effect, known as *contact stagger*, plays a role similar to that of stray delays in gate circuits.

Inputs are usually represented by the states of mechanically actuated switches having multiple back and front contacts, or by relays (called *primary* relays) controlled directly by input switches (another possibility is discussed shortly). State variables are represented by the states of Y-relays (*secondary* relays) that are controlled by networks of contacts from primary and secondary relays (x- and y-contacts, respectively).

The synthesis procedure follows the lines developed earlier. After the row assignment has been made, and the Y- and Z-logic functions specified, the contact networks realizing these functions are designed using any of the approaches developed for such circuits [CAL-1], with due precautions taken to avoid problems concerning combinational hazards.

It has been found that relay circuits are particularly vulnerable to essential hazards because of the fact that contact stagger is usually more pronounced between front and back contacts. The normal inertial-delay effect of the y-relays may be insufficient to cope with the problem, necessitating the use of particularly sluggish relays. A technique believed to be superior in many cases is to use *shunt control* of some of the secondary relays. It entails connecting the relay coil in series with the voltage supply and a resistor, with a contact network realizing the *complement* of the Y-function connected in parallel with the coil. By this means, it is often possible to replace races between complementary contacts on the same x-relay with races between like contacts, which generally act more nearly simultaneously.

Some special problems are associated with the input source. In cases in which the input signals are coupled to the circuit via primary relays, the effect is as though an inertial-delay element were connected in series with each input signal. A rigorous analysis of such a circuit (Subsection 4.5.1) would require each of these delays to be treated analogously to a state branch. In effect the primary relays would be considered as being controlled by the basic inputs (the signals controlling the coil excitations) with the relay responses being treated as y-signals. When only one x-signal at a time is permitted to change, this analysis yields nothing new, since the only effect of the primary relays is to delay the inputs.

But if several inputs may change at once, then a race condition, generally critical, exists among the primary relays. The effect of the primary relays is to increase the possible deviation from simultaneity to the point where it is comparable to the magnitude of the delays corresponding to the relays; therefore the inertial effect of the secondary relays cannot be relied upon to absorb the error. The only apparent remedy is to use two kinds of relays: a relatively fast type for the primary relays, and a slower type for the secondary relays. This, of course, represents a departure from our concept of a "proper" circuit (Section 4.3).

Sometimes the inputs to a relay sequential circuit are generated by other relay circuits in the form of transmissions to ground through contact networks (the Z-output in Fig. 4.21 might, for example, serve as such an input to another circuit). In such cases it is usually necessary to employ primary relays controlled by these inputs in order to obtain the necessary set of front and back contacts for the Y and Z circuits. But if the circuits can be so designed that a single front contact with one side grounded is sufficient for each input variable, then the inputs can be used directly and the primary relays dispensed with; for example, in Fig. 4.21 the x_2-contact in the upper left corner is the *only* contact used from the x_2-relay, and hence the x_2-relay can be eliminated and the switch used to control it employed directly in place of the x_2-contact. It is sometimes possible to achieve such situations deliberately by generating an appropriate row assignment. This is rather difficult however, and there are unsolved problems here.

SOURCES

The concept of the inertial delay and the particular realizations shown in Fig. 4.2b and Fig. 4.3 are due to Huffman [HUF-1, and in unpublished notes]. Friedman [FRM-1, 2] developed the realizations of Fig. 4.2a and Fig. 4.4. The basic theory of combinational hazards as presented here is the work of Huffman [HUF-3]. The statements of Lemmas 4.1 to 4.3 on hazards in two-stage logic are taken from McCluskey [McC-3, 4]. Eichelberger [EI-3] first defined and discussed hazards occurring during multiple input changes. He also developed the ternary algebra approach to combinational hazards, discussed in Subsection 4.5.3. Somewhat earlier, work along similar lines involving ternary logic was done by Yoeli and Rino [YOE-1]. The definitions of proper operation, essential hazards, d-trios and the results of Subsections 4.3.1 and 4.3.2 pertaining to synthesis with delayfree circuits, and the need for delay elements when essential hazards are present are due to Unger [UN-2, UN-3, UN-6] who also established the sufficiency of one delay element for the realization of any SOC function and devised the delay box of Fig. 4.13. Alternative proofs of Theorem 4.7 (need for delay elements) have been found by Hall [HAL-4] and Langdon [LA-1]. The latter reference also includes an extension of the definition of essential hazards to incorporate multiple input changes. The delay box shown in Fig. 4.14 was the work of Huffman, and the material in Subsection 4.3.3 dealing with the use of delay elements in the input leads is based on the work of Kliman and Lowenschuss [KL-1]. Friedman and Menon [FRM-5] conceived of the source box and the "Mealy-to-Moore" transformations as methods for designing one-delay circuits where multiple input changes are permitted (Subsection 4.3.4). The contents of Section 4.4, on delayfree realizations in cases in which stray delays are concentrated in gate outputs, represents work by Armstrong, Friedman, and Menon [AR-2]. Another solution to this problem (which is interesting, but not discussed here) was found by Langdon [LA-1,2], apparently a little later, but independently. The procedure for deriving flow tables from gate-type sequential circuits is an extension by Unger [UN-2] of the basic work of Huffman [HUF-1]. Lerner [LE-1] has looked further into the question of determining when and where delay elements are needed in particular circuits to prevent malfunctioning due to stray delays. The discussion of essential hazards in relay sequential circuits, including the proposal for the use of shunt control summarizes ideas of Marcus [MAR-1]. The problems pertaining to relay-circuit inputs were pointed out by Brzozowski [BRZ-1], who also developed some pertinent techniques not discussed here. Extensive treatments of relay-circuit design can be found in the books by Caldwell [CAL-1], and Keister, Ritchie, and Washburn [KE-1]. A different approach to the hazard problem is taken by Muller [MU-5].

PROBLEMS

*4.1   Given four delay elements as described below

Designation	Type	Magnitude
D_{p1}	pure	4
D_{p2}	pure	6
D_{i1}	inertial	4
D_{i2}	inertial	6

and input signals s_1, s_2, s_3, and s_4 consisting of isolated pulses of durations 2, 5, 8, and 14, respectively, what outputs would each of the following delay combinations produce for each of the input signals:
(a) D_{p1} cascaded with D_{p2}.
(b) D_{p2} cascaded with D_{i1}.
(c) D_{i1} cascaded with D_{i2}.
(d) What other combination of the given delays is equivalent to combination c above? State a general rule for such cases.

*4.2   What output is generated by the circuit of Fig. 4.4 when the input is a pulse of duration 5 and:
(a) $D_1 = 4$, $D_2 = 6$.   (b) $D_1 = 6$, $D_2 = 4$.

4.3   Write equations for hazardfree two-stage combinational circuits for the octally specified four-variable function $F = \Sigma(0, 4, 5, 7, 11, 13, 17)$. Use both sum and product forms. (Note that the numbers in the specification represent the states in *octal* form; that is, for example, 13 represents $x_1 x_2 x_3 x_4 = 1011$.)

4.4   Refer to the function of Problem 4.3.
(a) Change the sum form found so as to introduce hazards in the transitions $4 \rightarrow 5$ and $11 \rightarrow 13$. Draw the circuit. In this circuit introduce a pure-delay element at a point where it will prevent a false output change for the $4 \rightarrow 5$ transition. Would this delay also prevent a false output for transition $5 \rightarrow 4$?
(b) Change the product form so as to introduce a hazard for transition $2 \rightarrow 3$.

4.5   Draw a circuit corresponding to the expression $F = (\bar{A} + C)(B + \bar{D}) + (A\bar{D} + B)(\bar{B} + \bar{C})$. Specify all single-input-change and two multiple-change combinational hazards. Write a simple expression corresponding to a hazardfree circuit for the same function.

4.6   What are the hazardous transitions (if any) for single input changes in the contact network of Fig. P4.6.

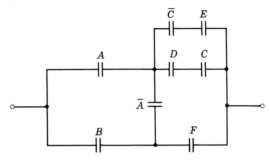

Figure P4.6

4.7   Are there two-stage AND-OR circuits that realize functions without single-input-change hazards and yet do not cover every prime implicant of the function realized? Prove your answer.

4.8   Find a four-variable function and a realization of that function that has *no* hazards for changes of single input variables, but which does have a logic hazard.

4.9   Prove that any function with more than one prime implicant has a static function hazard.

*4.10   Show that there exists a dynamic-logic hazard for a multiple input change in the circuit of Fig. P4.10.

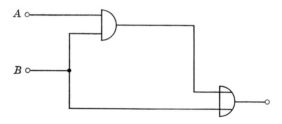

Figure P4.10

4.11   Identify all of the essential hazards of the function of Table P4.11.

Table P4.11

$$x_1 x_2$$

	00	01	11	10
1	①	2	3	①
2	1	②	4	②
3	1	③	③	③
4	④	3	④	2

*4.12   Determine if the row assignment shown for Table P4.12 is valid for a delayfree realization, assuming only one input variable at a time may change.

Table P4.12

	000	001	$x_1 x_2 x_3$ 011	010	100	y_1	y_2	y_3	y_4
1	①,0	2,0	3,0	①,0	5,0	0	0	0	0
2	②,1	②,0	3,0	②,0	5,0	0	1	1	0
3	4,0	2,0	③,0	③,0	5,0	0	1	0	0
4	④,0	2,0	3,0	④,1	5,0	0	1	0	1
5	⑤,0	⑤,0	3,0	⑤,0	⑤,0	1	0	1	1

4.13 Show how Table P4.13 can be realized using a delay box of the type shown Fig. 4.14. Multiple input changes are to be permitted.

Table P4.13

	00	$x_1 x_2$ 01	11	10
1	①,0	2,0	①,0	①,1
2	3,0	②,0	3,1	②,0
3	③,0	2,0	③,1	4,1
4	④,0	④,0	1,0	④,1

4.14 Suppose a sequential circuit is to be constructed using delay elements with tolerances such that, in order to guarantee a minimum delay value D_m, it is necessary to accept elements that have values as large as $(1 + E) D_m$. Assume that some transitions involve sequences of as many as n y-state changes. If D and d are the maximum and minimum, respectively, delays through the logic, how much time must be allowed between successive input changes in order to ensure proper operation?

4.15 Consider the flow matrix Table P4.15.

(a) If only pure delays are available, how many are needed for S-proper operation?

(b) If inertial delays cost 50¢ each, and pure delays 40¢ each, how can we most economically use them to assure S-proper operation?

(c) In what sense can we trade speed and delay elements for logical elements in a realization of this matrix?

(d) If we now desire to avoid transient, as well as steady-state hazards, how would our choice in (b) be constrained?

Table P4.15

	x 0	1	y_1	y_2	y_3
1	①,0	2,0	0	0	0
2	3,0	②,0	0	0	1
3	③,0	4,0	0	1	1
4	5,0	④,0	0	1	0
5	⑤,0	6,1	1	1	0
6	1,0	⑥,1	1	0	0

4.16   Assuming that circuits can be constructed with stray delays confined to the outputs of logic gates, synthesize the function of Table P4.16 without using delay elements.

Table P4.16

	$x_1 x_2$		
	00	01	11
1	①, 0	2 , 0	①, 0
2	3 , 1	②, 0	②, 0
3	③, 1	③, 0	1 , 0

4.17   Analyze the circuit of Fig. 4.18 using the signals at points a, c, and d as y_1, y_2, and y_3, respectively. Compare the result with Table 4.15e.

4.18   Using the ternary logic approach of Subsection 4.5.3, analyze the sequential circuit of Fig. 1.1 (derived from Table 1.2) to determine the result of changing x_2 when the system is initially in 1–10.

4.19   Derive a flow table specifying the behavior of the circuit of Fig. P4.19. Assume the initial state is 00–00.

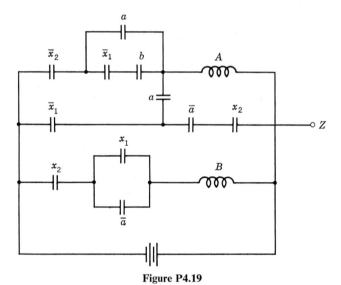

Figure P4.19

*4.20   Prove that the existence of a logic 0-hazard in an AND-to-OR circuit implies the presence of a p-term with complementary literals.

*4.21   Show that the function described by $\bar{A}B + B\bar{C}$ can be realized by an AND-to-OR circuit without a hazard for the transition $010 \rightarrow 110$, or without a hazard for the transition $000 \rightarrow 011$, but that no such circuit is free of *both* hazards. Is there *any* circuit that can realize this function without either hazard?

4.22   Specify the complete flow matrix for a delayfree realization of Table P4.22. Use no more state variables than necessary. Assume single-input-change operation.

Table P4.22

	$x_1 x_2$			
	00	01	11	10
1	①, 0	2 , 0	①, 0	①, 0
2	3 , 1	②, 0	②, 0	5 , 0
3	③, 1	2 , 0	③, 0	③, 0
4	3 , 1	④, 1	④, 0	5 , 0
5	⑤, 0	⑤, 1	4 , 0	⑤, 0

‡**4.23**   Table P4.23a and b each describe a SOC function in which multiple input changes *are permitted*. Specify a flow matrix for each of them so that there will be no steady-state *or* transient hazards. Use a minimum number of state variables, and indicate when delay elements are necessary.

Table P4.23

	$x_1 x_2$			
	00	01	11	10
1	①, 0	2 , 1	①, 0	①, 0
2	3 , 0	②, 1	1 , 0	②, 0
3	③, 0	③, 0	1 , 0	③, 1

(a)

	$x_1 x_2$			
	00	01	11	10
1	①, 0	2 , 0	①, 0	①, 0
2	3 , 0	②, 0	②, 1	3 , 1
3	③, 0	4 , 0	2 , 1	③, 1
4	④, 1	④, 0	1 , 0	3 , 1

(b)

CHAPTER 5

Feedback

In this chapter, the role played by feedback in asynchronous sequential circuits is discussed with respect to the circumstances under which it is required, the physical consequences of its presence, and synthesis techniques for designing circuits with a minimum number of feedback paths. The principal results apply to Huffman circuits, although some of the material is also pertinent to Muller circuits.

5.1 Necessity for Feedback

It is shown here that, for an important class of sequential switching functions, positive feedback is associated with each nonredundant state variable in any Huffman realization using the components discussed earlier, namely, logic gates and delay elements.

THEOREM 5.1 *Let M be a SOC flow matrix† free of critical races. Then, for every necessary state variable y_i used in the state assignment, there is a state of the other y-variables and the input variables where $Y_i = y_i$.*

This is equivalent to saying that each necessary Y_i is neither independent of y_i nor a monotone decreasing function of y_i. There must be some "positive" feedback from y_i to Y_i. In physical terms this means that if, in a Huffman circuit realizing a SOC function, there is a state variable y_j such that no path free of inverters (or with an even number of inverters) leads from y_j to Y_j, then we can say that y_j is superfluous.

It is important to understand that the feedback path referred to above must be a genuine feedback path around which signals can actually flow, not just any path which is *topologically* a circuit. For example, the path shown in

---

† Note that a *single* y-state is assigned to each row of the flow matrix and the next-state entry for each total state is the number of the row whose y-state determines the Y-values. As indicated in Chapter 3, the matrix may have been obtained from a flow table by assigning several y-states to each row and then expanding the table to provide a separate row for each y-state.

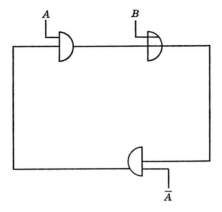

Figure 5.1 A pseudo-loop.

Fig. 5.1 is an example of a *pseudo-loop*, since at all times one or the other of the AND gates is off. Thus, if the circuit is cut at any point, the signal at the output end of the break is independent of the signal injected into the input end. Such pseudo-loops involving Y_i and y_i do *not* satisfy the requirement stated in the theorem that Y_i be a function of y_i.

The necessity for the SOC condition is illustrated by the circuit of Fig. 5.2, which realizes the function of Table 5.1, without *any* feedback. The double

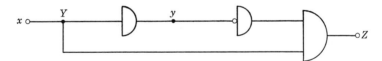

Figure 5.2 Circuit realizing Table 5.1 without feedback.

**Table 5.1   Flow Table
for a Function Producing
an Output Pulse**

	x	
	0	1
1	①, 0	2 , 1
2	1̄ , 0	②, 0

output change $0 \to 1 \to 0$ following the single input change $0 \to 1$ contradicts our hypothesis. Now for the proof.

PROOF.   First let us alter the output entries of the matrix by setting $Z(s, I) = Z(N(s, I), I)$ for all s and I. Thus, the output in every state becomes the same as that in the next stable state (or set of cycling states representing a stable flow-table state). This alteration does not change the essential behavior when a SOC function is being realized (see Section 2.6). Now assume that Y_j never increases with y_j and that r_0 and r_1 are any two rows whose y-assignments differ only in that y_j is 0 at r_0 and 1 at r_1. We shall show that r_0 and r_1 are essentially equivalent and that either can be deleted without changing the function realized or introducing critical races. If this deletion is made for every such pair of rows, then y_j is superfluous, as was to be shown.

1. Given any input I, there are just four ways in which Y_j-values can be assigned to r_0-I and r_1-I. One of them, the assignment of 0- and 1-values of Y_j to r_0-I and r_1-I, respectively, would make Y_j increase with y_j between r_0 and r_1 and is hence excluded by assumption. In each of the other cases, y_j is unstable in at least one of the two total states. Let us assume, without loss of generality, that y_j is unstable ($Y_j = 1$) in r_0-I. Then regardless of what values are assigned to the other Y-functions in r_0-I, the possibility exists that, after entering r_0-I, the system may go to r_1-I.

2. But $N(r_0, I)$ is also a state that the system may go to from r_0-I; hence, if this state is not equivalent to r_1-I, a critical race would exist. Since this possibility is excluded in the hypothesis of the theorem, it follows that r_1-I and $N(r_0, I)$ are equivalent.

3. Then $Z(r_1, I) = Z(N(r_0, I), I) = Z(r_0, I)$.

4. Hence r_0 and r_1 have the same outputs in every column.

5. By the same argument used in step 2, the stable states (or cycling sets of states) reached from r_1-I and $N(r_0, I)$ (and therefore from r_0-I) must also be equivalent, assuming that, as usual in asynchronous circuits, the input does not change until a steady-state condition is reached.

6. Then when starting in r_0 or r_1, all inputs result in the same output and lead to equivalent rows. Hence r_0 and r_1 are equivalent (assuming asynchronous operation—see Section 2.6).

7. Now let us delete each r_1 row from the table, and y_j from the set of y-variables (since y_j serves only to distinguish between r_0 and r_1 rows). The resulting flow *table*, considered as representing an asynchronous function, is equivalent to the original table, since each r_0 and r_1 of the given table is equivalent to the corresponding r_0 of the new table.

8. Suppose there is a critical race in the new matrix starting in some state s-I, with destination state $N(s, I) = d$-I, and involving variables y_p and y_q (possibly others as well). Then a corresponding race also involving y_p and y_q exists in the original matrix from r_0-I (where r_0 corresponds to s) to $N(r_0, I)$, since we did nothing to change assignments with respect to variables other than y_j. Either exactly the same set of variables would have been involved, or y_j would *also* have been a contestant. Every member of the transition set $T(s, d)$ would have had a counterpart in the race in the original matrix.

9. But since, by hypothesis, the given matrix has no critical races, neither can the new matrix have any, and the theorem is proved.

Although in the above theorem we have shown that an assignment free of critical races can be obtained from the original assignment by deleting y_j, there exist cases in which y_j *does* serve a useful purpose in the circuit. This would be the case if a delay element had been inserted in the *logic* in order to circumvent a static hazard (a technique mentioned in Section 4.2). In an analysis of such a circuit, the output of that delay would be designated as a state variable (see Subsection 4.5.1) meeting the description of y_j. Since presumably this y_j is not necessary to avert critical races, it could be dispensed with (as indicated by our theorem) if the logic were redesigned to be hazard-free, usually by adding one or more gates.

Observe that, in the terminology of the above proof, if in states r_0-I and r_1-I, Y_j were assigned values 1 and 0, respectively, so that it *decreased* as y_j increased, the circuit might, at least temporarily, oscillate between r_0-I and r_1-I. (The oscillation would necessarily be temporary if some *other* y-variable were unstable in *both* r_0-I and r_1-I so that eventually, when it changed, the system would enter some other state.) The existence of a "negative" feedback path, characterized by the existence of an odd number of inverters in some y_i to Y_i path through the logic always creates such oscillatory situations (which may or may not be undesirable). We see then that, if a circuit for the type of function under discussion has no superfluous state variables and has no oscillatory conditions, then each Y_i is a monotone increasing function of y_i. In other words, any irredundant expression for Y_i in which only individual literals are complemented (such as a minimal sum-of-products expression) will contain at least one y_i term and no $\bar{y}_i$ terms.

Note that, with respect to oscillations, the converse of the above statement is not generally true. The functions $Y_1 = y_2$ and $Y_2 = \bar{y}_1$, embedded in some larger functions in which Y_1 and Y_2 are still increasing functions of y_1 and y_2, respectively, can lead to oscillations through the *four* states 00, 01, 11, 10. In Section 5.6, a very interesting circuit is presented, in which stable states of a flow table are realized as oscillations among sets of y-states. (Theorem 5.1 is still valid in such cases.) It should also be pointed out that, although there may be circuit states between which oscillations are possible, it may be that constraints on the initial circuit states or on the input sequences are such that the oscillatory states are inaccessible under normal operation.

5.2 Amplification in Sequential Circuits

An important consequence of the feedback theorem just presented is the need for the presence of some sort of amplifier in every feedback loop.

Assume that the logical variables are represented in our circuits by voltages.

(The argument would run along parallel lines if some other physical parameter such as current or pressure were used instead.) Then there are nonoverlapping voltage ranges to represent logical 0- or 1-signals; for example, in certain portions of the circuit $e < 10$ might represent a 0, and $e > 20$ might represent a 1. Different ranges might be used elsewhere in the system.

Let part a of Fig. 5.3 represent a circuit realization of the type considered in Theorem 5.1, and assume that none of the state variables are redundant. Part b then represents the part of the circuit involving the y_k-state branch when the input variables and other state variables are such that $Y_k = y_k$. Such a condition must exist according to Theorem 5.1, and in these circumstances y_k may be stable at 0 or 1. The dotted line through the logic indicates the existence of a signal path logically joining y_k to Y_k. With respect to the logic, this is a static condition that remains as long as the other variables are held constant. If the circuit is now broken at some point B (shown in part b), then we can discuss its behavior in terms of the static voltage-transfer characteristic T, relating the response (e_r in Fig. 5.3c) at the right side of the break to a signal voltage e_i injected at the left side.

Now we observe that in the original, unbroken circuit, when $y_k = 0$, the voltage at point B must be less than 10 and when $y_k = 1$, this voltage must exceed 20. Since, when the loop is closed, e_i is identical to e_r, it follows that there must be points on the characteristic T where $e_i = e_r < 10$ *and* points where $e_i = e_r > 20$. Under the plausible physical assumption that the voltage at B does not grow indefinitely in magnitude, the points referred to must be in stable equilibrium. But in a positive feedback system, a point on the e_r vs. e_i curve can be in stable equilibrium only if the incremental gain $\Delta e_r / \Delta e_i$ is less than unity in some neighborhood of that point.

Putting together the above notions, we obtain in Fig. 5.4a a part of a satisfactory T-characteristic showing e_r plotted against e_i with equilibrium points at v_0 and v_1. In order to complete the curve, it is necessary to fill in the portion joining point p to point q. Regardless of how this is done (Fig. 5.4b depicts an example of a complete characteristic curve), the resulting transfer function will exhibit incremental gain in that, when the input swings between the values corresponding to p and q, the output changes by a larger amount. Thus voltage amplification must occur somewhere in the loop. Furthermore, since the output of the box shown in Fig. 5.2c is fed into the input end of the same box, it follows that the voltage amplification is taking place with the output current equal to the input current. Hence not only voltage but also power is being amplified.

Thus if we are realizing a sequential circuit with logic packages that do not provide voltage and power gain (diode gates, for example, and sometimes even gates constructed with transistors), we must explicitly provide amplifiers in the circuit in such a manner that every genuine (as opposed to pseudo)

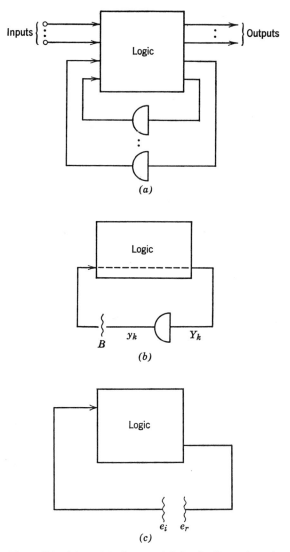

Figure 5.3   (a) Model of sequential circuit. (b) Portion of circuit showing y_k state branch when other variables are such that $Y_k = y_k$. (c) Equivalent circuit of (b) with loop broken.

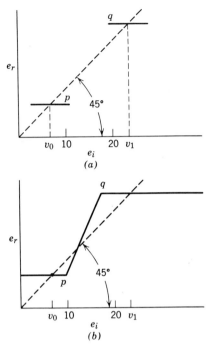

Figure 5.4 (*a*) A portion of a *T*-curve.
(*b*) An example of a valid *T*-curve.

feedback loop has a voltage gain in excess of unity. An obvious and always satisfactory place to insert such amplifiers is in each state branch. However, in the next section we see that it is possible to design circuits requiring fewer amplifiers if we do not insist on placing them in the state branches.

5.3 Minimizing Feedback

Given a logic circuit diagram of a sequential circuit, and assuming that amplifiers must be provided explicitly, the problem of locating the amplifiers in such a manner as to require a minimal number is that of locating a minimal *feedback cut set*, or set of points with at least one member in every loop. It should be borne in mind that pseudo-loops are to be ignored here. Thus the problem of synthesizing circuits requiring a minimum number of amplifiers corresponds to that of synthesizing circuits with minimum feedback index.

Another motive for designing minimum feedback circuits involves the question of verifying that a given circuit is free of faults. This task can be considerably simplified for an asynchronous circuit if we can temporarily interrupt all feedback paths and test the resulting *combinational* circuit. The amount of special gating necessary to accomplish this is, of course, proportional to the feedback index.

First we present a theorem that specifies for any flow table the *minimum* value of the feedback index for any circuit realizing that table.

THEOREM 5.2   *Given any reduced flow table with s_i stable states in the ith input column, any sequential circuit realizing this table, in which stable flow-table states are represented by stable circuit states, must have feedback index $f \geq \lceil \log_2 (\max_i [s_i]) \rceil$.*

PROOF.   Suppose that, for an arbitrary sequential circuit, a cut is made at each of the f members of a minimal feedback cut set and that the input ends of these cuts are treated as additional input terminals. Then if these new inputs as well as the original inputs are assigned fixed values, the *steady-state* signals at all other points in the circuit will be determined, since there will be finite logic circuits, possibly including some delay elements, but free of feedback, connecting the inputs to each point in the circuit. In particular, the vector y specifying the internal state of the circuit is determined. But this is tantamount to saying that when the *original* circuit is in the steady state, the input signals and the signals at the cut-set points determine y. If there are f points in this set, then for any input state there can be *at most* 2^f different y-states since at most 2^f different sets of values may be observed at these points and no more than one y-state can correspond to each f-state when the input is fixed. Hence, for any input state there can be at most 2^f stable circuit states, which is the essence of the theorem.

We now investigate the problem of realizing flow tables with minimum feedback circuits. Consider Fig. 5.3a, which is a general block diagram of a sequential circuit. Suppose there are n state variables and that all 2^n y-states are used in the course of the operation of the circuit. Then, since any of 2^n Y-states may occur at the output end of the logic box, it follows that there cannot be any cut made through the logic box, completely severing the input from the output, which does not involve cutting at least n wires. The argument here parallels that used in the proof of Theorem 5.2 and appears at first to discourage any attempt to find circuits with cut sets having fewer members than the number of state variables (unless one is prepared to create an illusion of success by employing superfluous state variables!).

But now suppose that in any one input column only a fraction of the 2^n y-states correspond to next-state entries. In this case, for each input column, the set of possible next y-states could be coded in terms of m binary variables, where $m < n$. Given x and y, a combinational circuit L_1 could compute, in the compact m-bit code, the next state and transmit this data, on m signal leads, to a second logic circuit L_2. If L_2 is also supplied with x, then it can decode the m-bit signal generating the appropriate Y-signals, which are fed to the inputs to the delay elements.

Figure 5.5 depicts a block-diagram implementation of the above scheme. The part of the figure enclosed in broken lines corresponds to the logic box of Fig. 5.3a. Note now that, if we cut the $m\,q$-wires linking the logic circuits L_1 and L_2, then all feedback loops are interrupted. Thus, if in no input column of the flow matrix are there more than 2^{n-1} different next-state entries, then the resulting circuit will have a feedback index less than the number of state variables.

The cut made to sever all feedback does *not* completely dichotomize the overall logic (the logic box in Fig. 5.3a) in that it does not cut the x leads going to L_2. As indicated at the start of the discussion leading to the development of this scheme, cutting all the way through the logic box would necessarily sever at least n wires. Hence, by using this method, as opposed to a conventional synthesis with the same row assignment, the feedback index is reduced by at most the number of leads necessary to code the inputs states.

As shown in the figure, the circuit outputs, z-signals, may be generated in L_1 or in L_2 since the necessary data is present at the inputs of both blocks.

As an example, consider the function of Table 5.2a. A racefree row assignment for this table is shown in Table 5.2b, in which the row labeled α has been used as an intermediate state in the $4 \rightarrow 5$ transition of the 00 column. There are three stable states in the 00 column, and so, according to Theorem 5.2,

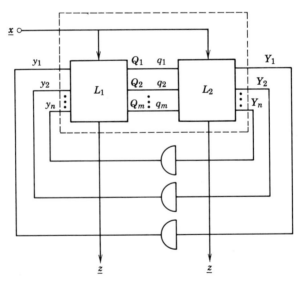

Figure 5.5 Block diagram of minimum feedback circuit.

Table 5.2

	x_1x_2 00	01	11
1	①,0	2,0	①,0
2	3,1	②,0	1,0
3	③,1	2,0	4,1
4	5,1	2,0	④,1
5	⑤,1	2,0	1,0

(a) Flow table.

	x_1x_2 00	01	11	10	y_1	y_2	y_3
1	①,0	2,0	①,0	–	0	0	0
2	3,1	②,0	1,0	–	0	1	0
3	③,1	2,0	4,1	–	0	1	1
4	α,1	2,0	④,1	–	1	1	1
5	⑤,1	2,0	1,0	–	0	0	1
α	5,1	–	–	–	1	0	1
	–	–	–	–	1	0	0
	–	–	–	–	1	1	0

(b) Flow matrix.

	x_1x_2 00	01	11	10	y_1	y_2	y_3
1	00	–	1–	–	0	0	0
2	01	–	1–	–	0	1	0
3	01	–	0–	–	0	1	1
4	11	–	0–	–	1	1	1
5	10	–	1–	–	0	0	1
α	10	–	–	–	1	0	1
	–	–	–	–	1	0	0
	–	–	–	–	1	1	0

(c) Q-matrix.

x_1x_2 00	01	11	10	q_1	q_2
000	010	111	–	0	0
011	010	111	–	0	1
101	010	000	–	1	1
001	010	000	–	1	0

(d) Y-matrix.

x_1x_2 00	01	11	10	q_1	q_2
0	0	1	–	0	0
1	0	1	–	0	1
1	0	0	–	1	1
1	0	0	–	1	0

(e) z-matrix.

a feedback index of at least 2 is necessary to realize this matrix. The relevant parameter for our procedure is the maximum number of *different* next-state entries in any column of the flow matrix and in this case there are four different excitations in the 00 column. Thus two Q-variables are sufficient to code the next-state information in each column; hence our process yields a circuit with the minimum feedback index of 2.

The next step is to code the next-state entries in each column in terms of the variables Q_1 and Q_2. In the 00 column these entries are 1, 3, α, and 5.

Any assignment of the four states of Q_1, Q_2 to these entries is workable, although the complexity of the logic is in general affected by the choice made. In the example, an arbitrary assignment of 00, 01, 11, and 10 has been made to 1, 3, α, and 5, respectively, and these code words have been substituted for the corresponding states in the 00 column of Table 5.2c. Since with input 01 the next state is *always* 2, there is no need to transmit any information to L_2 except the input. Hence the Q_1 and Q_2 values are optional in the 01 column. There are just two next-state entries in the 11 column, so that only one Q-variable is necessary to specify which is meant. Q_1 has been chosen in the example. Table 5.2c is now a specification of the L_1-logic.

The L_2-logic must now be specified by indicating, for each input state, the internal state corresponding to each q-state. (Although $q_i = Q_i$, for each i, and in fact label the same signals in Fig. 5.5, it later proves convenient to distinguish the outputs of L_1 from the corresponding inputs to L_2.) In column 00, we used the Q-states 00, 01, 11, and 10 to designate the next y-states as 000, 011, 101, and 001, respectively, and this accounts for the entries in the first column of Table 5.2d, which specifies $Y_1 Y_2 Y_3$ as a function of $x_1 x_2 q_1 q_2$. The second column entries all indicate state 2 as the next state, and the third column specifies the code for rows 4 or 1, depending on whether q_1 is 0 or 1, respectively.

The output z may be specified in terms of the y's directly from the flow matrix, or when the output is a function of the next state, as is the case here, it may be convenient to specify it in terms of the q-variables. (More is said about output circuits a little later.) The latter choice has been made in this example, so that the z-function, specified in Table 5.2e, may be realized in the L_2-logic box. (In this example z happens to be equal to Y_3.)

Using standard techniques on Table 5.2c and d we obtain the following expressions:

(5.1) $$Q_1 = \bar{y}_2 y_3 + \bar{x}_1 y_1 + x_1 \bar{y}_3,$$

(5.2) $$Q_2 = y_2,$$

(5.3) $$Y_1 = \bar{x}_2 q_1 q_2 + x_1 \bar{q}_1,$$

(5.4) $$Y_2 = \bar{q}_1 q_2 + \bar{x}_1 x_2 + x_1 \bar{q}_1,$$

(5.5) $$Y_3 = z = \bar{x}_2 q_2 + \bar{x}_2 q_1 + x_1 \bar{q}_1.$$

The resulting circuit is shown in Fig. 5.6. It is evident from this diagram that cutting the wires labeled Q_1 and Q_2 would interrupt all feedback.

In this example the amount of logic needed would be reduced by about a third if the same flow matrix were realized in the conventional manner with a two-stage logic circuit having feedback index 3. However, in many cases, the "factoring" process used here yields *simpler* logic than the standard

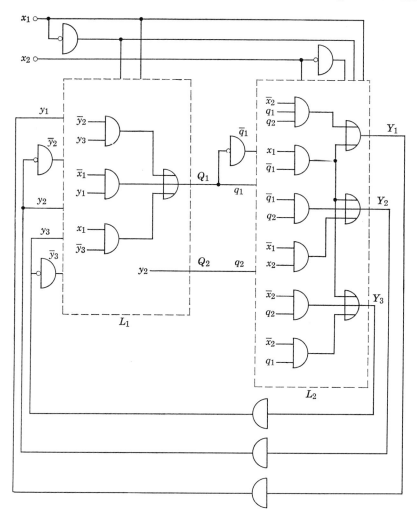

Figure 5.6 Logic circuit corresponding to Table 5.2.

synthesis procedure. Of course, the usual drawbacks of multistage logic, namely delay, and signal deterioration must be reckoned with.

Transient, false Y-signals are obviously possible if multiple input changes are permitted, but they must still be expected even if only one input variable at a time is permitted to change and if L_1 and L_2 are each hazardfree. This is because even if only one x-variable changes, two or more signal changes may occur in rapid succession at the input to L_2. One of them is the x-change, and and the other is a q-change resulting from the x-change at the L_1-input.

Under such conditions, as pointed out in Section 4.2, there may be no possibility of avoiding combinational hazards through logical design alone. Hence there is little point in paying the price for hazardfree Q and Y circuits. Instead, inertial y-delays capable of filtering out isolated short pulses must be used.

The z-signal is generated in the L_1-logic so as to avoid hazards due to multiple input changes to the L_2-logic. If multiple x-changes are permitted, then the flow table should be converted to Moore form (Section 4.3). MOC and UOC functions are treated in Section 5.5.

For the important case of SOC functions, the following procedure always yields circuits that meet the bound of Theorem 5.2:

PROCEDURE 5.1   *Synthesis of Minimum-feedback-index Huffman Circuits for SOC Functions*

1. Code the rows of the flow table using any unicode STT assignment (such as the Liu or Tracey assignments discussed in Subsection 3.3.2). Note that a characteristic of such assignments is that, if r_i appears in the flow matrix as a next-state entry, then in *that* column, the total state in row r_i is *stable*. In other words, the number of different next-state entries in any column is equal to the number of stable states in that column.
2. In the resulting flow matrix, the next-state entries in each column may now be coded in terms of a set of Q-variables whose cardinality is equal to the lower bound on the feedback index as specified in Theorem 5.2 ($\lceil \log_2 S_{max} \rceil$, where S_{max} is the maximum number of stable states in any one column). The L_1-logic may now be specified as in the previous example and logic for the Q-variables designed.
3. Using the inverse of the coding above, the L_2-logic, generating the Y-variables may now be obtained.
4. The z-logic is incorporated in L_1.

Within the above procedure, a great deal of scope exists in terms of the choice of a particular row assignment and the choice of Q-codes, which the designer can use to optimize other factors, such as logic complexity. Although, in general, as pointed out earlier, inertial delays are necessary in every state branch, in particular cases it may be possible that pure delays, or even no delays, are adequate in some branches. This aspect of the problem has not been fully explored. Of course, for particular *physical* circuits, the existing distribution of stray delays may be such as to render some or all of the delay elements unnecessary.

In the next section Procedure 5.1 is specialized to yield minimum feedback circuits that take into account the number of inverters required.

5.4   Minimum-transistor Circuits

Not many years ago semiconductor diodes were widely used in constructing AND and OR gates, and when inversion or amplification was needed, transistors were used. In that technology, since transistors were considerably more costly than diodes, it was very desirable to design circuits requiring relatively few inverters and amplifiers. The subject of this section is a development of the synthesis procedure of Section 5.3 that minimizes not only the number of amplifiers needed but also the number of inverters. Hence if double-rail inputs are available and diode-transitor logic is used, then the number of transistors needed is minimized, and in general at no great cost in diodes.

Technology, however, has swept on past the point where this technique would have been economically significant. Transistor NAND and NOR gates have captured the discrete component field, and in integrated circuit technology it appears at present that diodes are not significantly cheaper than transistors. However, there is always the possibility that further developments in the components art may again make desirable this type of optimization. Furthermore the method is sufficiently simple and elegant to warrant presentation for its intrinsic interest.

The structure of the circuits designed is that of Fig. 5.5, with amplifiers confined to the Q-branches. An amplifier is assumed to consist of two cascaded inverters, each built with one transistor, and the output of the first inverter is assumed to be available. Thus, as shown in Fig. 5.7, both q_i and $\bar{q}_i$ are available as inputs to the L_2 circuit. In addition, it is expected that the x-inputs are double-railed (each variable available both complemented and uncomplemented). The delays are assumed to be constructed of passive elements, such as resistors and capacitors. Clearly the L_2 circuit with all of its inputs being double-railed can consist entirely of AND and OR gates (realizable with diodes). The essence of the method is to choose the row assignment and Q-coding so that every Q-variable is a monotone increasing function of the y-variables. It is then possible to avoid inverting the y-variables while restricting the L_1-logic to AND and OR gates. The outputs are generated in the L_2-block to avoid the need for additional inverters. If transient output hazards exist (because of multiple L_2 input changes), then inertial delays must

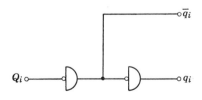

Figure 5.7   Two-transistor inverter-amplifier.

precede the corresponding z-terminals. They can be simple *RC* circuits (Fig. 4.2*b*) if steep leading and trailing edges are not required. Otherwise more complex elements such as the one shown in Fig. 4.4 must be used.

The state assignment used is the Liu assignment described in Subsection 3.3.2. Set lumping is *not* used so that within each column, *each* stable state is assigned a distinct substate.

PROCEDURE 5.2   *Minimum-transistor Synthesis of SOC Functions*

(Multiple input changes are permitted.) Table 5.2*a* is used here as a running example. First, the modified Liu assignment is developed, yielding a flow matrix (with the 10 column and intermediate y-states omitted) as shown in Table 5.3. The variables y_1 and y_2 are assigned on the basis of the 00 column, and y_3 is associated with the 11 column. Since, when the input is 01, there is only one stable state, no y-variables are needed for this column.

We now observe that a basic property of the modified Liu assignment is that, when input I_j is applied, the y-variables associated with I_j remain fixed and all other y-variables assume values determined by these fixed variables. For example, in Table 5.3, if, with the system in 4-11, x_1 and x_2 are turned off, then y_1 and y_2 remain fixed at 10, and y_3 assumes the value that it has in the stable state in the 00 column for which $y_1y_2 = 10$, namely, 0. Thus, for each input state, feedback paths are closed around each member of the associated set of y-variables, but the remaining y-variables are *not* included in any loops. Therefore, we can assign the Q-branches (containing the amplifiers) to the appropriate y-variables depending upon the input, and the L_2 circuit, receiving the q-inputs and the x-inputs, can then generate *all* of the Y-signals.

In our example we assign Q_1 and Q_2 to y_1 and y_2, respectively, in the 00 column, and Q_1 to y_3 in the 11 column. The input state alone is sufficient to generate all Y-values in the 01 column. The resulting Q-equations are

$$Q_1 = \bar{x}_1\bar{x}_2y_1 + x_1x_2y_3,$$
$$Q_2 = \bar{x}_1\bar{x}_2y_2.$$

Table 5.3   Truncated Flow Matrix Showing Liu Assignment for Table 5.2*a*

	00	01	11	y_1	y_2	y_3
1	①,0	2,0	①,0	0	0	0
2	3,1	②,0	1,0	0	1	0
3	③,1	2,0	4,1	0	1	1
4	5,1	2,0	④,1	1	0	1
5	⑤,1	2,0	1,0	1	0	0

Observe that the L_1 circuit simply connects Q-terminals to y-terminals under the control of the input state. Hence the *complements* of y-variables are never needed.

To complete the "locking up" of the y_1- and y_2-variables in input state 00, Y_1 and Y_2 are set to q_1 and q_2, respectively, for that state. Similarly, the y_3 lock-up for input state 11 is completed by setting Y_3 equal to q_1 for $x_1 x_2 = 11$. When the input is 00, Y_3 is determined as a function of y_1 and y_2 as transmitted through q_1 and q_2, respectively. Similarly, when $x_1 x_2 = 11$, the Y_1- and Y_2-values are determined by q_1 which is then equal to y_3. The q-values are not needed to compute the Y's when $x_1 x_2 = 01$. We now have the following Y-expressions:

$$Y_1 = \bar{x}_1 \bar{x}_2 q_1 + x_1 x_2 q_1,$$

$$Y_2 = \bar{x}_1 \bar{x}_2 q_2 + \bar{x}_1 x_2,$$

$$Y_3 = \bar{x}_1 \bar{x}_2 \bar{q}_1 q_2 + x_1 x_2 q_1.$$

By exploiting the fact that the input 10 is prohibited, we can determine whether or not the system input is 00 by observing whether or not $x_2 = 0$. Similarly, the input state is 11 if and only if $x_1 = 1$. The above equations can thus be simplified to yield

$$Q_1 = \bar{x}_2 y_1 + x_1 y_3,$$

$$Q_2 = \bar{x}_2 y_2,$$

$$Y_1 = \bar{x}_2 q_1 + x_1 q_1,$$

$$Y_2 = \bar{x}_1 q_2 + \bar{x}_1 x_2,$$

$$Y_3 = \bar{x}_2 \bar{q}_1 q_2 + x_1 q_1.$$

From Table 5.3, z can be computed as

$$z = \bar{x}_2 y_1 + \bar{x}_2 y_2 + x_1 y_3 = Q_1 + Q_2 = q_1 + q_2.$$

The corresponding circuit is shown in Fig. 5.8. Since the only transistors necessary are the four needed to realize the four inverters and since four transistors are necessary in any event to realize the two amplifiers known to be essential (it is generally accepted that two transistors are required to build a noninverting amplifier having a voltage gain greater than 1 and a current gain at least equal to 1), it follows that this is a minimum-transistor realization. The same process is applicable to any flow table under the specified assumptions.

Although the procedure presented here yields minimum-transistor circuits, it is sometimes possible to find other minimum-transistor realizations of the same functions which require fewer state variables; hence the possibility of

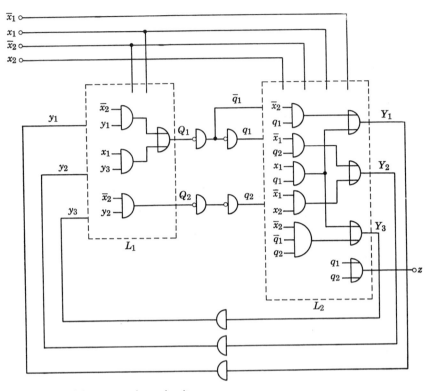

Figure 5.8 Minimum-transistor circuit.

simpler circuitry and fewer delay elements. There exists no procedure guaranteed to yield a minimum-transistor design with the smallest number of y-variables, although there does exist a method that sometimes achieves this end by examining those subsets of the y-variables generated by the above method which satisfy all of the Tracey conditions (see Subsection 3.3.2) for the flow table. Instead of presenting this method, we simply give an example. The reader may verify that four y-variables are necessary to code Table 5.4a in accordance with the synthesis procedure discussed here. However, using the row assignment shown and the Q-coding of Table 5.4b, the following expressions result:

$$Q_1 = I_1 y_1 + I_2 y_2 + I_3 y_1 y_2 + I_4 y_1,$$
$$Q_2 = y_3,$$
$$Y_1 = I_1 q_1 + I_2 \bar{q}_1 + I_3 q_1 + I_3 q_2 + I_4 q_1,$$
$$Y_2 = I_2 q_1 + I_3 q_1 + I_3 q_2 + I_4,$$
$$Y_3 = I_1 q_1 + I_3 q_2.$$

Table 5.4a Flow Table with Row Assignment Leading
to Minimum-Transistor Circuit

	I_1	I_2	I_3	I_4	y_1	y_2	y_3
1	①,0	4,0	①,0	2,0	0	0	0
2	1,0	②,0	1,0	②,0	0	1	0
3	③,1	4,0	5,0	6,0	1	0	1
4	3,1	④,0	1,0	6,0	1	0	0
5	3,1	2,0	⑤,0	6,0	1	1	1
6	3,1	2,0	⑥,1	⑥,0	1	1	0

Table 5.4b Coding for $Q_1 Q_2$

	I_1	I_2	I_3	I_4	y_1	y_2	y_3
1	0–	0–	00	0–	0	0	0
	–	–	–	–	0	0	1
	–	1–	–	–	0	1	1
2	0–	1–	00	0–	0	1	0
6	1–	1–	10	1–	1	1	0
5	1–	1–	–1	1–	1	1	1
3	1–	0–	–1	1–	1	0	1
4	1–	0–	00	1–	1	0	0

Since none of the y-variables appear in complemented form, these equations may be used to design L_1 and L_2 circuits without requiring any inverters other than those constituting the two necessary amplifiers.

Procedure 5.2 has the following advantages:

1. The number of transistors and the feedback index are minimized.
2. The price paid in terms of the overall amount of logic needed is not large.
3. The design procedure is simple.
4. Circuit operation is relatively fast, since an STT assignment is used.

However, in practice, these advantages may not be easy to realize (assuming, of course, that the first is relevant to the technology being used) because four stages of logic are usually required. This requirement not only has a detrimental effect on item 4 above, but it may be difficult to drive the logic with one stage of amplification.

The method is applicable only to SOC functions and it is not known at this time how to design minimum-transistor circuits with less restricted output sequences. However, in the next section, the synthesis of minimum-*feedback* circuits for such functions is described.

5.5   Minimum-feedback Synthesis of MOC Functions and UOC Functions

If multiple input changes are permitted, then the flow table must first be converted to Moore form as discussed in Section 4.3. First, MOC functions are considered. It is shown that the bound of Theorem 5.2 can be met.

The basic idea is to select two sets of y-variables: one, the y_S-variables, to designate the next stable state, and the other, the y_T-variables, to designate the transient states. The y_S-variables are controlled very much as the y-variables of Procedure 5.2 are, feedback being required; whereas the y_T-variables are realized by cascaded strings of delays not involved in any feedback loops. It is useful now to generalize the definition of *destination set*, a term introduced in Section 3.2 with reference to SOC functions. Applied to MOC functions, let the destination set D_{qi} be the set of internal states p such that if the system is in state p and input I_i is applied the *ultimate* stable state reached will be q. (D_{qi} is sometimes said to be a destination set *under* I_i.) In Table 5.5, which is used as an example in the following discussion, $D_{62} = \{1, 5, 6, 8\}$. We now present the procedure.

PROCEDURE 5.3   *Minimum-feedback Synthesis of MOC Functions*

1. As in Procedure 5.2, assign for each column I_i a set of y_S-variables with a unique coding for each destination set under I_i. In the example, y_{S1} distinguishes those states that input I_1 takes ultimately to 1 from those that it takes to 8. Similarly, y_{S2} and y_{S3} distinguish three destination sets under I_2, and y_{S4} and y_{S5} are used to code the destination sets of the I_3 column.
2. Within some column, let p_1 be a sequence of states of maximum length leading to stable state s_s. If there are k states in this "path," then assign k y_T-variables, to be referred to as the p_1-variables. Abbreviating a string of i x's as x^i, let the values of the p_1-variables be $0^{k-i}1^i$ for those states of p_1 at distance i from s_s. (In our example, in column I_1 let s_s be 1, and p_1 be $4 \rightarrow 3 \rightarrow 2 \rightarrow 1$. Then $k = 3$, and the p_1-variables are y_{T1}, y_{T2}, and y_{T3}.)

Table 5.5   Synthesis of MOC Function

	I_1	I_2	I_3	I_1 y_{S1}	I_2 y_{S2}	y_{S3}	I_3 y_{S4}	y_{S5}	I_1 y_{T1}	y_{T2}	y_{T3}	y_{T4}	y_{T5}	I_2 y_{T6}	y_{T7}	y_{T8}
1	①, 00	5 , 00	①, 00	0	0	0	0	0	0	0	0	0	0	1	1	0
2	1 , 10	3 , 00	②, 01	0	0	1	0	1	0	0	1	0	0	0	0	1
3	2 , 00	③, 01	7 , 00	0	0	1	1	1	0	1	1	0	0	0	0	0
4	3 , 11	④, 10	2 , 01	0	1	0	0	1	1	1	1	0	0	0	0	0
5	2 , 01	6 , 01	⑤, 11	0	0	0	1	0	0	1	1	0	1	0	1	0
6	5 , 11	⑥, 11	7 , 00	0	0	0	1	1	1	1	1	1	1	0	0	0
7	8 , 00	4 , 00	⑦, 00	1	1	0	1	1	0	0	1	0	0	0	0	1
8	⑧, 01	6 , 10	7 , 00	1	0	0	1	1	0	0	0	0	0	0	0	1

Suppose some other path p_{11} merges with p_1 at $s_m \neq s_s$. (In our example, such a path is $6 \rightarrow 5 \rightarrow 2 \rightarrow 1$, merging with p_1 at 2.) Then the p_1-variables are assigned to the members of p_{11} the same values they have at p_1-states equidistant from s_m. In order to distinguish between the corresponding p_1- and p_{11}-states, a new set of y_T-variables is introduced with cardinality t equal to the number of members of p_{11} above s_m. The p_{11}-variables are assigned values $0^{t-j}1^j$ at those states of $p_{11}\, j$ steps above s_m, and 0^t at all points on p_1. (In the example, $p_{11} = y_{T4}y_{T5}$.)

If other paths merge at s_m, then an additional set of y_T-variables is added for each of them and assigned the all-zero value for the states in all other paths. If other paths merge with p_{11} at points above s_m, then they are treated analogously to the way p_{11} is treated with respect to p_1. Other paths intersecting p_1 only at s_s are treated separately, with new y_T-variables being introduced. The variables associated with p_1 and its branches are set to 0 for all states on these new paths, and conversely, the new variables are set to 0 for all states on p_1 and its branches.

Within a column, since the q-states distinguish among the various destination sets, the same y_T-variables may be used, in different combinations if necessary, for paths in different destination sets. (In the example, y_{T3} is also used for the path $7 \rightarrow 8$ in I_1.) It is generally necessary to use different y_T-variables for each input. (In the example, $y_{T6}y_{T7}y_{T8}$ are used for I_2, and since no output changes occur within any destination set under I_3, no y_T-variables are needed for that input.)

3. As in Procedure 5.2, Q-variables are associate with the y_S-variables, and the Y_S- and Q-functions computed for minimum feedback. Thus, in the example, two Q-variables are necessary and they are used to transmit the appropriate y_S-variables in each column, namely, y_{S1} in I_1, y_{S2} and y_{S3} in I_2, and y_{S4} and y_{S5} in I_3. This gives us the expressions

$$Q_1 = I_1 y_{S1} + I_2 y_{S2} + I_3 y_{S4},$$
$$Q_2 = I_2 y_{S3} + I_3 y_{S5}.$$

The feedback loops locking up the stable variables in each column are then completed, and the y_S-variables in columns in which they are *not* locked up are assigned next-state values as functions of the stable variables (as transmitted by the q's). This yields

$$Y_{S1} = I_1 q_1 + I_3 q_1 q_2,$$
$$Y_{S2} = I_2 q_1 + I_3 q_1 q_2,$$
$$Y_{S3} = I_2 q_2 + I_3 \bar{q}_1 q_2,$$
$$Y_{S4} = I_1 q_1 + I_2 \bar{q}_1 + I_3 q_1,$$
$$Y_{S5} = I_1 q_1 + I_2 + I_3 q_2.$$

4. The Y_T-functions are now computed, and it can be seen that each Y_{Ti} is independent of all y_{Tj}, where $j \geq 1$, so that there is no feedback involving the y_T-variables. Within the column that generated it, Y_{Ti} is a function of the q-variables (which transmit the stable y_S's), and possibly of $y_{T(i-1)}$. In other columns it is a function only of the q's. Thus for Table 5.5 we obtain

$$Y_{T1} = I_2 \bar{q}_2,$$
$$Y_{T2} = I_1 y_{T1} + I_2 + I_3 q_1 \bar{q}_2,$$
$$Y_{T3} = I_1 y_{T2} + I_2 + I_3 q_1 + I_3 q_2,$$
$$Y_{T4} = I_2 \bar{q}_1 \bar{q}_2,$$
$$Y_{T5} = I_1 y_{T4} + I_2 \bar{q}_1 \bar{q}_1 + I_3 q_1 \bar{q}_2,$$
$$Y_{T6} = I_1 \bar{q}_1 + I_3 \bar{q}_1 \bar{q}_2,$$
$$Y_{T7} = I_1 \bar{q}_1 + I_2 y_{T6} + I_3 \bar{q}_2,$$
$$Y_{T8} = I_1 q_1 + I_3 q_2.$$

Only the q-terms appear in complemented form in the above equations, and this is true in general for this method.
5. The outputs must be generated in terms of the input and the corresponding y_S- and y_T-variables. The q-variables cannot be used since their use could introduce transient false signals. In the example, we obtain

$$Z_1 = I_1 y_{T1} + I_1 \bar{y}_{S1} \bar{y}_{T2} y_{T3} + I_2 \bar{y}_{S3} \bar{y}_{T7} \bar{y}_{T8} + I_2 \bar{y}_{S2} \bar{y}_{S3} y_{T8} + I_3 y_{S4} \bar{y}_{S5},$$
$$Z_2 = I_1 y_{T1} + I_1 y_{T5} + I_1 y_{S1} \bar{y}_{T3} + I_2 \bar{y}_{T6} y_{T7} + I_2 \bar{y}_{S2} \bar{y}_{T7} \bar{y}_{T8} + I_3 \bar{y}_{S4} y_{S5},$$
$$+ I_3 y_{S4} \bar{y}_{S5}.$$

Note that the Z-expressions may involve complements of y_S- and y_T-variables.

In the above procedure, no particular effort is made to reduce the number of state variables used, and it is quite likely that, even for the given example, solutions with fewer y_T's exist. The feedback index of the resulting circuit is $\max_i \lceil \log_2 s_i \rceil$ as defined in connection with Theorem 5.2.

Inertial delays are necessary for both the y_S- and y_T-variables, since multiple input changes (x's and q's) are possible at the inputs to the circuits generating the Y_S's and the Y_T's. As in the case discussed in Section 5.4, RC delays are adequate for the y_S's. However, since changing y_T-signals drive Y_T circuits and Z circuits, it is desirable to use as inertial delays devices producing better waveforms. In principle at least, the device shown in Fig. 4.4 seems to be satisfactory. It is doubtful, however, that one one could cascade many such devices without intervening amplifiers and obtain satisfactory results.

We now discuss the synthesis of minimal-feedback circuits for UOC functions. Such functions are characterized by the fact that, under certain conditions, the output cycles periodically through a sequence of states as long as the input remains fixed. (See, for example, Table 1.7b and c.) This cycling implies that the internal state is also varying.

Suppose a system is cycling through the sequence of states $s_1, s_2, \ldots, s_n$ and that the y-variables that change during the process are $y_1, y_2, \ldots, y_m$. If one of the Y_i-functions ($1 \leq i \leq m$) were independent of all of the changing y's, then y_i would soon assume a constant value, contradicting the statement that it never settled down. Hence, each of the y_i ($1 \leq i \leq m$) must be involved in a feedback loop with at least one member of the set (possibly itself). The basis for our synthesis procedure is a simple class of circuits with feedback index 1 for realizing cycles of any period without critical races.

Consider first the case in which the period is even, namely, $n = 2k$. The circuit of Fig. 5.9, consisting of k delay elements connected in cascade with an inverter, if started off in an appropriate initial state (such as all y's $= 0$), will cycle periodically through $2k$ states with one variable changing at a time. For example, if $k = 3$, the sequence is 000, 100, 110, 111, 011, 001, 000, ...

For odd length cycles, the simplest procedure that preserves uniformity is to use n delays and assign a *pair* of complementary y-states to each system state. Thus, for $n = 3$, the assignment to s_1, s_2, and s_3 may be (000, 111), (100, 011), and (110, 001), respectively.

The loop must contain an amplifier to prevent the signal from fading away. Those delays in the chain that receive inputs only from the preceding delay can be realized by pure-delay elements. As becomes evident shortly, at least one member of the chain receives inputs from q-variables, which may be incorrect for short intervals. Some sort of inertial delay is needed here. The type shown in Fig. 4.4 is not satisfactory, since there is no way (short of bounding delay elements above) of ensuring that intervals between input changes to this device will be spaced sufficiently far apart during cycles. An RC delay might be satisfactory, but, as mentioned earlier, the topic of inertial delay needs further study.

The method to be presented below is an extension of Procedure 5.3 in

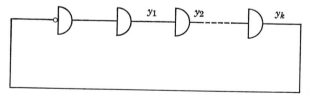

Figure 5.9 Realization of cycle of period $2k$.

which y_c-variables are added to take care of cycles. They are switched into position under the control of input variables and y_S-variables, with the feedback path being completed through a Q-variable.

For the following discussion, it is useful to extend further the definition of a *destination set under input* I_k, so that two states are said to be in the same *destination set under* I_i if starting in either state and holding the input at I_i takes the system to the same stable state *or* to the same set of cycling states. Let D_i be the number of destination sets of column I_i and let

$$K_i = \begin{cases} \lceil \log D_i \rceil, & \text{if there are no cycles in } I_i, \\ 1 + \lceil \log D_i \rceil, & \text{if there is a cycle in } I_i. \end{cases}$$

Then the feedback index of the circuits to be synthesized is $f = \max_i [K_i]$. This is probably the minimum achievable for f, but it has not been proven to be so.

PROCEDURE 5.4   *Synthesis of Minimal-feedback Circuits for UOC Functions*

1. For each input, select a set of y_S-variables to partition the states into destination sets under that input as in Procedure 5.3. (For the function of Table 5.6, which is used here as a running example, column I_1 has a transient terminating in stable state 1 and another transient terminating in 6, which is part of a cycle also involving 7 and 8. Thus, y_{S1} distinguishes between the destination sets $\{1, 2, 3\}$ and $\{4, 5, 6, 7, 8\}$.)
2. Each destination set with a stable state is treated as in Procedure 5.3. In addition, all states in cycles are treated as stable states for the purpose of assigning y_T-variables to states in paths that terminate in cycles. (In the example, y_{T1} and y_{T2} are used as in the earlier procedure to take care of the path $3 \rightarrow 2 \rightarrow 1$ in I_1. In addition, they are assigned to define the path $4 \rightarrow 5 \rightarrow 6$, which ends in a cycle.)
3. If a destination set includes a cycle of period n, then:

    3.1. If n is even ($n = 2k$), assign k y_C-variables to the cycle. Numbering the states around the cycle from some arbitrary starting point, assign the y_C-state $1^{i-1}0^{k+1-i}$ to the ith state for $1 \le i \le k$, and $0^{i-k-1}1^{2k+1-i}$ to the ith state for $k + 1 \le i \le 2k$.

    3.2. If n is odd, then assign n y_C-variables to the cycles, with y_C-state $1^{i-1}0^{n+1-i}$ and its complement being assigned to the ith state of the cycle. (In the example, note the assignment of pairs of states of $y_{C1}y_{C2}y_{C3}$ to the cycle involving 6, 7, and 8 in I_1.)

    Variables used as y_C's or as y_T's in one destination set may be used again in either capacity for other destination sets in the same column.
4. The number of Q-variables used in column I_i is K_i. For columns without cycles these are used as in Procedure 5.3 to transmit y_S-values. For

Table 5.6 Synthesis of UOC Function

	I_1	I_2	I_3	y_{S1}	y_{S2}	y_{S3}	y_{S4}	y_{T1}	y_{T2}	y_{C1}	y_{C2}	y_{C3}
1	①,00	①,00	5,00	0	0	0	0	0	0	0	0	0
2	1,01	4,00	②,00	0	1	1	1	0	1	0	0	0
3	2,11	③,00	5,00	0	0	1	0	1	1	0	0	0
4	5,11	④,00	5,00	1	1	1	0	1	1	0	0	0
5	6,10	3,00	⑤,00	1	0	1	0	0	1	0	0	0
6	7,00	⑥,00	2,00	1	1	0	1	0	0	{0 / 1}	{0 / 1}	{0 / 1}
7	8,01	6,00	2,00	1	1	0	1	0	0	{1 / 0}	{0 / 1}	{0 / 1}
8	6,11	6,00	2,00	1	1	0	1	0	0	{1 / 0}	{1 / 0}	{0 / 1}

columns with one or more cycles, one of the Q's is used to close the feedback loop composed of y_C-delays; hence, in columns with several loops, one of the Q's is dependent on y_C's and y_S's. (In the example,

$$Q_1 = I_1 y_{S1} + I_2 y_{S2} + I_3 y_{S4},$$
$$Q_2 = I_1 y_{C3} + I_2 y_{S3}.)$$

5. The expressions for Y_S's, Y_T's, and Z's are computed as before. Under the input for which it is chosen and in a destination set in which it is acting as a y_C-variable (as determined by the stable y_S's), $Y_{Ci} = \bar{q}_t$ if i is the lowest index in this cycle, where q_t is transmitting the value of highest indexed y_{Cj} in the cycle, or else $Y_{Ci} = y_{C(i-1)}$.

In the example, since the y_{S3} and y_{T2} columns are identical, we can use a single variable y_{S3T2} for both, with the Y_{S3T2}-expression computed as for Y_{T2}. The expressions are

$$Z_1 = I_1 y_{T1} + I_1 y_{S1} y_{S3T2} + I_1 y_{C2} \bar{y}_{C3} + I_1 \bar{y}_{C2} y_{C3},$$
$$Z_2 = I_1 \bar{y}_{S1} y_{S3T2} + I_1 y_{T1} + I_1 y_{C1} \bar{y}_{C3} + I_1 \bar{y}_{C1} y_{C3},$$
$$Y_{S1} = I_1 q_1 + I_2 q_1 + I_3 \bar{q}_1,$$
$$Y_{S2} = I_1 q_1 + I_2 q_1 + I_3 q_1,$$
$$Y_{S4} = I_1 q_1 + I_2 q_1 \bar{q}_2 + I_3 q_1,$$
$$Y_{T1} = I_2 q_2,$$
$$Y_{S3T2} = I_1 y_{T1} + I_2 q_2 + I_3,$$
$$Y_{C1} = I_1 \bar{q}_2,$$
$$Y_{C2} = I_1 y_{C1},$$
$$Y_{C3} = I_1 y_{C2}.$$

Note that the y_{S3}-literal in the Q_2-expression must be replaced by y_{S3T2}.

As noted after Procedure 5.3, we have not attempted to indicate above how to minimize the number of y-variables. It is quite possible, for instance, to use the same variables for different purposes in different columns (as in our example.) Such multiple usage can lead to the appearance of pseudo-loops in the circuit, but this does not cause any difficulty.

5.6 A Unity Feedback Solution

In the preceding section, an implicit analogy is made between a cycle and a stable state. Suppose now that we explore this analogy by removing the restriction imposed in Theorem 5.2 that stable flow-table states be represented by stable circuit states and allowing a stable state to be represented by a set of unstable circuit states. A rather surprising result of this deletion is a method for realizing *any* sequential function with a circuit having a feedback index of 1! Unfortunately, this method requires the use of inertial-delay elements having threshold properties that may be realizable only by circuits involving amplifiers and feedback.

Consider the circuit of Fig. 5.10, (the logic elements are all modulo 2 adders), assuming as a first approximation that there are no stray delays. Observe that every y is transmitted through two different paths to each adder controlling a Y to the right of it. One connection is direct, and the other is through the final adder and the feedback path. Since modulo 2 addition of any variable with itself yields zero, no Y is dependent on any y to the left of it. Because of the feedback, each Y_i is dependent on all the y's (including y_i) to the right of it so that we have for $1 \leq i \leq k$

$$Y_i = \sum_{j=i}^{k} y_j \qquad \text{(the addition being modulo-2).}$$

Hence, if an *even* number of y's to the right of y_i are equal to 1, then $Y_i = y_i$, and so y_i is stable in either state. On the other hand, if an *odd* number of y's to the right of y_i are equal to 1, then $Y_i = y_i \oplus 1$, so that y_i is unstable.

Suppose now that the rightmost y with value 1 is y_j, that is $y_j = 1$ and $y_i = 0$ for $j < i \leq k$. Then all the y's from y_j to the right will be stable (in state 100– –0), y_{j-1} will be unstable, y_{j-2} will be stable when y_{j-1} is equal to 1 and unstable when y_{j-1} equals 0, etc. Thus, the outputs of all the delays from the jth through the kth remain fixed at 100—0, while the signals to the left of the jth are varying in some manner depending upon the relative magnitudes of the delay elements. Note that the system has two stable states, one with *all* y's equal to 0, and the other with all but y_1 equal to 0.

As an example, consider the case in which $k = 3$. Figure 5.11 is a directed graph with an arc from state p to state q if state q is a possible successor of state p. There will be more than one successor to a state if several y's are

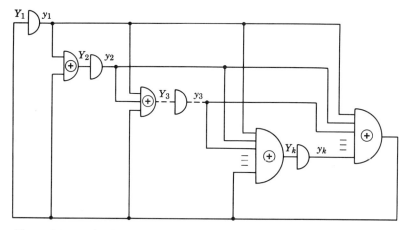

Figure 5.10 Unity feedback circuit with $k + 1$ states.

unstable in that state, so that there is a race condition. Note that there are four sets of states (called *final sets* by Muller) such that, if the system is in a state belonging to one of these sets, its next state must also be in that set. For the class of circuits under discussion, the final sets may be classified according to the states of their fixed variables (using a c to designate a changing variable), as 000, 100, c10, cc1. A more compact way is to specify the number of variables fixed at the value 0 (note that these are always the rightmost variables), namely, 3, 2, 1, and 0, respectively, in the example. In general, the final sets are k, $k - 1$, ..., 1, 0. Note that the variable immediately to the left of the leftmost fixed 0 is fixed at 1, so that this description of the final sets makes it clear that that they are mutually disjoint. Each final set is used to represent a stable state of the given flow table.

The synthesis procedure is indicated by applying it to the SOC flow table of Table 5.7. Extensions along the lines of the preceding section are straightforward.

As in the earlier procedures, a set of y-variables is associated with each

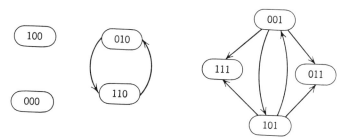

Figure 5.11 Final sets when $k = 3$.

Table 5.7   Example for Unity Feedback Synthesis

	x_1x_2 00	01	11	y_1	y_2	y_3	y_4
1	①,0	2,0	①,0	0	0	0	0
2	3,1	②,0	1,0	1	0	0	0
3	③,1	2,0	4,1	1	0	C	1
4	5,1	2,0	④,1	C	1	C	1
5	⑤,1	2,0	⑤,0	C	1	1	0

column. A final set of states of these variables is associated with each next-state entry. In Table 5.7 y_1 and y_2 are assigned to the 00 column, and the final sets 00, 10, and $C1$ (in terms of these variables) are assigned to the rows with next-state entries of 1, 3, and 5, respectively. No y-variables are needed for column 01, and y_3 and y_4 are assigned to the 11 column.

When input I_i is on, the y-variables associated with I_i are connected up as in Fig. 5.10, with the feedback being switched through the *single* Q-variable. The other y-variables are assigned values as functions of the I_i-variables, and the output is generated as a function of the input and the y's. The C's are treated as don't cares. In the example, the resulting expressions are

$$Z = \bar{x}_2 y_1 + \bar{x}_2 y_2 + x_1 y_4,$$

$$Q = \bar{x}_2(y_1 \oplus y_2) + x_1(y_3 \oplus y_4),$$

$$Y_1 = \bar{x}_2 q + \bar{x}_1 x_2,$$

$$Y_2 = \bar{x}_2(y_1 \oplus q) + x_1 y_4 + x_1 y_3,$$

$$Y_3 = \bar{x}_2 y_2 + x_1 q,$$

$$Y_4 = \bar{x}_1 y_1 \bar{y}_2 + x(y_3 \oplus q).$$

Note that Y_2 is a function of y_3, and Y_3 is a function of y_2, but since the input is never such that both relationships are true simultaneously, this is a pseudo-loop. All genuine feedback is through the Q-variable.

Now assume that stray delays exist in the circuit of Fig. 5.10 so that the effect of a change in y_i reaches Y_j, where $j > i$ and y_j is a stable variable, through one path before the second path transmits the change. Then during the interval between the arrivals, Y_j changes value improperly. This error will appear at the y_j-terminal unless the y_j-delay has inertial properties. Suppose then that the delay elements in the circuit are all inertial with minimum values D_m and that the maximum error interval as depicted above is $\mathscr{E}$ (a function of stray-delay values). Then each time a y to the left of y_j changes value, there may be an error signal at the input y_j of duration no greater than $\mathscr{E}$. Since there are at most $k - 1$ y-variables to the left of y_j (this value occurs when y_j is the rightmost variable, $j = k$) and since no inertial delay can change more than once during any interval of duration D_m, it follows that the maximum overall time during which Y_j is false within any interval of length D_m is $(k-1)\mathscr{e}$. Thus D_m may be chosen to be large enough so that the cumulative time during which the input to any delay is false is proportionately as small as desired. However, the individual false pulses may appear at any time and no control is possible over the spacing. Hence the type of delay of Fig. 4.4 cannot be used.

In the circuit of Fig. 5.10 a y-signal that is changing has a direct effect on its own excitation and on other Y-signals during the transition. (This is *not* true of the class of circuits typified by Fig. 5.8, for example.) Hence it is important that the transient interval during which the signal is ambiguous be small compared with the response times of the delays in the circuit. In this respect RC delays are unsatisfactory. What is needed is some sort of threshold device (see Section 4.1) that changes rapidly after a decision is made. Amplification and feedback seem to be associated with circuits that behave this way, although the problem has not been formulated with sufficient precision to allow a definitive answer. Of course, if feedback is necessary around each delay element, then the whole point of this approach would appear to be nullified. Nevertheless, one has the feeling that there may be some useful role for the ingenious circuit of Fig. 5.10.

SOURCES

Theorem 5.1 is an extension of a theorem proved by Unger [UN-1, UN-2] and the result discussed in Section 5.2 was also included in the latter referenc e Note that the need for gain around closed loops was recognized earlier by Huffman [HUF-2]. An example of a circuit with feedback index less than the number of state variables was first presented by Unger [UN-2]. Theorem 5.2 is due to Eichelberger [EI-1], and the general Q-variable synthesis method was the work of Huffman [HUF-4]. The idea of combining this method with an STT row assignment to achieve circuits meeting the bound of Theorem 5.2, the minimal-transistor-design method, the unity feedback circuit, and the basis for the approach to the minimum-feedback synthesis of functions with bounded output sequences (Section 5.5) are all due to Friedman [FRM-1, FRM-2]. The method referred to in the latter part of Section 5.4 which sometimes reduces the number of state variables required by Friedman's minimum-transistor-design method is due to Friedes [FRD-1]. Interesting work has been done with respect to the design of synchronous or pulsed circuits with minimal feedback. The problem seems quite different from the asynchronous case, and here Friedman has shown that unity feedback is definitely achievable [FRM-1, FRM-3].

PROBLEMS

*5.1 Synthesize an SR-FF with AND-OR-INVERTER logic, assuming that the AND and OR gates attenuate signals. Use a minimum number of inverters.

‡5.2 Synthesize a τ-FF that changes its output *after* the change pulse goes off; that is, it is triggered by the *trailing* edge of the input pulse. Assume a *single*-rail input and try to minimize the number of transistors used.

5.3 Find Y- and Q-expressions for a minimum-transistor realization of the flow table of Problem 3.15.

5.4 Find Y- and Q-expressions for a minimum-transistor realization of the flow table of Problem 3.12.

5.5 Find a minimum feedback realization of the function described by Table P5.5.

Table P5.5

	00	x_1x_2 01	11
1	①, 0	2 , 1	①, 0
2	②, 0	3 , 0	4 , 1
3	2 , 0	③, 1	1 , 0
4	④, 1	3 , 0	④, 1

CHAPTER 6

Other Modes of Operation

In Chapter 1 several classes of sequential circuits are discussed, and here we survey them as well as some others in greater detail. They differ with regard to the circumstances under which input changes are permitted, and in terms of internal structure. Objectives vary from maximizing average speed to minimizing design problems.

6.1 Circuits that Generate Completion Signals

These circuits, referred to in Section 1.6 as Muller circuits (also called *speed-independent* circuits), send back signals to the input source indicating when they are ready to accept new input states. In cases in which the time required to process an input is subject to large variations, dependent perhaps on the particular input or on the internal state, the potential increase in the average input rate is substantial.

Such an approach is possible only when the input source is under the control of the system or when a system-controlled buffer may be placed between the input source and the circuit. When the circuit must respond immediately to uncontrollable input changes, as is the case in many real-time applications, Muller circuits are not feasible. Perhaps their most natural environment would be in a digital computer, which is essentially a closed system after its memory has been loaded with the program and data for a given problem. It is also possible to use the completion-signal philosophy in parts of a system or to govern communications among the major blocks of a system, while using other approaches within certain of its subsystems.

As is made evident later, the same restriction on stray-delay locations that is imposed in Section 4.4 is necessary here, namely, that the delays in the lines be small compared with those in the gate outputs. However, whereas in all our earlier discussions we assume that there are known upper bounds on all stray-delay values (an obvious necessity in computing the minimum allowable spacing between input changes), in this section that assumption is not needed, and furthermore, delay elements are not used. We assume here that stray delays may be pure *or* inertial, although some workers in this field postulate inertial delays.

The design of combinational circuits is discussed first, and then the method is extended to include SOC sequential circuits. The final subsection deals with the problem of constructing networks of such systems. It should be noted at the outset that the methods to be presented in this section reflect only one of many approaches and that our treatment of this topic is much less comprehensive than that accorded to the subjects of the preceding chapters.

6.1.1   Combinational Circuits with Completion Signals

Probably the first case in which the completion-signal concept found application was that of the parallel binary adder, an iterative combinational circuit. It was realized that, depending on the numbers being added, the time required for the outputs to respond varies over a very wide range. When a carry bit must "ripple" through the entire circuit, the delay is a maximum. In cases in which there is no carry, the delay may be less than the maximum by a factor of about n for an n-bit adder. If the input numbers are randomly chosen, the *average* time required varies approximately as $\log_2 (5n/4)$(a formula given by Hendrickson [HE-1]). However, if the adder does not return some signal indicating when it has completed each computation, then it is necessary to allow the maximum time in every case.

In order to avoid this considerable waste of time, adders have been developed that generate completion signals so that they can process data at their average rate instead of at a rate limited by the worst-case situation. Such circuits may require as many as twice the number of components as a simple adder and are actually slower in operation; nevertheless, in an appropriate environment, they offer significant overall gains in efficiency. The technique employed in such adders [GIL-1] has been generalized to encompass a broad class of iterative circuits [WAI-1], but instead of discussing this technique, we present a method applicable to the realization of *any* combinational function. The two techniques are, however, related to some extent. Until further notice, it is understood that stray delays are confined entirely to gate outputs, line delays being zero.

We began by describing a condition that constitutes the principal obstacle to the successful design of Muller circuits, namely, the *delay hazard*. Consider Fig. 6.1, which depicts a two-stage AND-to-OR circuit realizing the function $\bar{A}\bar{B}\bar{C} + AB + AC$ without logic hazards (see Table 6.1a for a K-map of the function showing the product terms used). The input sequence 011, 111, 101 should produce the output sequence 0, 1, 1. Suppose that we observe both

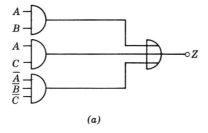

(a)

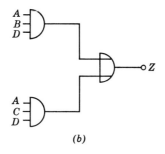

(b)

Figure 6.1 (a) A circuit with a 0101 delay hazard for input changes 011 → 111 → 101. (b) A circuit with a 01010 delay hazard for input changes 0111 → 1111 → 1110.

the input terminals (A, B, and C), and the output Z in order to determine when the effects of the first input change have ended and the circuit is ready for the second change. One might think that, after Z has changed from 0 to 1 in response to the change in ABC from 011 to 111 (the first change), the circuit is ready for the second change. But if this assumption is acted upon, the result could be a transient error. The initial input change excites both the AB- and the AC-AND gates. Suppose there is a relatively large delay associated with the AC gate. Then the AB gate would go on first and the OR gate might then respond to this signal *before* the AC gate goes on. If we then permit the second input change (to 101), the result might be to turn off the AB gate and the OR gate (hence Z) while the AC gate is still struggling to emit a 1-signal. When this gate finally does go on, Z again switches to 1. Hence the result is a Z-sequence of 0101 instead of 011. (Note that this process is quite similar to that described in Section 4.2 for generating a dynamic-hazard transient after a simultaneous change of several input variables.)

In general, we define a *delay hazard* as a condition in a circuit free of logic hazards such that a sequence of two consecutive input changes $I_1 \rightarrow I_2 \rightarrow I_3$

Table 6.1*a*

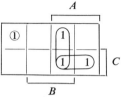

(*a*) Function realized by
Fig. 6.1*a*.

Table 6.1*b*

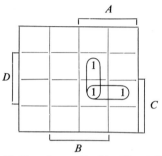

(*b*) Function realized by Fig. 6.1*b*.

can produce either of the following output sequences

1. $f(I_1), f(I_2), \overline{f(I_2)}, f(I_3)$, where $f(I_2) = f(I_3)$
2. $f(I_1), f(I_2), f(I_3), f(I_2), f(I_3)$, where $f(I_2) \neq f(I_3)$.

Figure 6.1*a* and Table 6.1*a* illustrate the first possibility, and Fig. 6.1*b* and Table 6.1*b* illustrate the second (assuming pure stray delays).

If bounds on the stray-delay values are known, then we can wait for a sufficient period after each input change to permit the effects of that change to reach *all* gate outputs before initiating the next change. If such bounds are not known or if we are unwilling to "assume the worst" in each case, then safe operation may require monitoring gates interior to the circuit, as well as the input and output signals. Note, however, that the delay-hazard trouble results from the fact that several of the OR-gate inputs go on during the course of the transitions. Once one of them goes on it is impossible to determine from the output signal whether or not another one is on. Hence we cannot tell if the circuit has *fully* absorbed the input change. If the circuit is such that only *one* input to the output OR gate is energized during a given transition, then we are able to tell from the output when the circuit has reached a stable state after an input change. A dual situation exists with respect to OR-to-AND circuits. Here the problem arises when more than one AND-gate input can be 0 so that the first input changing to 0 masks the status of the other inputs.

The overall objective is to design the circuit so that the input states may be changed as quickly as the circuit can respond to the changes, and so that the sequence of output states is appropriately related to the sequence of input states. In cases in which there are several output variables, the output state during transitions may, of course, assume values intermediate between consecutive desired states.

Our approach is to force the input to alternate between a state corresponding to a significant input state, called a *data word*, and a fixed *spacer word*. These words are so chosen that:

1. It is easy to determine when the input is a data word and when it is a spacer.
2. No data word is in the region spanned by the spacer and some other data word.

The second condition permits matters to be so arranged that exactly one data word occurs between consecutive spacers. The outputs can be similarly coded, although it is not necessary as we show later.

There are many kinds of codes satisfying the above conditions, only one of which, the *double-rail* method, is presented here. Each signal x is transmitted in double-rail fashion on two lines labeled x_0 and x_1. When $x = 0$, x_0 is set equal to 1 and x_1 is set to 0. The condition $x = 1$ is represented by $x_0 = 0$ and $x_1 = 1$. The spacer state is coded by setting all x_0- and x_1-signals equal to 0, for every variable. Under no conditions are both x_0 and x_1 allowed to equal 1. It is convenient to refer to x_1 as x and x_0 as $\bar{x}$ even though it must be borne in mind that, since both of these signals may simultaneously equal 0, they are not actually complements of one another.

This code clearly meets our criteria:

1. It is easy to determine when the input is a data word (one of each pair of input lines has a 1-signal) and when it is a spacer (*all* input lines have 0-signals).
2. When the input is changing from a spacer to a data word, none of the intermediate states is a data word (assuming no signal that is supposed to stay at 0 temporarily goes on.) The same is true for transitions from data words to spacers.

Consider now a system of the form shown in Fig. 6.2, assuming that the Z_i- and $\bar{Z}_i$-outputs are generated by two-stage AND-to-OR logic. Suppose that at the start the source emits a spacer (all x_i and $\bar{x}_i$ set to 0) and that this

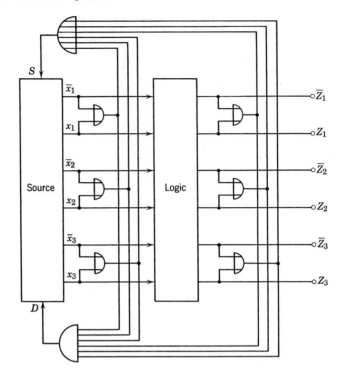

Figure 6.2 Block diagram of a combinational circuit generating return signals.

situation persists until all AND gates and OR gates in the logic block emit 0-signals. Then S, the output of the upper OR gate, and D, the output of the lower AND gate, both become 0. These signals are interpreted by the source as a request for a data word, which it proceeds to supply. The effect then is that 1-signals are generated by certain of the AND gates in the logic block, eventually causing, for each i, *either* Z_i or $\bar{Z}_i$ to go on. When this process is complete, the output corresponds to a data word and eventually D goes on. Meanwhile S is also turned on. The source interprets $S = D = 1$ as a request for a spacer and complies by turning off all x_i- and $\bar{x}_i$-signals. This in turn extinguishes all signals in the logic circuit, causing the output to enter the spacer state and switching S and D to 0. When this occurs, a new data word is supplied by the source and the entire process is repeated.

   Let us now examine the situation in further detail to determine under what circumstances correct operation is assured. Suppose that, for a particular data input, some Z_j is supposed to go on and that two of the AND gates feeding the Z_j-OR gate go on. If the delay at the output of one of the AND gates is very long, then the 1-signal may not get through that delay until after the next spacer and the next data input are produced. This condition constitutes a delay hazard and may cause an incorrect output to occur. To avoid it, we impose the restriction that the logic be so designed that, for any data input and for any i, exactly one AND gate in the circuits generating Z_i or $\bar{Z}_i$ be allowed to go on. If this is the case, then when S and D both go from 1 to 0, it must follow that there are no 1's lurking in any stray delay in the logic since the only AND gates that were on must have gone off. When a data input is fed to the logic, exactly one AND gate eventually goes on for each output pair Z_i and $\bar{Z}_i$. Note that there is no possibility of a false transient occurring anywhere (that is, there are no combinational hazards) since there are no inverters in the circuit. (It is *assumed* that the source operates as specified, never emitting spurious signals.)

The requirement that only one AND gate at a time be allowed to go on for each output pair means that each 1-point of each output function must be covered by exactly one product term. (The same is true for the complement of each function.) This means that in general it is not possible to realize all of the functions with sums of prime implicants, a factor that tends to increase the amount of logic circuitry needed. However, since as pointed out earlier, combinational hazards are not a factor, no special gates are needed to avoid them (see Section 4.2), hence leading to some reduction in the number of gates that would otherwise be required.

As an example, consider the functions mapped in Table 6.2a. The complements are shown in Table 6.2b. Selected product terms are marked in these

Table 6.2

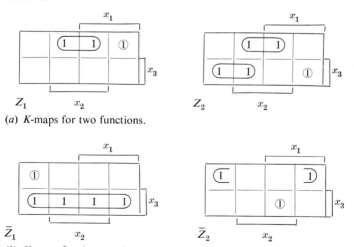

(a) K-maps for two functions.

(b) K-maps for the complements.

tables, leading to the expressions

$$Z_1 = x_2\bar{x}_3 + x_1\bar{x}_2\bar{x}_3,$$
$$\bar{Z}_1 = \bar{x}_1\bar{x}_2\bar{x}_3 + x_3,$$
$$Z_2 = x_2\bar{x}_3 + \bar{x}_1x_3 + x_1\bar{x}_2x_3,$$
$$\bar{Z}_2 = \bar{x}_2\bar{x}_3 + x_1x_2x_3.$$

The resulting circuit is shown in Fig. 6.3. It might be instructive for the reader to trace through in detail the operation of the circuit for the typical input sequence

$$001 \rightarrow 110 \rightarrow 111.$$

The specified response is

$$01 \rightarrow 11 \rightarrow 00.$$

In our circuit, the generated input sequence, including spacers, is

$$x_1\bar{x}_1x_2\bar{x}_2x_3\bar{x}_3 = 000000 \rightarrow 010110 \rightarrow 000000 \rightarrow 101001 \rightarrow 000000 \rightarrow 101010,$$

and the response, including spacers, is

$$Z_1\bar{Z}_1Z_2\bar{Z}_2 = 0000 \rightarrow 0110 \rightarrow 0000 \rightarrow 1010 \rightarrow 0000 \rightarrow 0101.$$

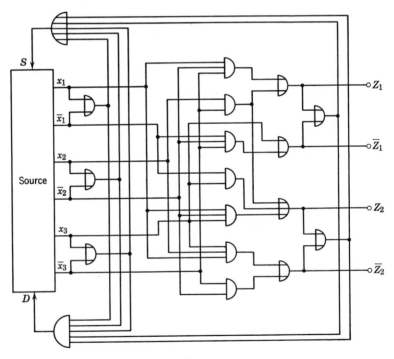

Figure 6.3   Circuit realizing Table 6.2.

It is possible to dispense with the output spacers if we are willing to use FF's at the output terminals. This technique, to be illustrated next, is of particular interest since the basic principle involved is applied shortly to the synthesis of sequential circuits.

As shown in Fig. 6.4, a single SET-RESET-FF is used for each output variable. For each data input either the SET or the RESET terminal of the Z_i-FF is energized, depending upon whether Z_i is specified at 1 or 0 for that input state. The logic block generating these signals is identical to the logic block of Fig. 6.2. When a given FF has received its excitation signal *and* responded to it, then the OR gate associated with that FF goes to 1. When the input corresponds to a data word (coded in double-rail form as before) and all output FF's have received excitations and responded, then the *D*-AND gate goes on. An OR gate is used to sense the presence of an input spacer and the fact that all FF excitations have returned to 0, thereby generating the *S*-signal, which in conjunction with the *D*-signal, controls the input source as discussed earlier.

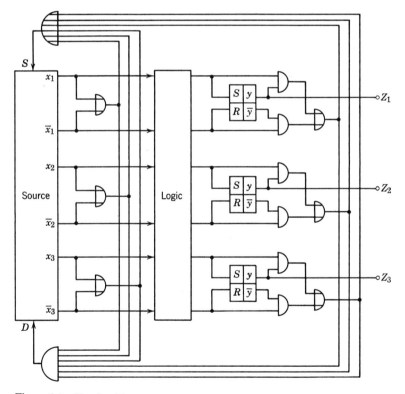

Figure 6.4 Circuit without output spacers.

In the case of a circuit of the form of Fig. 6.4 realizing the functions of Table 6.2, it may be seen that the input sequence

$$x_1 x_2 x_3 = 001 \rightarrow 110 \rightarrow 111$$

results as before in the source producing

$$x_1 \bar{x}_1 x_2 \bar{x}_2 x_3 \bar{x}_3 = 000000 \rightarrow 010110 \rightarrow 000000 \rightarrow 101001 \rightarrow 000000 \rightarrow 101010.$$

Now, however, the resulting output $Z_1 Z_2$ is

$$01 \rightarrow 11 \rightarrow 00.$$

Note that when, as in this example, several outputs are required to change for one transition, we can expect intermediate outputs to occur, depending on the stray-delay values. Thus the actual system output might be

$$01 \rightarrow 11 \rightarrow 01 \rightarrow 00 \qquad \text{or} \qquad 01 \rightarrow 11 \rightarrow 10 \rightarrow 00.$$

Let us now briefly summarize the results thus far. We begin with everything in a quiescent state (all gates emitting 0's); then an input word is fed to the circuit by the source. Regardless of how long the stray delays are or how unevenly distributed they are (recall that line delays are zero), the input is held constant until the outputs have assumed correct values. A signal is then sent back to the source indicating that a spacer signal may now be sent in to clear the circuit. When the spacer signal has been sent and the circuit is clear of all 1-signals, a request for the next relevant input state is sent back to the source.

Thus far it has been assumed that all line delays are zero. Now let us examine the extent to which this assumption can be relaxed. When nonzero delays are allowed in connecting wires (or in gate *inputs*—see Subsection 4.3), a signal change at a node (which may be an input terminal or a gate output terminal) that directly feeds several different points may affect these points at different times. This can lead to malfunction if any input change can occur and penetrate to a different terminal of a gate that is still receiving, at other terminals, signals derived from a previous input state. Such a situation can always be avoided if the line delay between connected pairs of nodes never exceeds the delay through the two stages of logic that generate the S- and D-signals. A conservative rule is that the largest line delay should never exceed half of the smallest gate delay. The relationship involved resembles that discussed in connection with the delayfree realizations of Section 4.4.

A very useful characteristic of the circuits we are discussing is that a wide class of circuit faults cause a prompt halt in system operation. Suppose that, at some node in one of these circuits, the signal becomes fixed at 0 or at 1. When, in the course of normal operation, the signal at this node is supposed to assume the opposite value, the effect is as if an infinitely large delay existed in the output of the gate (or possibly the source) that generates the signal at this node. This would freeze the input at the existing state. Thus, for example, if a 1-signal became permanently established at any node in Fig. 6.3, the S-signal would remain fixed at 1, and so the circuit would be unable to request the next data input. If some node became "stuck at 0," then as soon as an input state occurred for which a 1 at this node became essential in order to produce a 1-signal at some Z_i or $\bar{Z}_i$, the latter terminal would also become stuck at 0 and hence the next spacer input would never be requested. Clearly such behavior is a boon to a maintenance man.

We close this section by pointing out that there is no known method for realizing a source circuit with elements having unbounded stray delays. Such circuits are not difficult to design if components with bounded delays are available.

6.1.2 Sequential Circuits with Completion Signals

The concepts involved in the combinational-circuit model depicted in Fig. 6.4 can serve as the basis for synthesizing SOC sequential functions by simply feeding back to the input side of the logic block the outputs of some of the FF's as shown in Fig. 6.5. These y-FF's then serve as state devices; whereas the others, the Z-FF's, remain as output devices. The key problem is to generate satisfactory row assignments.

If an STT assignment is used, then, after an input change, the termination of any resulting change in the internal state is indicated unambiguously when all of the FF's are in states corresponding to their excitations (the principle exploited in Fig. 6.4). It remains, however, to restrict the class of row assignments further in order to avoid delay hazards.

As is the case for combinational-circuit synthesis, the Z_i or Y_i circuits in the logic block should be so designed that no more than one of the AND gates feeding any one of the output OR gates is 1 during the course of any transition. This means that not only must every 1-point in each Z- and Y-function be covered by exactly one product term, but in addition if there is an $i \rightarrow j$ transition in an input column in which Y_k (or Z_k) has 1-points for rows i and j, then a *single* product term should cover both of these 1-points in the Y_k (or Z_k) realization. But, as pointed out in Section 3.3, the Liu assignment has the property that, in each input column, a unique y-subcube is associated with each destination set, and this subcube is disjoint from all of those associated with the other destination sets of the same column. Since the Y-excitations are constant within each destination set, it follows that, for each Y-function, a set of disjoint product terms can cover the 1-points of the function in such a manner that, for any transition within that column, at most

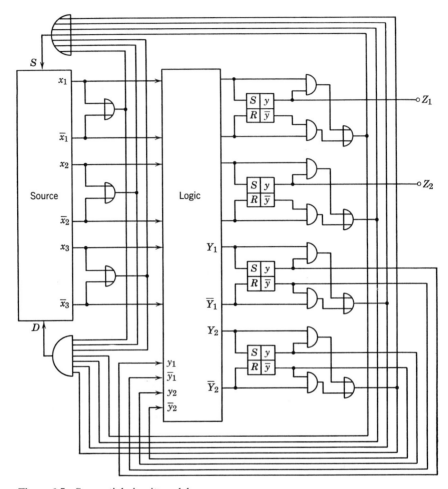

Figure 6.5   Sequential-circuit model.

one of the product terms is ever on. Since the Z-functions are constant within each destination set, they are also realizable in a similar manner.

Thus a satisfactory design is possible in the form of Fig. 6.5 provided that we use a Liu assignment and realize the Y- and Z-functions with maximal subcubes *within* each column, but with no multiple coverage of any 1-point. As is the case with the combinational circuits of the form of Fig. 6.4, it is necessary to generate Z_i-, $\bar{Z}_i$-, Y_j-, and $\bar{Y}_j$-signals for every i and j and for every data input. When the input spacer is on, all Y-, $\bar{Y}$-, and Z-, and $\bar{Z}$-signals are specified to be 0.

As an example, consider Table 6.3 a flow matrix with a Liu assignment.

Table 6.3 Flow Matrix with Liu Assignment

| | x_1x_2 | | | | | |
	00	01	11	y_1	y_2	y_3
1	①, 0	2 , 0	①, 0	0	0	0
2	3 , 0	②, 0	②, 0	1	0	0
3	③, 0	5 , 1	4 , 0	1	0	1
4	1 , 0	5 , 1	④, 0	0	0	1
5	⑤, 1	⑤, 1	4 , 0	0	1	1

The FF excitation expressions are derived by setting $S = Y$ and $R = \bar{Y}$, using product terms covering maximal subcubes within each column. Within each expression, the terms are chosen so as to be mutually disjoint.

$$S_1 = \bar{x}_2 y_1 + \bar{x}_1 x_2 \bar{y}_3 + x_1 x_2 y_1 \bar{y}_3,$$
$$R_1 = \bar{x}_1 \bar{x}_2 \bar{y}_1 + \bar{x}_1 x_2 y_3 + x_1 \bar{y}_1 + x_1 y_1 y_3,$$
$$S_2 = \bar{x}_2 y_2 + \bar{x}_1 x_2 y_3,$$
$$R_2 = \bar{x}_1 \bar{x}_2 \bar{y}_2 + \bar{x}_1 x_2 \bar{y}_3 + x_1,$$
$$S_3 = \bar{x}_2 y_1 \bar{y}_2 + \bar{x}_2 y_2 + x_2 y_3,$$
$$R_3 = \bar{x}_2 \bar{y}_1 \bar{y}_2 + x_2 \bar{y}_3,$$
$$Z = \bar{x}_2 y_2 + \bar{x}_1 x_2 y_3,$$
$$\bar{Z} = \bar{x}_1 \bar{x}_2 \bar{y}_2 + \bar{x}_1 x_2 \bar{y}_3 + x_1.$$

The above approach can be modified if desired to produce output changes separated by spacers analogously to the system for combinational circuits shown in Fig. 6.2. The modification can be accomplished by omitting the output FF's, and generating Z- and $\bar{Z}$-signals as before with OR gates to indicate when each output signal has been produced (see Fig. 6.6).

Combinational hazards and sequential hazards are no problem in circuits designed as described above, and the same "error-stop" feature described in the last subsection is also a property of these circuits.

6.1.3 Networks of Circuits

In a complex digital system, it may be desirable to interconnect a number of combinational and sequential circuits of the type treated in the two preceding subsections. Such connections necessitate the modification of the circuits to provide storage for their output states and a means for responding to requests for spacers or new outputs.

A simple chain of circuits is shown in Fig. 6.7, in which the leftmost circuit receives inputs from a source that it controls with S- and D-signals as discussed earlier. Each circuit interior to the chain processes data received from the circuit on its left and passes on the results as inputs to the circuit on its

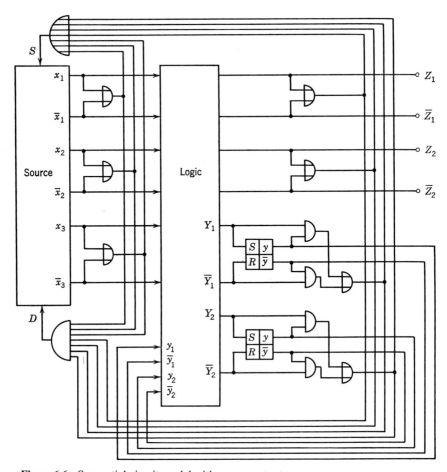

Figure 6.6   Sequential-circuit model with spacer output.

right. When the circuit on the right requests a spacer or a data input, the request is relayed to the circuit on the left. The receptor on the right end of the chain absorbs the overall result of the system and calls for spacers and data according to its own operating rate. We may think of the receptor as an output device such as a printer, and the source as a buffer memory.

A circuit requests a spacer (or data) when its output is data (or a spacer). This request is acted upon when the circuit to its left is emitting a spacer (or data) *and* the circuit to its right is requesting a spacer (or data). Thus, in a long chain, the effects of several different input states can appear at different circuits buffered by circuits with spacer outputs. In no case can the results of a later input overtake and thus garble the results of an earlier input.

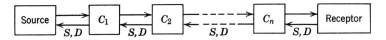

Figure 6.7   A cascade of circuits.

A combinational-circuit model suitable for inclusion in such a chain is shown in Fig. 6.8 which is based on Fig. 6.2 with FF's added for each Z_i and $\bar{Z}_i$. When the $(i + 1)$st module requests a spacer (SD = 10) and the input from the $(i - 1)$st module is a spacer, the upper AND gate is activated, causing all of the ith module output FF's to be reset, thus generating an output spacer. When this has occurred (note that the $\bar{y}$-outputs cannot go on until the S-signals go to 0), the lowest AND gate is energized, resetting the *request* FF Q, which then sends a request for data (SD = 01) signal to the $(i - 1)$st module.

The receipt of a data request (SD = 01) from the right activates the logic block (the D-signal is an input to each AND gate in that block), and if the Q-FF is in the RESET state, then eventually a data input will be fed to the logic from the left, setting various i-module FF's. When one member of each pair of Z_i-FF's reaches the SET state, the AND gate activating the SET terminal of the Q-FF goes on, causing a spacer request to go to the $(i - 1)$st module. Thus a sequence of inputs from the left is processed and the results transmitted to the right on request, with spacers intervening.

Next we consider how the sequential-circuit configuration of Fig. 6.6 can be modified so as to be compatible with the combinational circuits just discussed in systems such as that shown in Fig. 6.7. What is needed (see Fig. 6.9) is a pair of FF's for each output variable with the circuits needed to detect spacer outputs (as in Fig. 6.8.) A FF is used to record whether a spacer or data output occurred last, and another FF indicates whether or not all of the internal state FF's are both excited and stable (that is, for each FF, $S = 1$ and the FF is set, or $R = 1$ and the FF is reset). These two FF's control the *request* FF Q, which is set whenever both are set and reset whenever both are reset. Spacer or data inputs are requested from the left when Q is in the set or reset states, respectively. The S-signal from the right controls the resetting of the output FF's, and the D-signal controls all of the AND gates in the logic as in the case of the circuit of Fig. 6.8.

In cases in which a module feeds several other modules, the S- and D-signals from *all* of these modules must feed the AND gates, so that a change between spacer and data in the output of a module can occur only when requested by all of the successor modules.

The techniques described above indicate possible solutions to the problems discussed. In order to obtain speed-independent operation (that is, circuitry that functions properly regardless of the relative and absolute operating

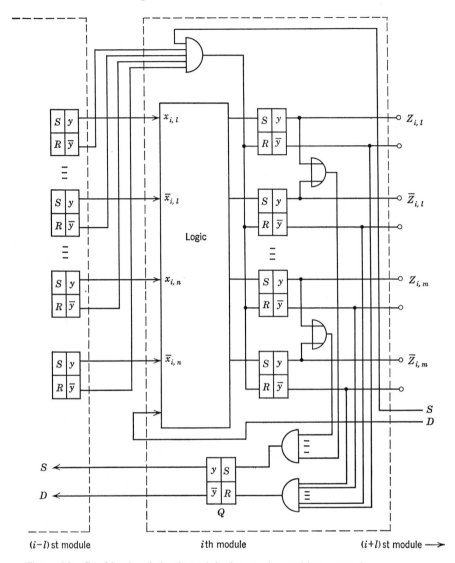

Figure 6.8   Combinational-circuit module that can be used in a network.

speeds of the components used), a substantial price is indicated in terms of the number of components required (a factor of perhaps 3), and since the logic paths have been lengthened by the addition of the various completion detection circuits, the maximum operating speed is decreased. However, if long chains of circuit modules are required, with significant variations in operation times, *effective* operating speeds may be increased, and there may also be gains

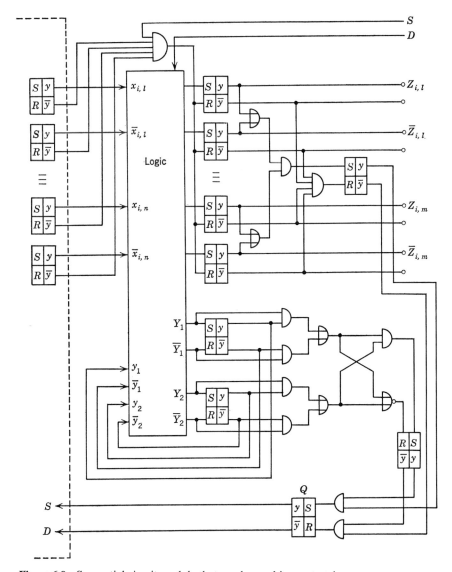

Figure 6.9   Sequential-circuit module that can be used in a network.

in reliability and maintainability. It may yet be found that this mode of
operation can be implemented with simpler circuitry.

The theory of speed-independent circuits has been largely concerned with
the realization of autonomous functions (no input variables) and so we show
how the ideas presented here can be applied to this problem. Table 6.4a

describes an autonomous function, in which it is assumed that the starting state is 1. In this example, the specified output consists of a transient sequence followed by a periodic sequence.

Our approach is to convert the table to a two-column table that generates the desired output when the input alternates. In our example, Table 6.4b is the expanded version of Table 6.4a, having two columns and twice as many rows. The expanded table is of the SOC type considered earlier and so is realizable by a module of the form of Fig. 6.9. Starting in 1-0 of Table 6.4b and changing x back and forth between 0 and 1 produces the same output sequence described by the given table. If the outputs are produced as in the model of Fig. 6.5, then the simulation will be exact in that no spacers will separate consecutive data outputs. What is needed to complete the design is a

Table 6.4a   Table for an Autonomous Function

1	2, 00
2	3, 01
3	4, 11
4	5, 01
5	6, 00
6	7, 10
7	4, 11

Table 6.4b   Expanded Version of a

	x	
	0	1
1	①, 00	1′ , 00
1′	2 , 01	①′, 00
2	②, 01	2′ , 01
2′	3 , 11	②′, 01
3	③, 11	3′ , 11
3′	4 , 01	③′, 11
4	④, 01	4′ , 01
4′	5 , 00	④′, 01
5	⑤, 00	5′ , 00
5′	6 , 10	⑤′, 00
6	⑥, 10	6′ , 10
6′	7 , 11	⑥′, 10
7	⑦, 11	7′ , 11
7′	4 , 01	⑦′, 11

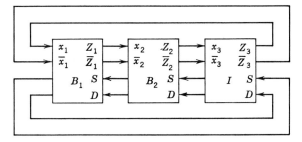

Figure 6.10 Circuit generating 010101 · · · .

means for generating the alternating x-signal with modules of the type under discussion. This can be accomplished with a closed chain of three simple combinational-circuit modules as shown in Fig. 6.10. Each circuit feeds its output to the next circuit and receives from it the S- and D-signals that we have discussed. Locally, each module behaves precisely as a module interior to the cascade of Fig. 6.7 producing data and spacer outputs under the same constraints. The I-block is an inverter ($Z_3 = \bar{x}_3$), and each of the B-blocks simply transmits the received input to the output ($Z_1 = x_1$ and $Z_2 = x_2$). An examination of this system, assuming that initially two outputs are spacers and the other output 0 or 1, will show that one module at a time changes its output (to or from a spacer) and that, at each module, consecutive data outputs alternate between 0 and 1. (There is some resemblance to the behavior of the circuit shown in Fig. 5.9.) For example, if $Z_1 = \bar{Z}_1 = Z_2 = \bar{Z}_2 = Z_3 = 0$ and $\bar{Z}_3 = 1$, then I will be requesting (and currently receiving) a spacer from B_2, B_2 will be requesting data from B_1, and B_1 will be requesting (and receiving) data from I. Hence only B_1 is in a position to change its output, and it will be to the data output $Z_1\bar{Z}_1 = 01$.

The output of any one of the modules of the circuit in Fig. 6.10 can be connected to the input of a sequential-circuit module (in the form of Fig. 6.9) realizing Table 6.4b as shown in Fig. 6.11. The S- and D- signals transmitted back from the sequential-circuit module control the release of inputs to that module, and so the system operates according to the rules presented earlier.

6.2 Pulse-mode and Synchronous Circuits

The advantages and disadvantages of pulse-mode circuits and, by extension, synchronous circuits are sketched briefly in this section.

Consider the flow matrix of Table 6.5, describing a function with three input states (I_1, I_2, and I_3) and two output states (O_1 and O_2). The function is to be realized by a pulse-mode circuit with three input terminals and two output terminals. An I_i-input is represented by a pulse on the I_i-terminal,

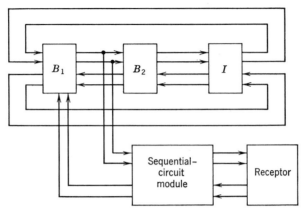

Figure 6.11   Realization of an autonomous function.

and an O_i-output is indicated by a pulse generated at output terminal O_i. At no time may more than one input terminal or more than one output terminal be pulsed. No more than one internal-state change is to occur for any one input pulse, and in between input pulses the internal state is to remain constant with all outputs dormant (the discussion of Fig. 1.3 and Table 1.6e in Section 1.6 is applicable here, except that there is no clock pulse in the present case).

A block diagram of the circuit to be derived is shown in Fig. 6.12. Using the given state assignment, we derive the necessary expressions as below:

$$S_1 = I_1\bar{y}_2 + I_3\bar{y}_2,$$
$$R_1 = I_1y_1 + I_2,$$
$$S_2 = I_1\bar{y}_2 + I_3,$$
$$R_2 = I_1\bar{y}_1y_2,$$
$$O_1 = I_1y_1,$$
$$O_2 = I_1\bar{y}_1 + I_2 + I_3.$$

Note that each product term in the O-expressions must include an I-term so that a pulsed output results. A basic feature of this mode of operation is

Table 6.5   Flow Matrix for a Sequential Function to be Realized by a Pulse-mode Circuit

	I_1	I_2	I_3	y_1	y_2
1	$3, O_2$	$1, O_2$	$3, O_2$	0	0
2	$1, O_2$	$2, O_2$	$2, O_2$	0	1
3	$2, O_1$	$2, O_2$	$3, O_2$	1	1

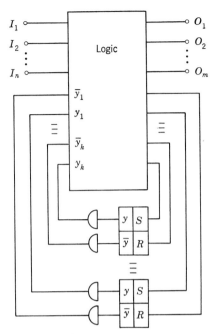

Figure 6.12 Form of pulse-mode sequential circuit.

that the only constraint on the state assignment is that no y-state be assigned to more than one row of the table.

Suppose now that, in the example, an I_1-input is applied with the system initially in state 3. Then a reset signal is applied to the y_1-FF, changing the y-state to 01, which corresponds to row 2. But if the I_1-pulse is so wide that it remains on *after* the new $\bar{y}_1$-signal emerges from the delay element and enters the logic block, the effect will be as though I_1 had been applied again with the system in row 2. The result will be that R_2 will go on, resetting the y_2-FF and thereby switching the system to the 1-state. Even if $2\text{-}I_1$ had been a stable state, the same situation would have resulted in a false O_2-pulse occurring. Thus, if the next state is unstable, or has a different output from the present state, the width of the input pulse must be less than the time it takes for a signal to pass through the logic, switch a FF, and pass through the logic again.

Of course there is a *minimum* allowable input pulse width that is determined by the time it takes to switch the slowest FF. As will be come evident, it is the combination of these two constraints that usually necessitates the delay elements shown in Fig. 6.12.

In order to obtain a quantitative picture of the situation, let us define D as the nominal delay-element value, T_S as the nominal time to switch a FF,

W as the pulse width, E_S as the normalized tolerance on T_S [the switching time varies between $(1 - E_S)T_S$ and $(1 + E_S)T_S$], and E_W as the normalized tolerance on W. We neglect the delays in the logic, which can easily be taken into account later. Then the first constraint illustrated above is expressed by

$$(6.1) \qquad\qquad W(1 + E_W) < T_S(1 - E_S) + D.$$

The second constraint can be expressed by

$$(6.2) \qquad\qquad W(1 - E_W) > T_S(1 + E_S).$$

If (6.2) is marginally satisfied, we have

$$(6.3) \qquad\qquad W = \frac{T_S(1 + E_S)}{1 - E_W}.$$

which when inserted in (6.1) yields

$$(6.4) \qquad\qquad \frac{D}{T_S} > \frac{2(E_S + E_W)}{1 - E_W}.$$

Clearly it may be necessary to insert a delay that is considerably larger than the FF operate time if the operate times and pulse widths cannot be specified precisely. This in turn means that the input pulses must be spaced further apart. Hence in order to obtain safe operation, the circuit must be operated at a rate governed by the variability of the available components as well as their speed.

We note a second effect that is pertinent. In our example, when I_3 is applied with the system in state 1, set signals go to both FF's. If the y_2-FF changes first and the resulting signal passes through the delay and the logic before the y_1-FF switches, the S_1-signal may be extinguished before it takes effect, thus leaving the system in state 2 instead of state 1. This critical race can be averted if

$$(6.5) \qquad\qquad (1 - E_S)T_S + D > (1 + E_S)T_S.$$

This inequality yields another constraint on D, namely,

$$(6.6) \qquad\qquad \frac{D}{T_S} > 2E_S.$$

When both (6.4) and (6.6) are applicable, it is clear that (6.4) dominates the situation uniformly.

It is important to understand that T_S is determined by delays in the feedback paths internal to the FF's (see Problem 5.1), which serve no useful purpose and slow down circuit operation. The D-elements are external to the loops and must be so chosen that they are sure to satisfy (6.4). Since these elements too have associated tolerances E_D, the nominal value of D, which must be used in computing the allowable input rate, must satisfy

(6.7)
$$\frac{D}{T_S} > \frac{2(E_S + E_W)}{(1 - E_W)(1 - E_D)}.$$

Knowing D and T_S, we can now specify the minimum interval T_I separating consecutive input signals. It must be such as to ensure that the effects of the preceding input signal have passed completely around the circuit; hence we have

(6.8)
$$T_I > (1 + E_D)D + (1 + E_S)T_S.$$

The above calculations may be taken as an indication of how this sort of problem can be attacked, and the results give us a general idea of how the operating rate is influenced by various tolerances and delays. Detailed differences in modes of operation are of course, reflected in variations in the constraints.

Synchronous sequential circuits can be treated in essentially the same manner, with W representing the clock-pulse width. The example given in Section 1.6 illustrates how the input can consist of the state of a set of two-level signals constrained to change only when the clock pulse is off. In some cases, as depicted in Fig. 1.3, the memory elements used (τ-FF's in this example) require for excitation input pulses constrained as to shape, amplitude, and duration. The first of these further complicates the engineering problems involved in designing reliable circuits. When capacitive coupling is used, one must allow for varying time constants that are effective during different states of the system, and the problem of spurious noise pulses becomes more serious. Such matters are treated in texts on electronics and digital circuit engineering. See for example Millman and Taub (MLM-1] or Maley and Earle [MAL-1].

6.3 Double-rank Sequential Circuits

In the mode of operation to be discussed in this section, delay elements are replaced by an escapement mechanism consisting of a bank of FF's controlled by a pair of clock pulses.

Consider first the function shown in Table 6.6a, and the block diagram of Fig. 6.13a. When the clock pulse C_1 (see Problem 6.4) goes on, the logic circuit generates the next state for the first rank of FF's as a function of the present input x and the state of the second rank of FF's. Operating on the same inputs, the output logic generates the output pulses in phase with C_1. The input x is assumed to remain constant while C_1 is on. As shown in Fig. 6.13b, the C_2 pulse goes on some time after C_1 goes off. During this phase,

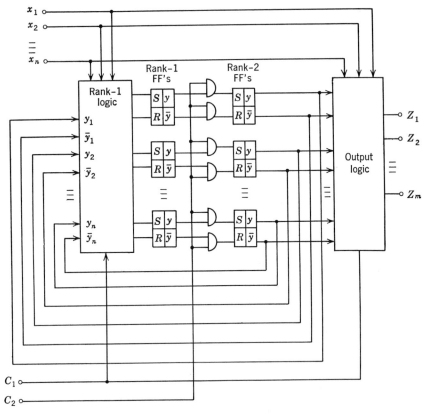

Figure 6.13a   Type-1 double-rank circuit.

the second rank of FF's is switched so as to assume the same state as the first rank.

Either of the circuits shown in Fig. 6.13c or d can be used to generate C_1 and C_2 from a single-phase clock C.

A key aspect of this mode of operation is the fact that during phase 1, when rank 1 is changing, rank 2, which controls the process, is held constant, and the reverse is true during phase 2, where the roles of the two ranks are switched. This obviates the need for delay elements, since a change in a FF

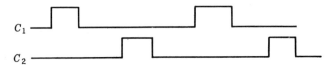

Figure 6.13b   Phasing of clock pulses.

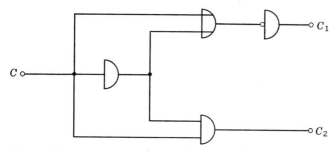

Figure 6.13c A method for generating a pair of separated pulses from a single pulse.

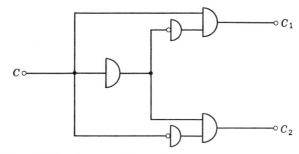

Figure 6.13d An alternative to (c).

state cannot feed back around the circuit to alter the excitation of some other FF's. (Note that C_1 controls the AND gates of the rank-1 logic, so that when $C_1 = 0$, no rank-1 FF can change. It controls the output in a similar manner.)

The clock-pulse widths must be long enough to allow the slowest FF's to change. Contrary to the situation depicted in the preceding section, there is no upper bound on these widths, provided only that C_1 and C_2 are never on simultaneously. The C_2-pulse and the second rank of FF's play the role of the delay elements used in the pulsed or synchronous circuits of the preceding section.

The logic can be designed without regard for combinational hazards, since all output signals and pulses to FF's result from clock pulses operating on circuits with all other inputs stable.

The design process is essentially the same as that for single-phase clocked circuits. First a state assignment is chosen, the only requirement being that a unique state be assigned to each row of the table. Different assignments in general affect the complexity of the resulting logic, and the same techniques used to find good assignments for single-phase synchronous circuits are applicable here. A suitable assignment is shown for our example in Table 6.6a. It is useful to think of the assignment as designating the states of rank 2.

Table 6.6a   A Sequential Function

	x_1x_2				y_1	y_2	y_3
	00	01	11	10			
1	3, 0	5, 0	2, 0	1, 0	0	0	0
2	2, 0	5, 0	4, 0	1, 0	0	0	1
3	5, 0	4, 0	3, 0	3, 0	0	1	0
4	5, 0	4, 0	5, 0	4, 0	0	1	1
5	3, 0	2, 0	2, 1	3, 0	1	0	0

Table 6.6b   Change Matrix

	x_1x_2				y_1	y_2	y_3
	00	01	11	10			
1	$\bar{S}S\bar{S}$	$S\bar{S}S$	$\bar{S}\bar{S}S$	$\bar{S}\bar{S}\bar{S}$	0	0	0
2	$\bar{S}\bar{S}R$	$S\bar{S}R$	$\bar{S}S\bar{R}$	$\bar{S}\bar{S}R$	0	0	1
3	$SR\bar{S}$	$\bar{S}RS$	$\bar{S}R\bar{S}$	$\bar{S}R\bar{S}$	0	1	0
4	SRR	$\bar{S}R\bar{R}$	SRR	$\bar{S}R\bar{R}$	0	1	1
5	$RS\bar{S}$	$R\bar{S}S$	$R\bar{S}S$	$RS\bar{S}$	1	0	0

Table 6.6c   FF Excitation Matrix

	x_1x_2				y_1	y_2	y_3
	00	01	11	10			
1	0–100–	100–0–	0–0–10	0–0–0–	0	0	0
2	0–0– –0	100–01	0–10–0	0–0–01	0	0	1
3	10010–	0– –010	0– –00–	0– –00–	0	1	0
4	100101	0– –0–0	100101	0– –0–0	0	1	1
5	01100–	010–10	010–10	01100–	1	0	0

$$S_1R_1S_2R_2S_3R_3$$

We introduce at this point the *change* matrix, a tool that is useful in designing circuits employing SR-FF's and that is of particular value for a generalization to be introduced later in this section. Table 6.6b is such a matrix for our example. It indicates for each of the y-FF's what excitation should be applied in each total state in order to ensure a correct transition to the next state indicated in the flow matrix. There are four possibilities for each FF:

1. If y_i is 0 in the present state and 1 in the next state, the *set* terminal must be excited, and the entry in our matrix is S.

2. If y_i is 1 in the present state and 0 in the next state, the entry is R, indicating that a reset signal is required.

3. If y_i is 0 in the current *and* next states, then an R-signal *may* be applied, but the S-terminal must *not* be excited. This case is indicated by an $\bar{S}$ entry in position i.

4. If y_i is and must remain 1, then no R-signal is allowed, and so the entry is $\bar{R}$.

From the change matrix we can easily derive the FF excitation matrix shown as Table 6.6c in the example. The SR entries for a given y-variable are 10, 01, 0–, and –0 corresponding to cases 1, 2, 3, and 4, respectively. In a routine manner, Table 6.6c yields the expressions for the rank-1 FF excitations (C_1 is added to each product term):

$$S_1 = \bar{x}_1\bar{x}_2 y_2 C_1 + \bar{x}_1 x_2 \bar{y}_1 \bar{y}_2 C_1 + x_1 x_2 y_2 y_3 C_1,$$
$$R_1 = y_1 C_1,$$
$$S_2 = \bar{x}_1\bar{x}_2\bar{y}_2\bar{y}_3 C_1 + x_1 x_2 \bar{y}_2 y_3 C_1 + \bar{x}_2 y_1 C_1,$$
$$R_2 = \bar{x}_1\bar{x}_2 y_2 C_1 + x_1 x_2 y_2 y_3 C_1,$$
$$S_3 = x_2 y_1 C_1 + \bar{x}_1 x_2 y_2 C_1 + x_1 x_2 \bar{y}_1 \bar{y}_2 C_1,$$
$$R_3 = \bar{x}_1\bar{x}_2 y_2 C_1 + \bar{x}_1 x_2 \bar{y}_1 \bar{y}_2 C_1 + x_1 x_2 y_1 C_1 + x_1 \bar{x}_2 \bar{y}_1 \bar{y}_2 C_1.$$

The output logic, derivable from Table 6.6a (with C_1 added to the AND gate), is

$$Z = x_1 x_2 y_1 C_1.$$

In general, it is necessary to provide special circuitry to set the initial state of a sequential circuit. Since in the case considered above, the internal state is represented by the state of the FF's of the second rank alone, it would appear to be feasible as well as desirable to be able to initialize such a system by initializing only the rank-2 FF's. This cannot be done, however, in the case of the circuit just designed because the rank-1 FF's are not all excited during the C_1-phase in every total state. For example, the y_1-FF is neither set nor reset in state 1-00. This means that, for such states, the next state of the rank-1 FF's is dependent in part on the previous state of this rank, and not just on the input and the state of rank 2. If we remedy this situation by making sure that every rank-1 FF is excited during each C_1-phase, then it is sufficient to initialize only the rank-2 FF's since the rank-1 FF's will assume the correct values after the initial C_1-pulse (which is assumed to precede the first C_2-pulse). The price paid for this feature (which has been called the *self-synchronizing property*) is the loss of some freedom in specifying the rank-1 logic, which in turn often leads to somewhat more complex circuitry. In the FF excitation matrix, the unspecified R (or S) entries must be filled in as the complements of the accompanying S (or R) entries for the same FF's. Thus the S- and R-functions for each FF will be complementary.

It is often possible to reduce the number of FF's in rank 1 by replacing the AND gates after this rank by a second block of logic, as shown in Fig. 6.14. Since there are no x-inputs to this block, there must be a unique state of the rank-1 FF's for each type of entry in the rank-2 excitation matrix. If we wish

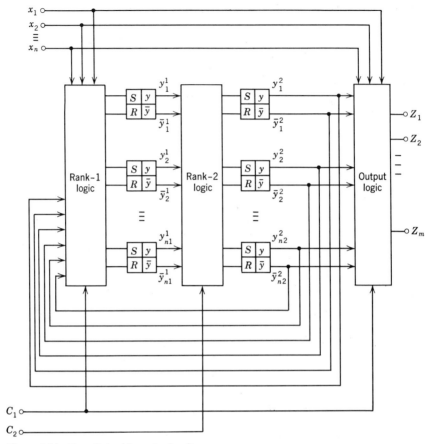

Figure 6.14   Type-2 double-rank circuit.

to use a minimal number of FF's, we must determine a minimal set of excitation entries such that every *change*-matrix entry is satisfied by at least one member of the set. For example, change-matrix entries $\bar{S}S\bar{S}$, $\bar{S}SR$, $RS\bar{S}$, and RSR are *all* satisfied by 011001. Two change-matrix entries may be defined as being *compatible* if there is no position in which one has an S and the other an $\bar{S}$ or R, and no position in which one has an R and the other an $\bar{R}$. It is not hard to see that a set of mutally compatible entries can all be satisfied by the same excitation entry. Thus in Table 6.6b, the entries $\bar{S}\bar{R}\bar{R}$, $R\bar{S}S$, and $\bar{S}\bar{R}S$ can all be satisfied by 010010. Since this type of compatibility has the same characteristics as the compatibility concept introduced in connection with flow-table reduction (Section 2.2), the methods presented earlier for finding maximal compatibles are applicable here. Once the maximal compatibles are found, a minimal set of them is derived so that every entry is covered by at least one member (the problem discussed in Subsection 3.3.2 in connection with Tracey assignments). For each of the MC's, there will be one excitation entry (possibly not fully specified) that will satisfy each component. For a given rank-2 assignment, this leads us to the minimal number of rank-1 FF's.

We illustrate this procedure by carrying through the synthesis of Table 6.6a in the form of Fig. 6.14. Before constructing a pair chart for the entries of Table 6.6b, we note that certain entries need not be explicitly considered; for example, *any* excitation satisfying RRS will *also* satisfy $R\bar{S}S$. Thus if both are change-matrix excitations, the latter need not be considered at all in finding the minimal set of excitations. In general an entry e_1 is dominated by another entry e_2, and may hence be ignored in finding the minimal excitation set, if their components are the same except for some $\bar{R}$ (or $\bar{S}$) elements of e_1 corresponding to S (or R) entries of e_2.

Applying this notion to Table 6.6b, we find that the entries *not* dominated by any others are

$$SRR, \; RS\bar{S}, \; \bar{S}\bar{R}S, \; R\bar{S}S, \; \bar{S}S\bar{R}, \; \bar{S}\bar{S}R.$$

By means of the pair chart of Table 6.7a, in which these entries are labeled a, b, c, d, e, and f, respectively, the maximal compatibles are found to be a, be, cd, ce, f. A minimal covering set is $\{a, be, cd, f\}$. Excitation-matrix entries satisfying the members of this set are: 100101, 011000, 010010, and 0–0–01. Each entry in Table 6.6b is satisfied by one of the above excitations, and if we label them as e_1, e_2, e_3, and e_4, respectively, we obtain Table 6.7b (it is convenient now to distinguish the variables of the two ranks by means of superscripts). Next, if we code the four excitations in terms of the rank-1 variables $y_1{}^1 y_2{}^1$ as 00, 01, 10, 11, respectively (any permutation of this coding will do, although the complexity of the logic may vary), we obtain the specifications for the rank-2 logic shown in Table 6.7c. The rank-1 logic is specified by Table 6.7d. Note that the role of the rank-1 y-variables closely resembles that of the q-variables used in designing minimum-feedback circuits (Section 5.3).

Expressions for the rank-2 logic are

$$S_1{}^2 = \bar{y}_1{}^1 \bar{y}_2{}^1 C_2,$$

$$R_1{}^2 = y_1{}^1 C_2 + y_2{}^1 C_2,$$

$$S_2{}^2 = \bar{y}_1{}^1 y_2{}^1 C_2,$$

$$R_2{}^2 = \bar{y}_1{}^1 \bar{y}_2{}^1 C_2,$$

$$S_3{}^2 = y_1{}^1 \bar{y}_2{}^1 C_2,$$

$$R_3{}^2 = \bar{y}_1{}^1 \bar{y}_2{}^1 C_2 + y_1{}^1 y_2{}^1 C_2.$$

Table 6.7a

(a) Pair chart for Table 6.6b entries.

Table 6.7b

| | $x_1 x_2$ | | | | | | |
	00	01	11	10	$y_1{}^1$	$y_2{}^1$	$y_3{}^1$
1	e_2	e_1	e_3	e_4	0	0	0
2	e_3	e_1	e_2	e_4	0	0	1
3	e_1	e_3	e_2	e_2	0	1	0
4	e_1	e_2	e_1	e_2	0	1	1
5	e_2	e_3	e_3	e_2	1	0	0

(b) Excitation matrix for Table 6.6b with minimal number of different excitations.

Expressions for the rank-1 logic are

$$S_1{}^1 = \bar{x}_2 \bar{y}_2{}^2 y_3{}^2 C_1 + \bar{x}_1 x_2 y_2{}^2 \bar{y}_3{}^2 C_1 + x_2 y_1{}^2 C_1 + x_1 \bar{y}_1{}^2 \bar{y}_2{}^2 \bar{y}_3{}^2 C_1,$$

$$R_1{}^1 = \bar{x}_1 \bar{x}_2 \bar{y}_3{}^2 C_1 + \bar{x}_2 y_1{}^2 C_1 + y_2{}^2 y_3{}^2 C_1 + \bar{x}_1 x_2 \bar{y}_1{}^2 \bar{y}_2{}^2 C_1 + x_1 y_2{}^2 C_1 + x_2 y_3{}^2 C_1,$$

$$S_2{}^1 = \bar{x}_2 \bar{y}_2{}^2 \bar{y}_3{}^2 C_1 + \bar{x}_1 x_2 y_2{}^2 y_3{}^2 C_1 + x_1 y_2{}^2 \bar{y}_3{}^2 C_1 + x_1 \bar{x}_2 C_1 + x_1 \bar{y}_2{}^2 y_3{}^2 C_1,$$

$$R_2{}^1 = \bar{x}_1 \bar{x}_2 y_3{}^2 C_1 + \bar{x}_1 y_2{}^2 \bar{y}_3{}^2 C_1 + \bar{x}_1 x_2 \bar{y}_2{}^2 C_1 + x_1 x_2 \bar{y}_2{}^2 \bar{y}_3{}^2 C_1 + x_1 x_2 y_2{}^2 y_3{}^2 C_1.$$

A further generalization of the double-rank concept that has not yet been explored is the use of x-inputs to the rank-2 logic. It would probably make possible simpler logic and fewer rank-1 FF's, but it would add the restriction that input changes would have to be prohibited while C_2 is on, as well as while C_1 is on.

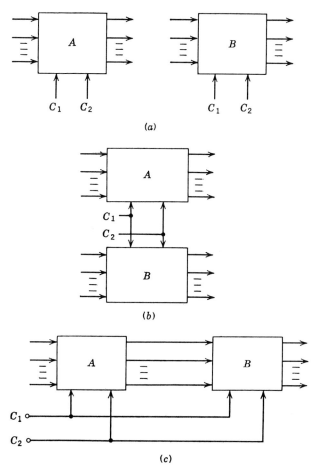

Figure 6.15   (*a*) Two double-rank circuits. (*b*) Parallel connection of *A* and *B*. (*c*) Serial connection of *A* and *B*.

Table 6.7c

	y_1^1	y_2^1	S_1^2	R_1^2	S_2^2	R_2^2	S_3^2	R_3^2
e_1	0	0	1	0	0	1	0	1
e_2	0	1	0	1	1	0	0	0
e_3	1	0	0	1	0	0	1	0
e_4	1	1	0	–	0	–	0	1

(*c*) Specifications for rank-2 logic.

Table 6.7d

$$x_1 x_2$$

00	01	11	10	y_1^2	y_2^2	y_3^2
0110	0101	1001	1010	0	0	0
1001	0101	0110	1010	0	0	1
0101	1001	0110	0110	0	1	0
0101	0110	0101	0110	0	1	1
0110	1001	1001	0110	1	0	0

$$S_1^1 R_1^1 S_2^1 R_2^1$$

(d) Rank-1 logic.

An interesting feature of double-rank circuits is that they can easily be connected in series or in parallel to form larger double-rank circuits, as shown in Fig. 6.15. This property is particularly useful for the synthesis of circuits of an iterative nature such as counters or shift registers.

SOURCES

The concept of speed-independent circuits, in which completion signals obviate the need for worst case designs based on estimates of maximum internal delays, was first introduced by Muller and his associates [MU-1-4, MU-6, HAML-1, RO-1, EL-1]. These sources deal principally with autonomous circuits, do not present general synthesis techniques, and are not easy to read. Chapter 10 of Miller's book [MLR-2] probably constitutes the most lucid survey of the Muller approach. A narrower, briefer summary is by Hall [HAL-1]. Note the reference in Section 6.1 to the work of Gilchrist, Pomerine, and Wong [GIL-1] on completion signals in adders and the generalization of this work by Waite [WAI-1]. The material in Section 6.1 which emphasizes synthesis, permits inputs, and fits in well with the Huffman approach is due to Armstrong, Friedman, and Menon [AR-1]. Sims and Gray [SIM-1] and McNaughton [MCN-1] have also treated various aspects of these problems, the latter in a fairly comprehensive manner.

The treatment presented in Section 6.2 of timing problems and tolerances in synchronous and pulsed circuits is based on work by Unger [UN-1], although practicing logic designers doubtless have made similar computations from the inception of the art. General material on this topic can be found in many books [McC-4, MIR-2, WOO-1]. More detailed treatments of the engineering aspects are available as noted earlier [MAL-1, MLM-1].

The double-rank concept of Section 6.3 was introduced by Ware [WAR-1] in connection with counters and shift registers. At about the same time, in a different context, Huffman [HUF-1] discussed a similar notion in more general form, using the term "escapement circuit." The specific ideas presented here follow those of Hall [HAL-2, HAL-4].

Two interesting modes of operation not treated here have been developed by Gerace [GE-1, 2] and Eichelberger [EI-1, 2].

PROBLEMS

‡6.1 Find a suitable row assignment for Table 4.9 and write logic expressions for a logic box, of the form of the one in Fig. 6.5, which realizes the table with a Muller-type circuit.

6.2 A type of FF often used in clocked systems is the JK-FF, which has three inputs. One of them is a clock pulse C and the others are set S and reset R inputs. A change of state can only occur when C goes on. If at that time signals are present at the S or R-terminals, the output state goes to the set or reset condition, respectively. If *both* the S- and R-terminals are energized when C is on, then the FF *changes* its state. Thus it combines the characteristics of the SR-FF and the τ-FF. Realize Table 1.6*e* using JK-FF's.

6.3 A three-stage synchronous mode shift register is shown in Fig. P6.3. Design a three stage double-rank shift register using a minimal number of FF's.

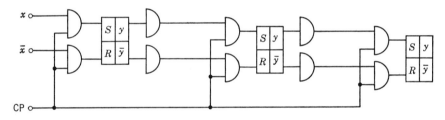

Figure P6.3

6.4 Find flow tables for the circuits of Fig. 6.13*c* and *d* which generate two-phase clock signals from single-phase clock signals.

CHAPTER 7

Counters

Binary counters have long been components of digital systems of all types. Even before such systems became prominent, binary electronic counters were important tools of the experimental physicist. As a result of this relatively long technological history (long in the perspective of a very young field), and wide area of application, a great deal of thought has gone into the design of these devices, and many interesting variations have been developed.

Although we present a number of these variations here, discussing some in detail, our goal is not to produce a comprehensive treatise on the topic. Rather it is to use these circuits to illustrate many of the principles and techniques incorporated in the preceding chapters.

A number of interpretations can be applied to the concept of a counter. They include single input circuits which for some positive integer n emit:

1. An output signal after every nth input signal.
2. A different output state after each of the first n inputs, repeating this sequence for successive sets of n inputs.
3. In sequence, binary representations of the numbers 0 through $n - 1$ for the first n inputs.

The third category, which is a subset of the second, is the one we focus on. In our examples n is a power of 2, although it is usually a straightforward matter to incorporate the logic necessary to recycle a counter after it reaches the desired maximum value.

In order to understand the operation of the various counters to be discussed, it is necessary to have a clear picture of how the component bits of a binary number change when the number is incremented by 1. The flow chart of Fig. 7.1 should be helpful in clarifying this process, and the reader is advised to study it carefully. Basically, what happens is that, starting at the least-significant end, every bit is changed up to and including the first 0-bit.

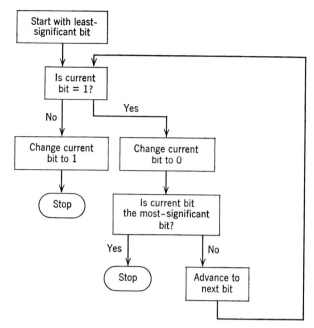

Figure 7.1   Description of counting process.

7.1   The Domino Counter

One of the earliest and simplest forms of binary electronic counter, depicted in Fig. 7.2, consists of a chain of τ-FF's (see Section 1.6) coupled by capacitors and with the input signal A, going only to the first member of the chain. The binary representation that constitutes the output is taken from the y-terminals of the FF's, with the least-significant bit on the left.

Operation is as follows, assuming that logical 1's are represented by the more positive voltages and that the FF's respond only to positive pulses. Each time an A-pulse occurs, FF-1 changes state, which of course means that y_1 behaves correctly as the least-significant bit by changing each time the counter is advanced. When $\bar{y}_1$ changes from $1 \to 0$, the capacitor transmits a negative-going pulse to τ_2, which by assumption produces no effect. But when FF-1 changes to the reset state, meaning that $\bar{y}_1$ goes on, a *positive* pulse goes to FF-2 causing it to change state. Hence y_2 changes value whenever the advance pulse causes y_1 to go from 1 to 0. Again, this situation is as it should be if y_2 is to represent the next binary digit of the count. Assume now that the first i FF's properly represent the i least-significant bits of the output of the counter. Then the $(i + 1)$st FF will receive an input pulse only after an A-pulse has occurred when all FF's to the left are in the set state. Since

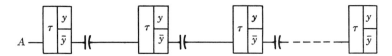

Figure 7.2   Domino counter.

this is precisely the way this FF should behave if its y-output represents the $(i + 1)$st bit of a counter, it follows by induction that the circuit is indeed a counter. Its maximum value for m stages is $2^m - 1$. The term "domino counter" is suggested by the fact that, when the k least-significant FF's are each in the 1-state, the advance signal "knocks over" the first FF (into the 0-state) which, in the act of "falling" knocks over the next FF, etc., until the last 1-FF in the string spoils the analogy somewhat by "standing up" the first 0-FF.

Observe that it may take up to m times the switching time of one FF and its coupling capacitor to advance the count of an m-stage counter by 1. If it is necessary to perform some operation on the basis of each consecutive state of the counter, then consecutive advance pulses must be separated by intervals at least equal to the above amount. However if the counter is to be read only after a series of advance pulses have occurred (as would be the case if the object were to count the number of pulses), then the pulses in that series need be separated only by intervals corresponding to the switching time of the slowest FF and its coupling capacitor. This is because once an advance pulse has switched the first FF and perhaps initiated a train of action, a second pulse may be applied even while this action is still occurring. The indicated minimum spacing ensures that the action of a subsequent pulse will not overtake that caused by an earlier pulse.

The problems entailed in designing such counters, particularly those associated with the charging and discharging of the coupling capacitors so as to obtain pulses of appropriate shape and magnitude are such as to require rather slow operating rates if reliable operation is to be assured. This factor is compounded by the serial nature of the circuit.

7.2   Pulse-mode Counters—Parallel Feed

By using the same basic FF as the domino counter, but replacing the coupling capacitors with logic elements, it is possible to arrange matters so that, except for logic delays, all FF's that are supposed to change receive their change pulses simultaneously. Such a counter is shown in Fig. 7.3a, where it is evident that the advance pulse is gated to a FF iff every FF to its left is in the set state. The delay elements are necessary for the reason presented in Section 6.2, namely, to prevent the effects of a FF change caused by a particular

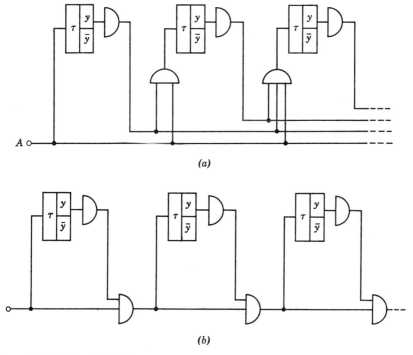

Figure 7.3 (a) Parallel-feed counter with minimal length signal paths. (b) Parallel-feed counter with minimal fan-in and fan-out.

advance pulse from propagating through the logic while that pulse is still on. In general, the considerations discussed in Section 6.2 govern the constraints on the advance pulse width, delay values, etc. This circuit can be operated at a considerably higher speed than the domino counter can.

There are, however, some serious fan-in and fan-out problems associated with counters of this form when m, the number of stages, exceeds 4 or 5. The AND gate feeding the kth FF has k inputs, the advance pulse fans out to m circuits, and the kth FF feeds $m - k$ circuits. One solution to this problem is shown in Fig. 7.3b, where the logic is of a more serial nature, with both fan-in and fan-out limited to 2. This solution, however, leads to two other problems, namely, slower operation due to longer signal paths through the logic, and signal deterioration when the AND gates do not contain amplifying elements. Compromises between the circuits of Fig. 7.3a and b are possible to meet various fan-in and fan-out constraints (see Problem 7.1), and such circuits are in common use.

The general disadvantages of pulse-mode counters are those indicated in Section 6.2 for the general class of pulsed and synchronous circuits.

7.3   Circuits Responsive to Trailing Edges

The circuits of the preceding section can be converted to asynchronous form, eliminating the need for the upper bound on the width of the advance pulse, by employing τ-FF's that behave according to Table 7.1. Such an asynchronous τ-FF is characterized by the fact that its outputs respond only to the *trailing* edge of the input pulse; that is, no response occurs for τ changing $0 \to 1$, but the output does change when the pulse goes off (τ changes from $1 \to 0$).

If such FF's are used, then regardless of how long the A-signal remains on in either of the circuits of Fig. 7.3, only those FF's that are supposed to change will receive τ-signals, since by the time any FF outputs change, A is back to 0. The essential hazards may be counted by making sure that for each stage the delays in the path through the FF exceed the delays in the path around the FF. A delay element at the output of each FF accomplishes this (though it may be unnecessary), and no other delay elements are needed external to the FF's.

Asynchronous τ-FF's can be synthesized in a straightforward manner. One design has already been presented (see Problem 5.2). A second solution, involving a pair of SR-FF's is shown in Fig. 7.4a. When $\tau = 0$, the upper FF copies the state of the lower one, and when $\tau = 1$, the lower FF assumes the state *opposite* to the state of the upper FF. In order to combat the essential hazard inherent in Table 7.1, an inertial delay can be used inside one of the FF's. An alternative approach, which also eliminates the need for external delay elements in the counter, is to make sure there is a suitable interval during which the gating signals p and q are both 0 following *each* change in τ. The circuit of Fig. 7.4b (see also Fig. 6.13 c and d) accomplishes this when inserted between p and q in place of the inverter in Fig. 7.4a.

Those readers with some knowledge of electronics might be interested in analyzing the FF shown in Fig. 7.5, a realization of Table 7.1 with just *three* transistors. Counters employing this type of circuit have been found to be practical.

**Table 7.1   Flow Table
for   an   Asynchronous
τ-FF**

	τ	
	0	1
1	①, 01	2 , 01
2	3 , 10	②, 01
3	③, 10	4 , 10
4	1 , 01	④, 10

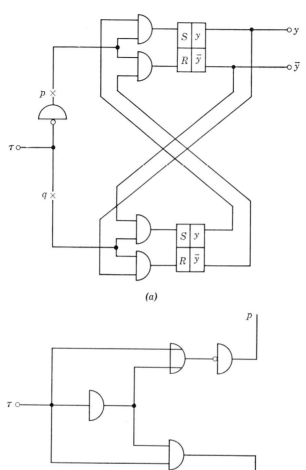

(a)

(b)

Figure 7.4   (a) An asynchronous τ-FF. (b) Input circuit for part (a) to combat essential hazards.

7.4   The Gray-code Counter

Suppose now that we wish to design a counter with the speed and reliability advantages of asynchronous operation. A straightforward approach would be to construct an appropriate flow table and then to find a suitable row assignment. In the latter part of Subsection 4.3.3 this is done for a four-state counter (see Table 4.10). A Gray-code assignment is used, and the same process is

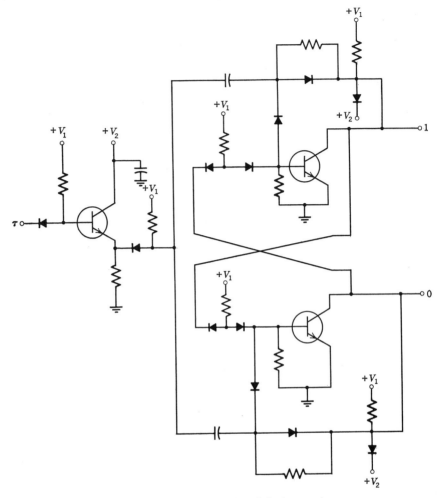

Figure 7.5 A FF that triggers on the trailing edge of the input pulse.

clearly applicable to the design of counters with maximum values corresponding to any power of 2. It is pointed out earlier that only one delay element is
necessary in a circuit constructed from such a flow matrix, an inertial delay
associated with the most frequently changing y-variable.

Unfortunately this approach does not appear to lead to a simple circuit
pattern that is easily iterated for an arbitrary number of stages. Furthermore
since the output variables do not correspond to state variables (except for the
most-significant variable), special logic is needed to generate the output.
When realized in iterative form (a Gray-code to binary-code circuit), which is

the least costly approach, there are long chains of logic involved which result in a loss of effective operating speed. For these reasons, counters of this type are rarely, if ever, used.

7.5 The Ware Counter

The approach of Section 7.4 can be modified to meet the principal objections. As shown in Table 7.2 a Liu-type row assignment (see Subsection 3.3.2) is made in which the substates assigned to the destination sets of each column correspond to the desired sequence of binary numbers. Thus the need for generating a separate set of output signals is eliminated, as the outputs can be taken directly from the FF's representing the y-variables chosen for the 0 column.

Now, assuming that SR-FF's are to be used as state devices, we observe that, when a Liu assignment is used as in this case, the variables associated with a given column remain stable in that column. Hence the y^0-FF's are not excited when $x = 0$, and the y^1-FF's are not excited when $x = 1$. Furthermore, the excitations for the y^1-FF's in column 0 are functions only of the y^0-variables, and the y^0-FF excitations in column 1 depend only on the y^1-variables. Examination of Table 7.2 reveals that, in the stable states of column 0, $y_i^1 = y_i^0$ for $i = 1$, 2. Hence the excitations for the y^1-FF's can be specified, for $i = 1$, 2, as

$$S_i^1 = \bar{A}y_i^0,$$
$$R_i^1 = \bar{A}\bar{y}_i^0.$$

Further examination reveals that, in the stable states of column 1, the y^0-state when regarded as a binary number exceeds by 1 the y^1-state when similarly regarded and that the y^1-state is the same as the *preceding* y^0-state. Thus the y^0-FF's that must change state correspond precisely to the y^1-FF's

Table 7.2 Flow Matrix for the Ware Counter

| | A | | | | | |
	0	1	y_2^0	y_1^0	y_2^1	y_1^1
1	①	2	0	0	0	0
2	3	②	0	1	0	0
3	③	4	0	1	0	1
4	5	④	1	0	0	1
5	⑤	6	1	0	1	0
6	7	⑥	1	1	1	0
7	⑦	8	1	1	1	1
8	1	⑧	0	0	1	1

that would have to be changed if the y^1-FF's alone constituted the counter. It follows that $y_1{}^0$ should always assume the value $\bar{y}_1{}^1$ when $A = 1$ so that we have

$$S_1{}^0 = A\bar{y}_1{}^1,$$

$$R_1{}^0 = Ay_1{}^1.$$

Also, $y_2{}^0$ should remain fixed, or change to $\bar{y}_2{}^1$ if $y_1{}^1 = 1$, thus yielding

$$S_2{}^0 = Ay_1{}^1\bar{y}_2{}^1,$$

$$R_2{}^0 = Ay_1{}^1y_2{}^1.$$

Clearly the above reasoning can be extended to counters that have 2^m states for any integer m simply by continuing Table 7.2 and observing that all of the above arguments remain valid. The expressions for $S_i{}^1$ and $R_i{}^1$ remain unchanged as i is permitted to increase, and we can generalize the expressions for the S^0- and R^0-terms as below:

$$S_1{}^0 = A\bar{y}_1{}^1,$$

$$S_i{}^0 = A\bar{y}_i{}^1 \prod_{j=1}^{i-1} y_j{}^1, \qquad \text{for} \qquad i = 2, 3, \ldots, m,$$

$$R_i{}^0 = A \prod_{j=1}^{i} y_j{}^1, \qquad \text{for} \qquad i = 1, 2, 3, \ldots, m.$$

Now the second problem referred to in Section 7.4 has been solved, since the logic generalizes in a simple manner as the size of the counter is increased, though at the price of nearly doubling the number of FF's. A logic circuit implementing this scheme is shown in Fig. 7.6.

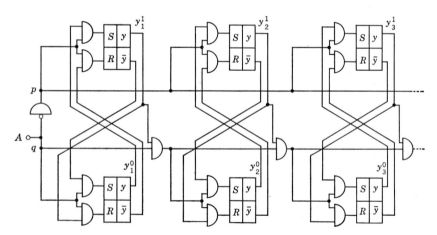

Figure 7.6 The Ware counter.

An inspection of this circuit reveals that it is virtually the same as the circuit referred to, but not shown, in Section 7.3 in which asynchronous τ-FF's of the form of Fig. 7.4a are connected according to the scheme of Fig. 7.3b! (We could also, of course, have constructed our circuit to conform to Fig. 7.3a or anything in between while realizing the same excitation expressions.) The same choices exist for combatting hazards discussed earlier. In particular we could replace the A-signal and its complement with the circuit of Fig. 7.4b, thereby eliminating the need for *all* other delays in the circuit. This approach is a special case of the "delayed-input" method of countering hazards described in Subsection 4.3.3.

Examining once more the reasoning that led to Fig. 7.6, paying particular attention to the roles played by the two sets of FF's, we see still another familiar pattern emerge. During one input state, the y^1-FF's copy the y^0-FF's, and during the other input state, the y^0-FF's assume states dependent on the y^1-values. This is precisely the mechanism of the type-1 double-rank circuit illustrated in Fig. 6.13 and discussed in Section 6.3. The y^1-FF's correspond to rank 2 and the y^0-FF's to rank 1, while the roles of the C_1 and C_2 clock pulses are played by the q- and p-signals, respectively, of the input circuit of Fig. 7.4b (which is the same as the circuit of Fig. 6.13c proposed as a means for obtaining suitably related C_1- and C_2-pulses from a single clock-pulse source). Note that there are *no* inputs to our counter corresponding to the x-inputs of the general model. The output may be taken from either rank, though if we take it from the y^0-FF's, only this set need be initialized, assuming we start with $A = 0$.

The Ware counter was in fact conceived from the point of view of double-rank circuits (well before the development of the theory leading to the initial approach presented here) and was the prototype for the class of double-rank circuits. It is considered to be fast, efficient, and reliable.

7.6 The Mayne Counter

As we have seen in Section 6.3, it is sometimes possible to reduce the number of FF's in one rank of a double-rank circuit by using nontrivial logic to excite *both* ranks. The question thus arises of whether a double-rank counter can be constructed with only *one* of the ranks representing the binary number constituting the output and with the other rank containing a smaller number of FF's.

Before approaching this question directly we examine it briefly in terms of state assignments. Referring now to the Tracey method for finding a USTT assignment (Subsection 3.3.2), we note that, in a flow table for a counter (such as Table 7.2), a row assignment in which the states correspond to the desired outputs—that is, an ordered sequence of binary numbers (such as the y^0-variables in the example)—covers all of the dichotomies in one column (the 0 column in this case) and *some* of the dichotomies [(12, 56), for example] in the other column. Hence we may reasonably hope that the remaining dichotomies may be covered by a smaller number of additional state variables. Since there seems to be no obvious way to approach this question in a general manner and since testing this hypothesis for a particular case would be a tedious, though straightforward chore, we shall not pursue this aspect further.

Now let us see how we can synthesize the eight-state counter described by Table 7.3a in the form of a type-2 double-rank circuit (Fig. 6.14). We begin by assigning the states of the rank-2 FF's to correspond to the output, as shown in Table 7.3b. Next we generate the change matrix Table 7.3c, and apply the techniques of Section 6.3 to determine a minimal set of excitation entries that satisfy all of the change-matrix entries, namely $S_1 R_1 S_2 R_2 S_3 R_3 =$ 000010, 001001, 100101, 010101. This leads to the excitation matrix Table 7.3d. Next, the four excitation states are coded in terms of rank-1 variables

Table 7.3

				y_1^2	y_2^2	y_3^2
1	2, 000	1	2, 000	0	0	0
2	3, 001	2	3, 001	0	0	1
3	4, 010	3	4, 010	0	1	0
4	5, 011	4	5, 011	0	1	1
5	6, 100	5	6, 100	1	0	0
6	7, 101	6	7, 101	1	0	1
7	8, 110	7	8, 110	1	1	0
8	1, 111	8	1, 111	1	1	1

(a) Flow table.	(b) Flow matrix.

		y_1^2	y_2^2	y_3^2
1	$\bar{S}\bar{S}S$	0	0	0
2	$\bar{S}\bar{S}R$	0	0	1
3	$\bar{S}RS$	0	1	0
4	SRR	0	1	1
5	$\bar{R}\bar{S}S$	1	0	0
6	$\bar{R}SR$	1	0	1
7	$\bar{R}\bar{R}S$	1	1	0
8	RRR	1	1	1

	S_1^2	R_1^2	S_2^2	R_2^2	S_3^2	R_3^2	y_1^2	y_2^2	y_3^2
1	0	0	0	0	1	0	0	0	0
2	0	0	1	0	0	1	0	0	1
3	0	0	0	0	1	0	0	1	0
4	1	0	0	1	0	1	0	1	1
5	0	0	0	0	1	0	1	0	0
6	0	0	1	0	0	1	1	0	1
7	0	0	0	0	1	0	1	1	0
8	0	1	0	1	0	1	1	1	1

(c) Change matrix.	(d) Excitation matrix.

Table 7.3 (*continued*)

						y_1^1	y_2^1
0	0	0	0	1	0	0	0
0	0	1	0	0	1	0	1
1	0	0	1	0	1	1	0
0	1	0	1	0	1	1	1

$S_1^2 \quad R_1^2 \quad S_2^2 \quad R_2^2 \quad S_3^2 \quad R_3^2$

(*e*) Matrix for rank-2 excitation logic.

					y_1^2	y_2^2	y_3^2
1	0	1	0	1	0	0	0
2	0	1	1	0	0	0	1
3	0	1	0	1	0	1	0
4	1	0	0	1	0	1	1
5	0	1	0	1	1	0	0
6	0	1	1	0	1	0	1
7	0	1	0	1	1	1	0
8	1	0	1	0	1	1	1

$S_1^1 \quad R_1^1 \quad S_2^1 \quad R_2^1$

(*f*) Matrix for rank-1 excitation logic.

$y_1^1 y_2^1$ as 00, 01, 10, and 11, respectively, as shown in Table 7.3*e*. Finally, the entries in the excitation matrix of Table 7.3*d* are replaced by excitations for rank-1 FF's that in each case takes these FF's to states that, according to part *e*, generate the original entries of part *d*. The result is the rank-1 excitation matrix shown as Table 7.3*f*. We could now proceed in a routine manner to derive the rank-1 and rank-2 logic from Table 7.3*f* and *e* respectively, bearing in mind that signals corresponding to $\bar{A}$ (or *p*) and *A* (or *q*) of Fig. 7.6 must be used to gate the rank-1 and rank-2 outputs, respectively.

Instead of doing that, let us attempt to generalize our procedure to cover counters with any number of stages. An inspection of the change matrix, Table 7.3*c*, indicates that to increment the counter when y_3^2 (the least-significant bit) = 0, we should switch y_3^2 to 1. When $y_3^2 = 1$ and $y_2^2 = 0$, we should switch y_3^2 to 0 and y_2^2 to 1. When $y_3^2 = y_2^2 = 1$ and $y_1^2 = 0$, we should switch the first 2 to 0 and turn on y_1^2. Finally, if all three *y*'s are 1, we must switch them all off. This situation, of course, conforms to our verbal description of Fig. 7.1; namely, that to increment a counter by 1, we simply switch to 0 all consecutive 1-bits, beginning at the least-significant end, and change the first 0 encountered to a 1. It follows then that to increment an *m*-bit counter, we must perform one of $m + 1$ actions, depending on the present state (there are of course 2^m possible states). Which of these actions is to be performed depends on whether the number of consecutive 1's starting at the least-significant end is 0, 1, 2, . . . , or *m*. In our current example, where $m = 3$, the number of possible actions is thus four, which explains why we found that the excitation matrix Table 7.3*d* could be constructed with only four different entries. The function of the rank-1 FF's is to record in some form *which* of the $m + 1$ actions must be performed on the rank-2 FF's. We code this information as a binary representation of the number of consecutive leading 1's in rank 2 (although there is no particular reason to think that this code is necessarily the best one possible). Thus the rank-1 logic must compute this number from rank 2 and excite the rank-1 FF's accordingly.

In Fig. 7.7 this is accomplished for our example, by first computing the signals B_i for $i = 0, 1, 2,$ and 3, corresponding to the desired number, and then setting the rank-1 FF's to the binary representation of i. For instance, if $y_1{}^2 y_2{}^2 y_3{}^2 = 010$, then B_2 is activated, and it in turn sets $y_1{}^1$ and resets $y_2{}^1$.

During phase 2 ($A = 1$ or $q = 1$), certain of the rank-2 FF's are changed in accordance with the information stored in rank 1. In particular, if i is stored in rank 1, then C_i is activated and the i low-order rank-2 FF's are reset, and the $(i + 1)$st FF (if $i + 1 \leq m$) is set. For our current example, the logic accomplishing this can be seen in Fig. 7.7. Thus if $i = 2$ ($y_1{}^1 = 1$ and $y_2{}^1 = 0$), then during phase 2, C_2 goes on causing $y_3{}^2$ and $y_2{}^2$ to be reset and $y_1{}^2$ to be set.

In general then, if the counter is to have 2^m states (m FF's in rank 2), then $\lceil \log_2 (m + 1) \rceil$ rank-1 FF's are necessary. Thus, for the Mayne counter, $m + \lceil \log_2 (m + 1) \rceil$ FF's are needed to count from 0 to 2^m as opposed to $2m$ for the Ware counter, $m + 1$ for the Gray-code counter, and m for the domino or pulse-mode counter.

The Mayne counter shares the advantages of the Ware counter with respect to speed and reliability. As may be seen by comparing Figs. 7.6 and 7.7, the Mayne counter apparently requires more logic than the Ware counter, in contrast to the savings in number of FF's. (It has been pointed out to the author by A. Friedes that in Fig. 7.7 it is sufficient to feed only the B_0-signal to the reset terminals of the rank-1 FF's, since B_0 is energized during alternate phase-1 intervals. This economy eliminates the need for the OR gates at these terminals, but makes it necessary to initialize the rank-1 FF's as well as the rank-2 FF's if the counter is started at an odd-numbered value.) Quite possibly the complexity of the logic for the Mayne counter might be significantly cut by the use of iterative circuit techniques whereby components might be saved at the price of introducing longer logic paths (as is done at a simpler level for the case of Fig. 7.3). Consideration might also be given to finding an alternative coding of the rank-1 logic, a possibility alluded to earlier.

SOURCES

The author has been unable to trace the origins of the domino counter or of the parallel-feed counters of Section 7.2. The FF of Fig. 7.5 was invented by W. B. Cagle et al. [CAG-1] who used it in a counter. W. H. Ware is responsible for the Ware counter [WAR-1]. R. H. Mayne is the inventor of the Mayne counter [MAY-1]; he also developed a variation of this counter to include a parity check bit [MAY-2]. Some other interesting papers on counters that are

Rank 1   Rank 2

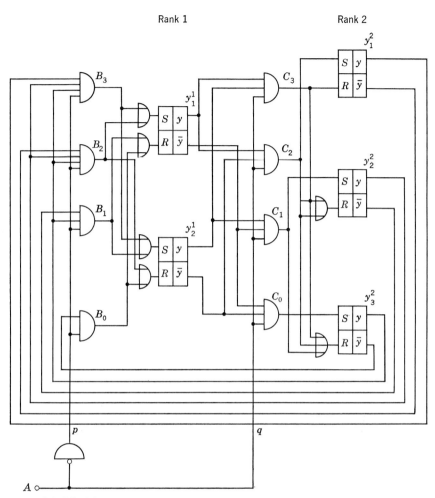

Figure 7.7   The Mayne counter.

not discussed here are by Kain [KA-1] and Marcus [MAR-3]. Additional material on counters can be found in a book by Richards [RIC-1].

PROBLEMS

*7.1   Design a pulse-mode five-stage parallel-feed counter in which no AND gate has a fan-in or fan-out in excess of 3, and in which no signal passes through more than two stages of logic.

*7.2   Design a pulse-mode parallel-feed counter that counts from 0 to 5 and then cycles back to 0 on the next count.

7.3   Design a domino counter using τ-FF's that trigger on the trailing edges of the input pulses.

References

Although no claim to completeness is made, the references listed here include the principal works dealing with the subject matter of this book, as well as a number of books and papers of collateral interest. Direct references are made to this material in the sections on "sources" that conclude each chapter, and there are also a few references made in the body of the text.

Several introductory texts on switching circuit theory which deal at most marginally with asynchronous circuits may be brought to the reader's attention. They are (in no particular order) by Prather [PRA-1], Marcus [MAR-4], Torng [TOR-1], Wood [WOO-1], Krieger [KRI-1], Phister [PHI-1], Humphrey [HUM-1], Bartee, Lebow, and Reed [BAR-1], and Hill and Peterson [HI]. Moore [MO-1] has edited an interesting collection of papers in the field, and books edited by McCluskey and Bartee [McC-5] and by Biorci [BIO-1] contain a number of interesting papers, both tutorial and otherwise. Some books treating "finite automata," which are clocked sequential circuits considered in terms of relations between input and output sequences, are by Booth [BOO-1], Hennie [HENN-1], Gill [GILL-1], Ginsburg [GIN-4], and Harrison [HARR-1]. The first two are the most up-to-date treatments.

The most important journal with respect to papers on switching theory is the *IEEE Transactions on Computers* (*IEEE-TC*, formerly *IEEE-TEC* and *IRE-TEC*), with the *Journal of the Association for Computing Machinery* (*JACM*) in second place. Other important sources, particularly for early publication of results are the *Proceedings of the Annual Symposia on Switching and Automata Theory*.

AR-1   D. B. Armstrong, A. D. Friedman, and P. R. Menon, "Design of asynchronous circuits assuming unbounded gate delays," Bell Laboratories internal memorandum, 1967. (To appear in *IEEE-TC* in 1969.)

AR-2   D. B. Armstrong, A. D. Friedman, and P. R. Menon, "Realization of asynchronous sequential circuits without inserted delay elements," *IEEE-TC*, **C-17**, No. 2, 129–134 (February 1968).

BAR-1 T. C. Bartee, I. L. Lebow, I. S. Reed, *Theory and Design of Digital Machines*, McGraw-Hill, New York, 1962.

BE-1   J. Beatty and R. Miller, "Some theorems for incompletely specified sequential machines with applications to state minimization," *Proc. 3rd Ann. Symp. Switching Circuit Theory, Logical Design*, 123–136 (September 1962).

BE-2   J. Beatty and R. Miller, "An approach to state minimization for incompletely specified sequential machines," *IBM Research Report*, **RC-1055** (September 1963).

BIO-1   G. Biorci, ed., *Network and Switching Theory, A NATO Advanced Study Institute*, Academic Press, New York, 1968.

BOO-1   T. L. Booth, *Sequential Machines and Automata Theory*, John Wiley & Sons, New York, 1967.

BRE   T. H. Bredt and E. J. McCluskey, "Analysis and synthesis of control mechanisms for parallel processes," *Symposia on Parallel Processing Systems and Applications*, Naval Postgraduate School, Monterey, California, June 25–27, 1969.

BR-1   J. A. Brzozowski, "Some problems in relay circuit design," *IEEE-TEC*, **EC-14**, No. 4, 630–634 (August 1965).

BR-2   J. A. Brzozowski and S. Singh, "Definite asynchronous sequential circuits," *IEEE-TEC*, **C-17**, No. 1, 18–26 (January 1968).

CAG-1   W. B. Cagle, R. S. Menne, R. S. Skinner, R. E. Staehler, and M. D. Underwood, "No. 1 ESS logic circuits and their application to the design of the central control," *BSTJ*, **43**, 2055–2095 (September 1964).

CAL-1   S. H. Caldwell, *Switching Circuits and Logical Design*, John Wiley & Sons, New York, 1958.

EI-1   E. B. Eichelberger, "Sequential circuits synthesis using hazards and delays," Ph.D. Dissertation, Dept. of Electrical Engineering, Princeton University, March 1963.

EI-2   E. B. Eichelberger, "Sequential circuit synthesis using input delays," *Proc. 4th IEEE Annual Symp. on Switching Circuit Theory and Logical Design*, **S-156**, 105–116 (September 1963).

EI-3   E. B. Eichelberger, "Hazard detection in combinational and sequential switching circuits," *IBMJ*, **9**, No. 2, 90–99 (March 1965).

EL-1   B. Elspas, J. Goldberg, R. A. Short, and H. S. Stone, "Investigation of propagation-limited computer networks," Final Report—Phase II, Stanford Research Institute, July 1965.

FE-1   D. Ferrari and A. Grasselli, "A cellular structure for sequential networks," *IEEE Conference Record of 8th Annual Symposium on Switching and Automata Theory*, 210–225 (October 1967).

FRD-1   A. Friedes, "State reduction and state assignments for asynchronous sequential machines," Ph.D. Dissertation, Department of Electrical Engineering, Columbia University, 1967.

FRM-1   A. D. Friedman, "Feedback in synchronous and asynchronous sequential switching circuits," Ph.D. Dissertation, Department of Electrical Engineering, Columbia University, 1965.

FRM-2   A. D. Friedman, "Feedback in asynchronous sequential circuits," *IEEE-TEC*, **EC-15**, No. 5, 740–749 (October 1966).

FRM-3   A. D. Friedman, "Feedback in synchronous sequential circuits," *IEEE-TEC*, **EC-15**, No. 3, 354–367 (June 1966).

FRM-4   A. D. Friedman, R. L. Graham, J. D. Ullman, "Universal single transition time asynchronous state assignments," *IEEE-TC*, **C-18**, No. 6, 541–547 (June 1969).

FRM-5   A. D. Friedman and P. R. Menon, "Synthesis of asynchronous sequential circuits with multiple input changes," *IEEE-TEC*, **C-17**, No. 6, 559–566 (June 1968).

GE-1   G. B. Gerace and G. Gestri, "State assignments for reducing the number of delay elements in sequential machines," *Information and Control*, 10, No. 3, 223-253 (March 1967).

GE-2   G. B. Gerace and G. Gestri, "Sequential machines with less delay elements than feedback paths," June 1967, unpublished (submitted to *TEC*).

GILB-1   E. N. Gilbert, "Gray codes and paths on the *n*-cube," *BSTJ*, **37,** 815–826 (May 1958).

GILC-1   B. Gilchrist, J. H. Pomerine, and S. Y. Wong, "Fast carry logic for digital computers," *IRE-TEC*, **EC-4,** 133–136 (December 1955).

GILL-1   A. Gill, *Introduction to the Theory of Finite State Machines*, McGraw-Hill, New York, 1962.

GIM-1   J. F. Gimpel, "A reduction technique for prime implicant tables," *IEEE-TEC*, **EC-14,** no. 4, 542–552 (August 1965).

GIN-1   S. Ginsburg, "A synthesis technique for minimal-state sequential machines," Natl. Cash Register Co .internal report, July 1958.

GIN-2   S. Ginsburg, "On the reduction of superfluous states in a sequential machine," *JACM*, **6,** 259–282 (April 1959).

GIN-3   S. Ginsburg, "A technique for the reduction of a given machine to a minimal-state machine," *IRE-TEC*, **EC-8,** No. 3, 346–355 (September 1959).

GIN-4   S. Ginsburg, *An Introduction to Mathematical Machine Theory*, Addison-Wesley, Reading, Mass. 1962.

GR-1   A. Grasselli and F. Luccio, "A method for minimizing the number of internal states in incompletely specified sequential networks," *IEEE-TEC*, **EC-14,** No. 3, 350–359 (June 1965).

GR-2   A. Grasselli, "Minimal closed partitions for incompletely specified flow tables," *IEEE-TEC*, **EC-15,** No. 2, 245–249 (April 1966).

GR-3   A. Grasselli and F. Luccio, "A method for combined row-column reduction of flow tables," *Proc. 7th Ann. Symp. Switching Theory, Automata* (September 1966).

HAL-1   A. D. Hall, Jr., "Introduction to the theory of speed independent asynchronous switching circuits," Report No. 50, Digital Systems Laboratory, Princeton University, July 1966.

HAL-2   A. D. Hall, Jr., "Synthesis of double rank sequential circuits," Report No. 53, Digital Systems Laboratory, Princeton University, Dec. 1966.

HAL-3   A. D. Hall, Jr., and F. S. Acton, "Scheduling university course examinations by computer," *CACM*, **10,** No. 4, 235–238 (April 1967).

HAL-4   A. D. Hall, Jr., "Treatment of delays in asynchronous networks," Ph.D. Dissertation, Dept. of Electrical Engineering, Princeton University, 1966.

HAMG-1   R. W. Hamming, "Error detecting and correcting codes," *BSTJ*, **29,** 147–160 (April 1950).

HAML-1   D. Hammel, "Ideas on asynchronous feedback networks," *Proc. 5th Ann. Symp. Switching Theory, Logical Design, Princeton University, November* 11–13, 1964. pp. 4–11.

HARR-1   M. A. Harrison, *Introduction to Switching and Automata Theory*, McGraw-Hill New York, 1965.

HART-1   J. Hartmanis and R. E. Stearns, *Algebraic Structure Theory of Sequential Machines*, Prentice-Hall, Englewood Cliffs, N.J. 1966.

HAZ-1 B. Hazeltine, "Encoding of asynchronous sequential circuits," *IEEE-TEC*, **EC-14**, 727–729 (October 1965).

HEND-1 H. C. Hendrickson, "Fast high-accuracy binary parallel addition," *IRE-TEC*, **EC-9**, No. 4, 465–469 (December 1960).

HENN-1 F. C. Hennie, *Finite State Models for Logical Machines*, John Wiley & Sons, New York, 1968.

HI F. J. Hill and G. R. Peterson, *Introduction to Switching Theory and Logical Design*, John Wiley & Sons, New York, 1968.

HUF-1 D. A. Huffman, "The synthesis of sequential switching circuits," *J. Franklin Institute*, **257**, No. 3, 161–190 (March 1954); and No. 4, 275–303 (April 1954). Also reprinted in [MO-2].

HUF-2 D. A. Huffman, "A study of the memory requirements of sequential switching circuits," Technical Report No. 293, Research Laboratory of Electronics, MIT, March 14, 1955.

HUF-3 D. A. Huffman, "Design of hazard-free switching circuits," *JACM*, **4**, 47–62 (January 1957).

HUF-4 D. A. Huffman, unpublished paper delivered at Princeton University Symposium on Switching Theory, Princeton, N.J. January 1962.

HUM-1 W. S. Humphrey, Jr., *Switching Circuits with Computer Applications*, McGraw-Hill, New York, 1958.

KA-1 R. Y. Kain, "Synthesis of up-down counters," *IEEE-TEC*, **EC-16**, No. 2, 146–151 (April 1967).

KE-1 W. Keister, A. E. Ritchie, and S. H. Washburn, *The Design of Switching Circuits*, D. Van Nostrand, Princeton, N.J., 1951.

KI-1 L. L. Kinney, "A characterization of some asynchronous state assignments," *IEEE Conf. Rec. of Ninth Ann. Symp. on Switching and Automata theory*, pp. 20–27, Oct. 1968.

KI-2 L. L. Kinney, "Decomposition of asynchronous sequential switching circuits," Ph.D. dissertation, Electrical Engineering Dept., University of Iowa, February 1968.

KL-1 M. Kliman and O. Lowenschuss, "Asynchronous electronic switching circuits," 1959 *IRE National Conv. Rec.*, Pt. 4, 267–271.

KRI-1 M. Krieger, *Basic Switching Circuit Theory*, The Macmillan Co., New York, 1967.

LA-1 C. G. Langdon, Jr., "Analysis and synthesis of asynchronous circuits under different delay assumptions," Ph.D. dissertation, Electrical Engineering Dept. (also *Technical Report* TR67-14), Syracuse University, October 1967.

LA-2 G. G. Langdon, Jr., "Delay-free asynchronous circuits with constrained line delays," *IEEE-TC*, *V.C.*-17, 1131–1143 (December 1968).

LE-1 S. B. Lerner, "Hazard correction in asynchronous sequential circuits," *IEEE-TEC*, **EC-14**, No. 2, 265–267 (April 1965).

LIU-1 C. N. Liu, "A state variable assignment method for asynchronous sequential switching circuits," *JACM*, **10**, 209–216 (April 1963).

MAL-1 G. A. Maley and J. Earle, *The Logic Design of Transistor Digital Computers*, Prentice-Hall, Englewood Cliffs, N.J., 1963.

MAR-1 M. P. Marcus, "Relay essential hazards," *IEEE-TEC*, **EC-12**, 405–407 (August 1963).

MAR-2 M. P. Marcus, "Derivation of maximal compatibles using Boolean algebra," *IBMJ*, **8**, No. 5, 537–538 (November 1964).

MAR-3 M. P. Marcus, "Cascaded binary counters with feedback," *IEEE-TEC*, **EC-12**, 361–364 (August 1963).

MAR-4   M. P. Marcus, *Switching Circuits for Engineers*, Prentice-Hall, Englewood Cliffs, N.J., 1962.

MAY-1   R. H. Mayne, "The binary counter: a novel logical design," unpublished Bell Laboratories memorandum, October 1958.

MAY-2   R. H. Mayne, "A binary counter with associated parity bit," unpublished Bell Laboratories memorandum, Nov. 1958.

McC-1   E. J. McCluskey, "Fundamental mode and pulse mode sequential circuits," *Proc. IFIP Congress* 1962, *Munich Germany*, *Information Processing*, North-Holland Publishing Co., Amsterdam, pp. 725–730.

McC-2   E. J. McCluskey, "Minimum-state sequential circuits for a restricted class of incompletely specified flow tables," *BSTJ*, **4,** 1759–1768 (November 1962).

McC-3   E. J. McCluskey, "Transient behavior of combinational logic networks", in *Redundancy Techniques for Computing Systems*, Spartan Books, pp. 9–46, 1962.

McC-4   E. J. McCluskey, *Introduction to The Theory of Switching Circuits*, McGraw-Hill New York, 1965.

McC-5   E. J. McCluskey and T. C. Bartee, eds., *A Survey of Modern Switching Circuit Theory*, McGraw-Hill, New York, 1962.

McN-1   R. McNaughton, "Badly timed elements and well timed nets," Moore School Report No. 65–02, University of Pennsylvania, June 10, 1964.

ME-1   G. H. Mealy, "A method for synthesizing sequential circuits," *BSTJ*, **34,** 1045–1079 (September 1955).

MLM-1   J. Millman and H. Taub, *Pulse, Digital, and Switching Waveforms*, McGraw-Hill, New York, 1965.

MLR-1   R. E. Miller, *Switching Theory*, Vol. I: *Combinational Circuits*, John Wiley & Sons, New York, 1965.

MLR-2   R. E. Miller, *Switching Theory*, Vol. II: *Sequential Circuits and Machines*, John Wiley & Sons, New York, 1965.

MO-1   E. F. Moore, "Gedanken experiments on sequential machines" in [SH-1].

MO-2   E. F. Moore, *Sequential Machines: Selected Papers*, Addison-Wesley, Reading, Mass., 1964.

MU-1   D. E. Muller and W. S. Bartky, "A theory of asynchronous circuits I," Report No. 75, University of Illinois, Digital Computer Laboratory, Nov. 1956.

MU-2   D. E. Muller and W. S. Bartky, "A theory of asynchronous circuits II," Report No. 78, University of Illinois, Digital Computer Laboratory, March 1957.

MU-3   D. E. Muller and W. S. Bartky, "A theory of asynchronous circuits," *Proc. of an Int. Symp. on the Theory of Switching*, vol. 29, Annals of the Computation Laboratory of Harvard University, Harvard University Press, pp. 204–243, 1959.

MU-4   D. E. Muller, "The general synthesis problem for asynchronous digital networks," *IEEE Conference Record of Eighth Ann. Symp. Switching, Automata Theory*, 71–82 (October 1967).

MU-5   D. E. Muller, "Treatment of transition signals in electronic sequential circuits by algebraic methods," *IRE-TEC*, **EC-8,** No. 3, 401 (September 1959).

MU-6   D. E. Muller, "Asynchronous logics and application to information technology," *Proc. of a Symp. on the Application of Switching Theory in Space Technology*, Stanford University Press, March 1962.

NA-1   R. Narasimhan, "Minimizing incompletely specified sequential switching functions," *IRE-TEC*, **EC-10,** No. 3, 531-532 (September 1961).

PA-1   M. C. Paull and S. H. Unger, "Minimizing the number of states in incompletely specified sequential switching functions," *IRE-TEC*, **EC-8,** No. 3, 356–367 (September 1959).

PA-2   M. C. Paull and G. Waldbaum, "A note on state minimization of asynchronous sequential functions," *IEEE-TEC* **EC-16**, No. 1, 94–97 (February 1967).

PA-3   M. C. Paull, "The minimization of the number of states of a completely specified sequential function having restrictions on its allowable input sequences," unpublished Bell Telephone Laboratories memorandum, 1966.

PHI-1   M. Phister, *Logic Design of Digital Computers*, John Wiley & Sons, New York, 1956.

PRA-1   R. E. Prather, *Introduction to Switching Theory: A Mathematical Approach*, Allyn and Bacon Inc., Boston, 1967.

RE-1   I. S. Reed, "Some remarks on state reduction of asynchronous circuits by the Paull-Unger method," *IEEE-TEC*, **EC-14**, No. 2, 262–265 (April 1965).

RIC-1   R. K. Richards, *Arithmetic Operations in Digital Computers*, D. Van Nostrand, Princeton, N.J., 1955.

RO-1   J. E. Robertson, "Problems in the physical realization of speed independent circuits," *Proc. 2nd AIEE Symp. on Switching Circuit Theory and Logical Design, Detroit, Michigan*, **S-134**, 106–108 (October 1961).

SA-1   G. Saucier, "Encoding of asynchronous sequential networks," *IEEE-TEC*, **EC-16**, No. 3, 365–369 (June 1967).

SH-1   C. E. Shannon and J. McCarthy, eds. *Automata Studies*, Princeton University Press, 1956.

SIM-1   J. C. Sims, Jr., and H. J. Gray, "Design criteria for autosynchronous circuits," *Proc. Eastern Joint Computer Conf.*, Dec. 3–5, 1958, pp. 94–99.

SIN-1   S. Singh, "Asynchronous sequential circuits with feeback," Dept. of Electrical Engineering, University of Ottawa, Technical Report, No. 68–9, May 1968.

SMI-1   R. J. Smith, II, J. H. Tracey, W. L. Schoeffel, and G. K., Maki, "Automation in the design of asynchronous sequential circuits," *Proc. Spring Joint Computer Conf.*, pp. 55–60, 1968.

TA-1   C. J. Tan, "Note on general race-free assignment for asynchronous circuits," unpublished note, Columbia University Dept. of Electrical Engineering, February 19, 1967.

TA-2   C. J. Tan, "State assignment for asynchronous sequential machines," *Bell Telephone Laboratory Report* (August 1967).

TA-3   C. J. Tan, "Synthesis of asynchronous sequential switching circuits," Ph.D. Dissertation Dept. of Electrical Engineering, Columbia University, 1969.

TA-4   C. J. Tan, "Computer aided design of asynchronous sequential switching circuits," *First Ann. Houston Conf. on Circuits, Systems and Computers*, U. of Houston (May 22, 23, 1969).

TA-5   C. J. Tan, P. R. Menon, A. W. Friedman, "Simplification and decomposition of asynchronous sequential circuits," to appear in *IEEE-TC* (September 1969).

TOR-1   H. C. Torng, *Introduction to the Logical Design of Switching Systems*, Addison-Wesley, Reading, Mass. 1964.

TR-1   J. H. Tracey, "Internal state assignments for asynchronous sequential machines," *IEEE-TEC*, **EC-15**, No. 4, 551-560 (August 1966).

UN-1   S. H. Unger, "A theorem on feedback in sequential switching circuits," Quarterly Progress Report, Research Laboratory of Electronics, MIT (April 15, 1955).

UN-2   S. H. Unger, "A study of asynchronous logical feedback networks," Technical Report No. 320, Research Laboratory of Electronics, MIT (April 1957). Also Sc.D. Dissertation, Dept. of Electrical Engineering, MIT, 1957.

UN-3   S. H. Unger, "Hazards and delays in asynchronous sequential switching circuits," *IRE Trans. on Circuit Theory*, **CT-6**, 12–25 (March 1959).

UN-4   S. H. Unger, "Simplification of state tables," *AIEE Fall Meeting, Chicago* (October 1960). Reprinted in [McC-5], pp. 145–170.

UN-5   S. H. Unger, "Flow table simplification—some useful aids," *IEEE-TEC*, **EC-14,** No. 3, 472–475 (June 1965).

UN-6   S. H. Unger, "A row assignment for delay-free realizations of flow tables without essential hazards," *Proc. 7th Ann. Symp. on Switching and Automata Theory, Berkeley California, October,* 27, 1966. Also in *IEEE-TC*, **C-17,** No. 2, 146–158 (February 1968).

UN-7   S. H. Unger, "Timing considerations in clocked switching circuits," Quarterly Progress Report, Research Laboratory of Electronics, MIT, pp. 113–115 (January 16, 1956).

WAI-1 W. M. Waite, "The production of completion signals by asynchronous, iterative networks," *IEEE-TEC* **EC-13,** 83–86 (April 1964).

WAR-1 W. H. Ware, "The logical principles of a new kind of binary counter," *Proc. IRE,* **41,** No. 10, 1429–1437 (October 1953).

WOO-1 P. E. Wood, Jr., *Switching Theory*, McGraw-Hill, New York, 1968.

YOE-1 M. Yoeli and S. Rino, "Application of ternary algebra to the study of static hazards," *JACM,* **11,** No. 1, 84–97 (June 1964).

YOU-1 D. H. Younger, "Minimum feedback arc sets for a directed graph," *IEEE Trans. on Circuit Theory,* **CT-10,** 238–245 (June 1963).

Problem Solutions

1.1 The output goes on after the second consecutive X_2-change and remains on until X_1 is changed. An X_1-change always turns Z off, and two consecutive X_2-changes are required to turn Z on.

1.4

	X		C_1	C_2
	0	1		
	①	2	0	0
	3	②	1	0
	③	4	0	0
	1	④	0	1

2.2

	X	
	0	1
1	1, 0	2, 0
2	3, 0	1, 0
3	2, 1	1, 0

(a)

	X	
	0	1
1	1, 1	2, 0
2	3, 0	1, 0
3	2, 1	1, 0

(b)

Tables *a* and *b* are clearly irreducible. We *can* however reduce the given table to the following two-row table:

	X		Rows of given table
	0	1	
1	2, 0	1, 0	12
2	1, 1	1, 0	13

2.6 The final pair chart is

1					
36	2				
× ×	14 × ×	3			
13 × ×	16	× ×	4		
	12	× ×	15	5	
12	× ×	46	45	14 25 26 × ×	6

The MC's are: 245, 46, 36, 125, 16 with the implication graph as below:

$$(24) \rightarrow (16) \rightarrow (12) \rightarrow (36) \rightarrow (46) \rightarrow (45) \rightarrow (15)$$
$$(25)$$

This leads to the minimal closed covering 45, 46, 36, 125 and hence the solution

$$X_1 X_2$$

	00	01	11	10	
1	2, 0	1, 0	1, 1	1, 1	125
2	–, 1	1, 1	4, 0	3/4, 1	36
3	1, 0	1/3, –	1, 1	1, 1	45
4	1, 0	1, 1	2/4, –	3, 1	46

2.8 (*a*) The final pair chart and MC's are

1								MC's
23 45								568
	2							
46	56							469
		3						
×	×	×						457
			4					
×	×	×	13					456
				5				
×	×	×		12				123
					6			
×	×	×			×			
						7		
×	×	×	×			×		
							8	
×	×	×		×		×	×	9

The impliction graph is

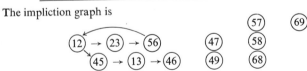

$$(12) \rightarrow (23) \rightarrow (56) \qquad (47) \qquad (57) \quad (69)$$
$$(45) \rightarrow (13) \rightarrow (46) \qquad (49) \qquad (58)$$
$$(68)$$

Note that although 123 implies 45, 46, and 56 it does *not* imply 456; hence our covering is closed without 456. The reduced table is

	A	B	C	D	
1	1, 0	2, 0	4, 0	3, 0	123
2	1, 0	1, 1	4, 1	2, 0	457
3	1, 1	1, 1	–, 1	1, 1	469
4	1, 1	1, 1	3, 0	2, 0	568

Reduced table

(*b*) The final pair chart and MC's are

MC's

1   568

23									469
45									
	2								
									457
12	13								
46	56								456
		3							
×	×	×							123
			4						
×	×	×	13						
				5					
×	×	×							
					6				
×	×	×			×				
						7			
×	×	×	×			×			
							8		
×	×	×		×		×	×	9	

The implication graph is

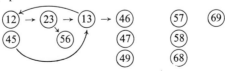

As far as *pairwise* compatibility goes, the *same* set of MC's used in part *a* is closed, namely, {123, 457, 469, 568}. But in this case 123 → 456, and so this is *not* a closed set. One solution is {123, 457, 469, 568, 456}. Another solution is {123, 456, 7, 8, 9}. The reduced table is

	A	B	C	D	
1	1, 0	2, 0	–, 0	3, –	123
2	1, 1	1, 1	–, 1	1, 0	456
3	–, 0	–, 1	4, –	–	7
4	–, 1	–, 0	5, –	–	8
5	–, 1	–, 1	–	1, 1	9

Reduced table

2.11 (a) Let i_a and i_b be row i of table a or table b, respectively, and let $i_a \, \mathbf{c} \, j_b$ mean that row i_a *covers* row j_b. Only 3_a can cover 2_b (because of outputs):

$$3_a \, \mathbf{c} \, 2_b \rightarrow 1_a \, \mathbf{c} \, 3_b \rightarrow 1_a \, \mathbf{c} \, 1_b.$$

But 1_a cannot cover 1_b because the output for 1_a is unspecified in column B; whereas the corresponding 1_b-output *is* specified. Hence table a does *not* cover table b.

2.15 Find largest sets of classes for which simultaneous exams are OK. (See [HAL-3])

Checks indicate compatible classes

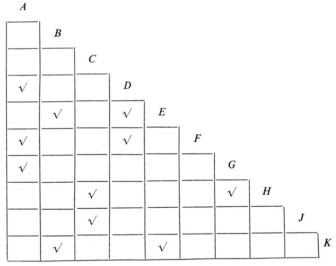

MC's are: *GH, BEK, DE, ADF, AG, CH, CJ*
Minimal covering set is *BEK, CJ, ADF, GH*

A satisfactory schedule would therefore be:
MON   TUE   WED   THU
BEK   *CJ*   *ADF*   *GH*

3.3 See Table 4.8 on p. 155.

3.8 The destination sets in the four columns are

$$(12, 34, 56), \quad (14, 26, 35), \quad (16, 23, 45), \quad (135, 24, 6).$$

They are satisfied by

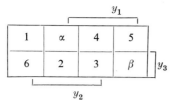

The resulting flow matrix is

	00	01	11	10	y_1	y_2	y_3
1	①	α	①	5	0	0	0
2	α	②	②	α	0	1	1
3	4	③	2	③	1	1	1
4	④	④	5	④	1	1	0
5	β	β	⑤	β	1	0	0
6	⑥	2	1	⑥	0	0	1
α	1	4	–	4	0	1	0
β	6	3	–	3	1	0	1

3.12 The dichotomies that must be covered are

Column
00: (12, 35)(14, 35)
01: (12, 35)
11: (13, 4)(13, 5)(23, 4)(23, 5)
10: (1, 34)(1, 45)(2, 34)(2, 45)(1, 2)

The row appearing in the largest number of these dichotomies is 3, and so we base our *ordered* dichotomies on 3 to obtain 14 different ordered dichotomies:

$A[12, 35]$, $B[14, 35]$, $C[4, 13]$, $D[5, 13]$, $E[4, 23]$, $F[5, 23]$, $G[1, 34]$, $H[2, 34]$, $I[1, 45]$, $\bar{I}[45, 1]$, $J[2, 45]$, $\bar{J}[45, 2]$, $K[1, 2]$, $\bar{K}[2, 1]$.

A covering set of MC's is BEK, $CDEF\bar{I}\bar{J}$, $AGHIJ$. They correspond to [14, 235], [45, 123], and [12, 345], respectively, and if we take the complement of the second of them (to allow 000 to be assigned to row 1), we obtain the following flow matrix:

| | X_1X_2 | | | | | | |
	00	01	11	10	y_1	y_2	y_3
1	①, 0	2, 0	3, 0	①, 0	0	0	0
2	1, 0	②, 0	3, 0	②, 1	1	0	0
3	③, 1	5, 0	③, 0	4, 0	1	0	1
4	1, 0	–	④, 0	④, 0	0	1	1
5	3, 1	⑤, 0	⑤, 1	4, 0	1	1	1
	1, 0	–	3, 0	4, 0	0	0	1
	1, 0	–	–	–	0	1	0

3.19 Using methods described elsewhere [HAR-1], we find SP partition (146, 235), but no other SP partition with fewer than five blocks separates 2 and 3. Hence no solution exists based on partitions. There are many SP set systems. Consider $\alpha_1 = (1234, 256)$ and $\alpha_2 = (1, 25, 23, 46)$; both are SP set systems, though their product is not 0. Suppose we convert α_1 and α_2 into the partitions $\alpha_1' = (12_p 34, 2_q 56)$ and $\alpha_2' = (1, 2_p 5, 2_q 3, 46)$, respectively, splitting state 2 into two states, 2_p and 2_q. Then $\alpha_1' \alpha_2' = 0$. An expanded equivalent version of the given table can be found corresponding to the split and such that α_1' and α_2' are SP partitions of this table. Then T_1 and T_2, the flow tables corresponding to α_1' and α_2', respectively, constitute the components of a parallel decomposition of the given table provided that $N(1, B)$ of T_2 is set equal to 2. With the state assignments as shown for tables T_1 and T_2, the resulting decomposition amounts to coding the states of the given table as:

$$1(000), 2(001 \text{ and } 111), 3(011), 4(010), 5(101), 6(110).$$

The $N(3, D)$ entry in T_2 was changed to 2 to permit a 2-variable state assignment free of critical races. Note that a serial decomposition of T_2 exists based on the SP partition (14, 23), which corresponds to the partition (146, 235) on the states of the given table.

	A	B	C	D	y_1
1	①	①	2	①	0 $(12_p 34)$
2	1	②	②	1	1 $(2_q 56)$

Table T_1

	A	B	C	D	$y_2 y_3$
1	①	2/3	4	①	00 (1)
2	3	②	②	1	01 $(2_p 5)$
3	③	③	2	2	11 $(2_q 3)$
4	1	3	④	④	10 (46)

Table T_2

4.1 (a) All signals delayed by 10 units.
(b) s_1 does not get through (blocked by D_{i1}).
The other signals are delayed by 10 units.
(c) S_1 and S_2 are blocked, while S_3 and S_4 are delayed by 10 units.
(d) A cascade of inertial- and pure-delay elements is completely characterized by the magnitude of the largest inertial delay and the sum of *all* of the delay-element values. Hence in this case we can replace the smaller inertial delay D_{i1} with a pure delay D_{p1} of equal magnitude without affecting the behavior of the circuit.

4.2 (a) A pulse of duration 1 beginning 4 units of time after the leading edge of the input pulse.
(b) Same pulse as in (a) but starting 6 units of time later.

4.10 The circuit is described by $AB + B$. Suppose B and A change in opposite directions. Then we can let $B = \bar{A}$ and obtain the expression $A\bar{A} + \bar{A}$ which obviously has a hazard (for changes between 01 and 10 in our original expression). The same conclusion follows directly from Theorem 4.5 if we let $I_1 = 01$ and $I_2 = 10$ and consider the superscripted expression $A^1 B^2 + B^3$.

4.12   According to Procedure 4.1 and Theorem 4.6, covering the following dichotomies is
sufficient:

$$(12, 5)(23, 5)(24, 5)(1, 34)(2, 34)(34, 5)(12, 34).$$

All except the last of them are covered by the given assignment. The (12, 34) dichotomy is relevant to the transition beginning 1-000 → 1-001. In this case, the danger
is that $T(1, 2)$ will intersect $T(3, 4)$ where, in the 000 column, the next-state entries
must be 4. Because of stray delays, some Y-variables may "see" the system in such a
column-000 state and the result could be that the system ends up in 5-001 instead of
2-001. This in fact would be a possibility in our example, if it were not for y_1. Since
y_1 separates 1234 from 5, it precludes the possibility and hence renders the assignment
satisfactory.

4.20   If there is a *logic* 0-hazard for transitions between input states I_1 and I_2, then $f(x) = 0$
for every x in $T(I_1, I_2)$, and there must be a p-term p_j that goes on during the transition
and then off again. But if p_j does *not* contain complementary appearances of some
literal, then it must be on in the *steady state* for some x between I_1 and I_2. Hence the
function has a 1-point in this region, which contradicts our initial assertion (thus
making the hazard a *function* hazard).

4.21   Examine the K-map below on which $\bar{A}B + B\bar{C}$ is plotted. If we do *not* use the p-
term $B\bar{C}$, then there will be a 1-hazard for 010 → 110. But if we *do* use this p-term,
then during the 000 → 011 transition, the corresponding gate may go on and then
off again before the gate corresponding to the p-term covering 011 goes on, thus
manifesting a dynamic hazard. Hence an AND-OR circuit must have at least *one* of
these hazards, though either can be avoided.

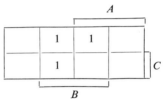

A circuit corresponding to $B(\bar{A} + \bar{C})$ has *neither* hazard as can be seen by applying
the methods of Section 4.2.

4.23   (*a*) First we modify the table by changing the output entry for 1-01 to 0, and splitting
3 into two rows. Note that row 2 does *not* have to be split since no false transients
can occur when multiple input changes are made starting in either stable state. An
STT assignment is easily found by inspection. Each y-variable must be inertially
delayed, and this can be accomplished using the delay box of Fig. 4.14.

	x_1x_2				Y_1	Y_2
	00	01	11	10		
1	①, 0	2 , 0	①, 0	①, 0	0	0
2	3A , 0	②, 1	1 , 0	②, 0	0	1
3A	③A, 0	③A, 0	1 , 0	3B , 1	1	1
3B	3A , 1	3A , 1	1, 1	③B, 1	1	0

5.1   The flow matrix is

	00	01	11	10	y
1	①, 0	①, 0	–	2 , –	1
2	②, 1	1 , –	–	②, 1	0

(column group header: *SR*)

$$Y = S + \bar{R}y, \quad Z = y$$

If we use the Y-expression directly, then we will need an inverter to get $\bar{R}$ from R and *two* inverters in the feedback loop to supply gain, as well as to generate $\bar{Z}$. Instead we may recast the Y-expression as

$$Y = S + \overline{(R + \bar{y})}.$$

This transformation eliminates the need for complementing R and places two inverters between Y and y. The resulting circuit is

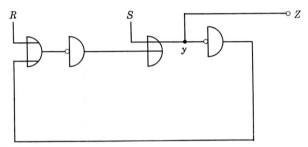

Figure S2

Note that with the circuit in this form, we might consider taking Z from the output of the left inverter, making

$$Z = \overline{(R + \bar{y})} = \bar{R}y.$$

This expression also satisfies the specifications, and we may take the other FF output from the other inverter. If this is done, then the form of the circuit becomes that of a pair of cross-coupled NOR gates as below:

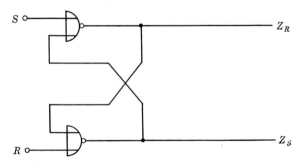

Figure S3

The outputs (Z_s and Z_R are labeled y and $\bar{y}$ elsewhere in this book when these FF's are usually used as state devices) are not always complementary in that both may be zero while $R = 1$. No delay element is needed in the circuit since there is only one y-variable.

5.2   The flow matrix is

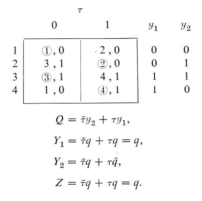

| | τ | | | |
	0	1	y_1	y_2
1	①,0	·2,0	0	0
2	3,1	②,0	0	1
3	③,1	4,1	1	1
4	1,0	④,1	1	0

$$Q = \bar{\tau}y_2 + \tau y_1,$$

$$Y_1 = \bar{\tau}q + \tau q = q,$$

$$Y_2 = \bar{\tau}q + \tau\bar{q},$$

$$Z = \bar{\tau}q + \tau q = q.$$

Thus three transistors are needed, including one to invert τ. (A different three-transistor solution is shown in Section 7.3 based on the use of capacitors or the hole storage effect.)

6.1   The destination sets for the four columns, respectively, are (1, 23, 4), (12, 34), (14, 23), (14, 23). We may lump together 1 and 4 in column 1; hence a Liu assignment corresponding to (12, 34) and (14, 23) is satisfactory. The $y_1 y_2$-states for rows 1, 2, 3, 4 are, respectively, 00, 01, 11, 10. The logic must be designed so that, in the course of any transition within a column, only *one* product term is activated. (This precludes the use of $\bar{x}_1 y_1$ in the Y_1-expression.) The resulting expressions are

$$Y_1 = \bar{x}_1 \bar{x}_2 y_2 + \bar{x}_1 \bar{x}_2 y_1 \bar{y}_2 + \bar{x}_1 x_2 y_1 + x_1 x_2,$$

$$\bar{Y}_1 = \bar{x}_1 \bar{x}_2 \bar{y}_1 \bar{y}_2 + \bar{x}_1 x_2 \bar{y}_1 + x_1 \bar{x}_2,$$

$$Y_2 = \bar{x}_1 \bar{x}_2 \bar{y}_2 + \bar{x}_1 x_2 \bar{y}_1 + x_1 y_2,$$

$$\bar{Y}_2 = \bar{x}_1 \bar{x}_2 \bar{y}_2 + \bar{x}_1 x_2 y_1 + x_1 \bar{y}_2,$$

$$Z = \bar{x}_1 \bar{x}_2 y_1,$$

$$\bar{Z} = \bar{x}_1 \bar{x}_2 \bar{y}_2 + \bar{x}_1 x_2 + x_1.$$

7.1

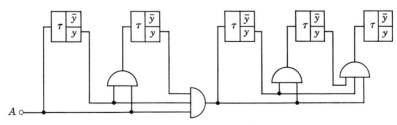

$A \circ$ ————

Figure S4

7.2

		y_1	y_2	y_3				y_1	y_2	y_3
1	2	0	0	0	0	0	1	0	0	0
2	3	0	0	1	0	1	1	0	0	1
3	4	0	1	0	0	0	1	0	1	0
4	5	0	1	1	1	1	1	0	1	1
5	6	1	0	0	0	0	1	1	0	0
6	1	1	0	1	1	0	1	1	0	1
					τ_1	τ_2	τ_3			

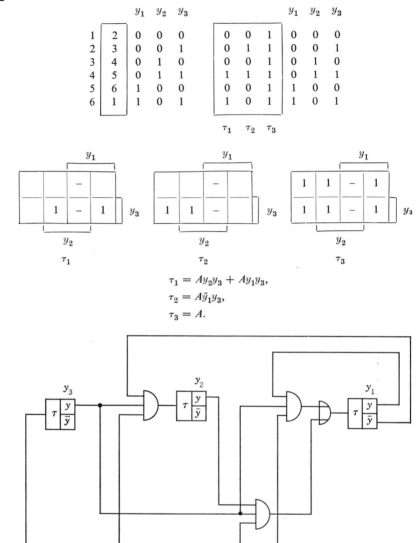

$$\tau_1 = Ay_2y_3 + Ay_1y_3,$$
$$\tau_2 = A\bar{y}_1y_3,$$
$$\tau_3 = A.$$

Figure S5

Index